Handbook for Engineering Design using Standard Materials and Components

by

Peter Mucci
D.I.C. C.Eng. F.I.Mech.E.

in association with
BSI

FOURTH EDITION

Published by
BSI Standards
Linford Wood, Milton Keynes MK14 6LE

Copies of this book are obtainable direct from BSI Standards on Tel. (0908) 221166 or Fax. (0908) 322484 or through bookshops.

Published by
BSI Standards
Linford Wood
Milton Keynes MK14 6LE.

First published 1986
Second Edition 1987
Third edition 1990
Reprinted 1991
Fourth edition 1994

ISBN 0 580 22585 2 Fourth edition

GENERAL

The British standards mentioned in this book include those published up to July 1993.

No BSI committee has been involved in the production of this publication. The statements made represent the views of the author. It is necessary to point out that this publication is intended for guidance and the text is not intended to serve as a substitute for the British Standards concerned.

Certain withdrawn and obsolescent British Standards are referred to by virtue of their limited use required by legislation, regulation and/or other reasons.

DISCLAIMER

Whilst every care has been taken to ensure the accuracy and completeness of this publication, neither the author nor BSI will accept responsibility for loss, damage etc. however arising occasioned by the use of this publication.

REVIEW OF PUBLICATIONS

Some of the material in this book has been extracted from British Standards. Readers are reminded that standards are continuously under review. New standards, revisions and amendments are published frequently. Up to date information may be obtained from BSI Standards, Information Services.

SUBSCRIBING MEMBERSHIP OF BSI

Certain advantages and facilities are available to subscribing members, not the least of which is a 50% discount on British and most Foreign National Standards. Further information may be obtained from BSI Standards, Membership Services.

INTRODUCTION

This handbook aims to provide a quick and compact design reference source for the selection, application and supply of a wide range of standard materials and components. It is biased towards, although not exclusive to, the mechanical engineering industries and it is hoped that it will provide engineers with a 'first reference' for much of the data so often dispersed among several different sources.

Since the information available for each subject alone would easily fill a book, careful control has been exercised over the amount of data presented in tables and charts accompanying the text. In most cases this has been done by excluding those specifications for materials and components which are not readily available from suppliers or which are at the extreme ends of ranges commonly used by engineers. If details of complete ranges are needed then the references to standards and the suppliers address lists at the end of each section should make it easy to obtain the required information.

The great majority of subjects included in the book have been chosen because they are supported by full specifications published by the British Standards Institution. This means that they have been accepted by representative industries as standards and are often the result of many years' experience and product development, a process which ensures that, when the design engineer properly applies them, a level of quality and 'fitness for purpose' is assured.

Obtaining large amounts of information is a very time-consuming process and it is anticipated that this book will help to solve the problem and at the same time go some way towards fulfilling the growing demand in industry for practical books to support design work. For most kinds of design project, realistic materials and component knowledge is vital otherwise a lot of time can be wasted 're-inventing the wheel' when there is a ready made solution at hand. The book should therefore be useful as well for students on all years of the new B. Eng. and M. Eng. degree courses with their emphasis on engineering applications.

The author is indebted to the British Standards Institution for its practical support and encouragement given during the research for this book and to all the industrial suppliers, large and small, who have helped along the way.

PREFACE TO FOURTH EDITION

The fourth edition has been extensively revised and reset with many textual changes to include latest practices and recommendations from industry. In particular FASTENERS, METALS, PLASTICS, OTHER MATERIALS and ADHESIVES have been given close attention. Existing references to British Standards have been updated and new standards included where relevant. In addition a number of relevant European Standards have been introduced, and some Aerospace and Automobile specifications referred to where high quality or high production are priority requirements.

The list of British Standards at the back (Appendix F) has been revised to indicate those with corresponding European and International Standards and many changes have been made to the text to keep up to date with changing technology.

Peter Mucci

CONTENTS

CONTENTS

GENERAL ADDRESSES

Address	Telephone	Fax
British Standards Institution Linford Wood Milton Keynes MK14 6LE	0908 220022	0908 320856
The Design Council 28 Haymarket LONDON SW1Y 4SU	071 839 8000	071 925 2130
Institution of Mechanical Engineers 1 Birdcage Walk LONDON SW1H 9JJ	071 222 7899	071 222 4557
(Also PO Box 23 Northgate Avenue Bury St. Edmonds IP32 6BN)	(0284 763277)	(0284 704006)
Institution of Engineering Designers Courtleigh Westbury Leigh WESTBURY Wiltshire BA13 3TA	0373 822801	0373 858085
Institution of Electrical Engineers (IEE)* Savoy Place LONDON WC2R 0BL	071 240 1871	071 240 7735
Institution of Production Engineers (IPE) (now merged with IEE)		
Production Engineering Research Association (PERA) MELTON MOWBRAY Leicester LE13 0PB	0664 501501	0664 501264
Engineering Equipment and Materials Users' Association 14 Belgrave Square LONDON SW1X 8PS	071 235 5316 / 7	071 245 6937
Engineering Industries Association 16 Dartmouth Street LONDON SW1H 9BL	071 222 2367	071 799 2206
Federation of British Electrotechnical and Allied Manufacturers Association (BEAMA) 8 Leicester Street LONDON WC2H 7BN	071 437 0678	071 437 4901

*Also referred to as:- 'Institution of Manufacturing Engineers'

GENERAL ADDRESSES

Address	Telephone	Fax
Machine Tool Technologies Association (MTTA) 62 Bayswater Road LONDON W2 3PS	071 402 6671	071 724 7250
Department of Trade and Industry (DTI) 123 Victoria Street LONDON SW1E 6RB	071 215 5000	071 828 3258
Science and Engineering Research Council (SERC) Polaris House, North Star Avenue SWINDON SN2 1ET	0793 411122	0793 411020
Federation of Engineering Design Companies Suite 106 Grosvenor Gardens House LONDON SW1W 0BS	071 828 0625	

USING THE HANDBOOK

For ease of reference and to give a structured introduction to the subject, each page of text and data is self-contained so that important information, such as performance ratings for components, can be found easily. Where a large amount of data has to be presented, as in the case of mountings for electric motors, then a page is devoted to individual types.

It is not possible in a book of this size to reproduce all ranges and all variations of materials and components so *it is essential* that for detail design work, especially when complete tables of data are needed, further reference is made to the relevant full British or European Standard Specifications and suppliers' publications. To help in this task, a list of B.S. numbers and suppliers' addresses is given at the end of each section, as well as a few addresses of other useful organizations.

A complete index of the British and European Standards used in this book is given in Appendix F and Appendix G contains information on the British Standards Institution (BSI).

Although this book is concerned mainly with design information, equally important are the *build* and *test* phases of a project, and it is recommended that when these stages are reached, full use is made of published standards on quality and test methods.

BS 5750 Quality Systems (see Appendix A) is of particular importance in this regard since it is concerned with total product quality and is a fully recognised International Standard.

Enquiries about British Standards should be addressed to
BSI Standards,
Information Services,
Linford Wood,
Milton Keynes,
MK14 6LE.
Tel: 0908 226888.

SAFETY

Much time is spent considering safety aspects when standards are drafted and often an 'obvious' way of doing something is avoided because there could be safety implications. If a change from established practice is being considered, especially in the areas of *pressurized systems*, *transmissions* and *electrical machines* advice should be sought from suppliers, technical officers at BSI and the HSE (Health and Safety Executive).

PLEASE NOTE

It is the responsibility of the designer to make judgements based on complete and accurate information from suppliers of materials and components and to refer, where necessary, to the full texts of published standards and current legislation relating to products and services.

The author, publisher, BSI and all other individuals and organisations contributing to this book accept no liability to any party for any loss or damage, whatever the cause, which may be claimed from its use.

SECTION 1 – MEASUREMENT

1.1 S.I. UNITS

1.1.1 Table of common units and prefixes;
Base units, derived units, prefixes.

1.2 CONVERSION FACTORS

1.2.1 Tables of sample conversions of common units;
Length, area, volume, mass, force, density.
Pressure, energy, power, temperature, velocity.

S.I. UNITS 1.1.1

Tables of common units and prefixes : Source – BS 5555

BASE UNITS

Quantity	Name of base S.I. Unit	Symbol
length	metre	m
mass	kilogram	kg
time	second	s
electric current	ampere	A
thermodynamic temperature	kelvin	K
amount of substance	mole	mol
luminous intensity	candela	cd

SUPPLEMENTARY UNITS

Quantity	Name of supplementary S.I. Unit	Symbol
plain angle	radian	rad
solid angle	steradian	sr

UNITS OF PRACTICAL IMPORTANCE

Quantity	Name of unit	Unit Symbol	Definition
time	minute	min	1 min = 60 s
	hour	h	1 h = 60 min
	day	d	1 d = 24 h
plane angle	degree	°	1° = (π/180) rad
	minute	′	1′ = (1/60) ″
	second	″	1″ = (1/60) ′
volume	litre	l	1 l = 1 dm^3
mass	tonne	t	1 t = 10^3 kg

PREFIXES

Factor by which the unit is multiplied	PREFIX Name	Symbol
10^{18}	exa	E
10^{15}	peta	P
10^{12}	tera	T
10^{9}	giga	G
10^{6}	mega	M
10^{3}	kilo	k
10^{2}	hecto	h
10	deca	da
10^{-1}	deci	d
10^{-2}	centi	c
10^{-3}	milli	m
10^{-6}	micro	μ
10^{-9}	nano	n
10^{-12}	pico	p
10^{-15}	femto	f
10^{-16}	atto	a

MEANING OF MILLION, BILLION, etc.

Term	Significance	Corresponding decimal factor UK	USA
million	thousand x thousand	10^6	(10^6)
billion	million x million	10^{12}	(10^9)
trillion	million x billion	10^{18}	(10^{12})
quadrillion	million x trillion	10^{24}	(10^{15})

DERIVED UNITS

Quantity	Name of derived SI unit	Symbol	Expressed in terms of base or supplementary SI units or in terms of other derived SI units
frequency	hertz	Hz	1 Hz = 1 s^{-1}
force	newton	N	1 N = 1 kg m/s^2
pressure, stress	pascal *	Pa	1 Pa = 1 N/m^2
energy, work, quantity of heat	joule	J	1 J = 1 N m
power	watt	W	1 W = 1 J/s
electric charge, quantity of electricity	coulomb	C	1 C = 1 A s
electric potential, potential difference, electromotive force	volt	V	1 V = 1 J/C = 1 W/A
electric capacitance	farad	F	1 F = 1 C/V
electric resistance	ohm	Ω	1 Ω = 1 V/A
electric conductance	siemens	S	1 S = 1 $Ω^{-1}$
magnetic flux, flux of magnetic induction	wieber	Wb	1 Wb = 1 V s
magnetic flux density, magnetic induction	tesia	T	1 T = 1 Wb/m^2
inductance	henry	H	1 H = 1 Wb/A
luminous flux	lumen	lm	1 lm = 1 cd sr
illuminance	lux	lx	1 lx = 1 lm/m^2
activity (radioactive)	becquerel	Bq	1 B1 = 1 s^{-1}
absorbed dose (of ionizing radiation)	gray	Gy	1 Gy = 1 J/kg

SPECIALIZED UNITS

Quantity	Name of unit	Unit symbol	Definition
energy	electronvolt	eV	1 electronvolt is the kinetic energy acquired by an electron in passing through a potential difference of 1 volt in vacuum; 1 eV = 1.602 19 x 1^{-19} J (approximately)
mass of an atom	atomic mass unit	u	1 (unified) atomic mass unit is equal to the fraction 1⁄12 of the mass of an atom of the nuclide ^{12}C; 1 u = 1.660 57 x 10^{-27} kg (approximately)
length	astronomic unit	(AU)	1 AU = 149 598 x 10^6 m (System of astronomical constants, 1964)
	parsec	pc	1 parsec is the distance at which 1 astronomic unit subtends an angle of 1 second of arc: 1 pc = 206 265 AU = 30 857 x 10^{12} m (approximately)
pressure of fluid	bar *	bar	1 bar = 0.986 923 atm (10^5 Pa) (atmospheres)

* Note : Although the Pascal is the standard unit for pressure, the Bar is very widely used in engineering fluid technology.

BS 5555 : 1981 (1987) Specification for SI units and recommendations for the use of their multiples and of certain other units

CONVERSION FACTORS 1.2.1

Tables of sample conversions of common units

LENGTH

Unit		Sample values			
metre	m	1	0.001	0.0254	0.305
millimetre	mm	1000	1	25.4	305
inch	in	39.37	0.03937	1	12
foot	ft	3.281	0.00328	0.083	1
yard	yd	1.094	0.00109	0.028	0.333

AREA

Unit		Sample values			
square metre	m^2	1	$1x10^{-6}$	0.093	$1x10^4$
square millimetre	mm^2	$1x10^{-6}$	1	$9.3x10^4$	$1x10^{10}$
square inch	in^2	1550	0.155	144	$1.55x10^8$
square foot	ft^2	10.764	$1.08x10^{-5}$	1	107639
hectare	ha	$1x10^{-4}$	$1x10^{-10}$	$9.3x10^{-6}$	1

VOLUME

Unit		Sample values			
cubic metre	m^3	1	0.001	$1.64x10^{-5}$	$0.57x10^{-3}$
litre	l	1000	1	0.0164	0.568
cubic inch	in^3	$6.1x10^4$	61	1	34.7
pint (UK)	pt	1.760	1.76	0.029	1
gallon (UK)	gal	220	0.220	$3.6x10^{-3}$	8

MASS

Unit		Sample values			
kilogram	kg	1	0.001	0.4536	1000
gram	g	1000	1	453.6	$1x10^6$
pound	lb	2.205	0.0022	1	2205
tonne	t	0.001	$1x10^{-6}$	$4.53x10^{-4}$	1
ton (UK)	ton	$9.84x10^{-4}$	$9.84x10^{-7}$	$4.46x10^{-4}$	0.984

FORCE

Unit		Sample values			
newton	N	1	9.806	4.448	9964
kg-force	kgf	0.102	1	0.453	1016
lb-force	lbf	0.225	2.205	1	2240
ton-force (UK)	tonf	$1.0x10^{-4}$	$9.8x10^{-4}$	$4.46x10^{-4}$	1

DENSITY

Unit		Sample values			
kilograms per cubic metre	kg/m^3	1	1000	27680	16.02
grams per cubic centimetre	g/cm^3	0.001	1	27.68	0.016
pound per cubic inch	lb/in^3	$3.6x10^{-5}$	0.036	1	$5.8x10^{-4}$
pound per cubic foot	lb/ft^3	$6.24x10^{-2}$	62.43	1728	1

PRESSURE (STRESS)

Unit		Sample values			
Pascal (=N/m^2)	Pa	1	$1x10^5$	$9.8x10^4$	6895
bar	bar	$1x10^{-5}$	1	0.981	0.069
kg-force per square cm	kgf/ cm^2	$1.02x10^{-5}$	1.02	1	0.0703
lb-force per square inch	lbf/ in^2	$1.45x10^{-4}$	14.5	14.22	1
Newton per square mm	N/mm^2	$1.x10^{-6}$	$1x10^{-1}$	$9.8x10^{-2}$	$6.895x10^{-3}$

ENERGY

Unit		Sample values			
Joule	J	1	$3.6x10^6$	4.1868	1.356
kilowatt hour	kWh	$2.78x10^{-7}$	1	$1.16x10^{-5}$	$3.77x10^{-7}$
calorie	cal	4.1868	859845	1	0.324
foot pound force	ft lbf	1.356	$2.65x10^5$	3.088	1
British thermal unit	Btu	1055	3412	$3.97x10^{-3}$	$1.28x10^{-3}$

POWER

Unit		Sample values			
Watt	W	1	9.806	1.356	746
kg-force metre per second	kgf m/s	0.102	1	0.138	76
foot lb-force per second	ft lbf / s	0.737	7.23	1	550
horsepower	hp	$1.34x10^{-3}$	0.0131	$1.82x10^{-3}$	1
calorie per second	cal/s	0.239	2.342	0.323	178.1

TEMPERATURE

Unit		Sample values			
celsius	°C	0	1	20	100
fahrenheit	°F	32	33.8	68	212
rankine	°R	459.67	461.47	495.67	639.67
kelvin	K	273.15	274.15	293.15	373.15

VELOCITY – LINEAR

Unit		Sample values			
metre per seconds	m/s	1	0.278	0.447	0.305
kilometre per hour	km/h	3.6	1	1.61	1.097
miles per hour	mph	2.237	0.621	1	0.682
foot per second	ft/s	3.281	0.911	1.467	1
knot (international)	kn	1.944	0.54	0.869	0.592

VELOCITY – ANGULAR

Unit		Sample values			
radian per second	rad/s	1	0.0167	6.283	0.105
radian per minute	rad/min	60	1	377	6.283
revolution per second	rev/s	0.159	0.0026	1	0.0167
revolution per minute	rpm	9.55	0.159	60	1
degree per second	°/s	57.3	0.955	360	6

REFERENCES:

BS 350 : 1983 Conversion factors and tables (see also supplement No. 1 – 'Additional Tables')

BS 5775 : 1982 (1989) Specification for quantities, units and symbols

Notes

SECTION 2 – MATERIALS

METALS 2.1.1

Ferrous metals: forms, processes, selection and use

TYPICAL APPLICATIONS : Widest used material group in mechanical engineering because of its strength, cheapness, availability and versatility. It is remarkable for its range of uses, from fine wires to supertankers, offering consistency of quality and performance unrivalled by most other materials.

DEFINITIONS : Cast irons, steels and alloys whose major component is iron.

FORMS AND PROCESSES :

Supplied to standard sizes and shapes, with black or bright surface finishes depending on steel. Black is oxidised surface layer, bright is exposed metal finished to more accurate sizes. Ferrous metals, with the exception of stainless steel, require anti-corrosion protection by painting, electroplating, plastic coating or other method depending on cost and service use. Ferrous metals may be machined, drawn, pressed, cast, welded, hardened, or case-hardened, depending on the steel selected. Addition of lead aids machineability without affecting mechanical properties except some welding processes.

NOTES ON SELECTION AND USE :

When selecting steels care must be taken to meet the priority need for any particular application (e.g. weldability, malleability, or good machine finish) as no steel will excel in all properties. The mild steel groups are chosen for most general engineering, from large machined parts to thin section stampings and pressings, and a high variety of accurate sectional and sheet forms are easily available. For higher strength, higher performance, **hardenable steels** are used which can be through-hardened easily and which have particularly high wear resistance. The forms of supply for these steels include gear blanks, making gear machining very cost effective. **Case hardening steels** are normally available as simple bars or plates which, after machining, can be hardened giving a wear resistant surface and a tough core. These steels are not suitable for very small parts or thin sections and where close tolerances are needed, post-hardening finishing is necessary. **Tool steels** can be used for intricate work, are very tough, shock resistant, and maintain their hardness at high temperature, but their cost normally limits their use to 'one-off' jig and tool work. **Stainless steels** are normally resistant to corrosion and irradiation and can be polished to a high finish. They are particularly suited to the marine, petrochemical and nuclear environments, but very careful selection is needed to avoid aggressive environmental attack such as crevice corrosion. **Cast irons** cannot be cold worked and have relatively low tensile strengths. They are normally supplied in billet forms for general foundrywork. They are cost-effective materials for producing complex shapes in quantity which require minimum machining. For each of the groups described there is a wide choice of grades of material. When selecting it is essential that the relevant Standard be studied and the supplier consulted so that grades may be matched to applications. This is important where high performance hardenable steels are used since within the broad headings of light, medium and heavy duty steels, a wide variety of tensile strengths is available.
Always put BS numbers on drawings and avoid just using the terms 'mild steel' or 'Cast Iron'.

REFERENCES :

BS 970 :	Specification for wrought steels for mechanical and allied engineering purposes (see also BS EN 10083)
BS 1407 : 1970 (1987)	Specification for high carbon bright steel (silver steel)
BS 1452 : 1990	Specification for flake graphite cast iron
BS 1501 :	Steels for fired and unfired pressure vessels : plates
BS 1503 : 1989	Specification for steel forgings (including semi-finished forged products) for pressure purposes (see also BS 1502 and BS 1504)
BS 2789 : 1985	Specification for spheroidal graphite or nodular graphite cast iron
BS 3920 :	Derivation and verification of elevated temp. properties for steel products for pressure purposes
BS 4659 : 1989	Specification for tool and die steels
BS 6258 : 1988	Specification for hollow steel bars for machining
BS 6323 :	Spec. for seamless & welded steel tubes for automobile, mech. & general engineering purposes
ISO 683-9: 1988	Heat treatable steels, alloy steels and free cutting steels
BS EN 10027	Designation systems for steel
BS EN 10020	Definition and classification of grades of steel
BS EN 10131 : 1991	Cold rolled low carbon steel flat products (etc)

METALS 2.1.2

Ferrous metals: Table of properties

Properties of common steels	British Standard Specification (source BS 970) 1955 (EN No.)	1991	Tensile Stress * see notes	Yield Stress	Young's Modulus	Density	Coeff. of Linear Expansion	Weldability: Resistance	Flame	Arc	Brazing	Hardness (Brinell No) see BS 131, 240, 427 and 4175	Charpy Impact (J)	Supplied	Supply Condition	Remarks
			MN/m²	MN/m²	GN/m²	kg/m³	µm/K					** see notes below		Section		
Freecutting Mild Steel	(1A)	220M07 230M07	367-446	215	208	7833	12.6	×	×	×	✓✓	103 Min.	–		As rolled/ Normalised	High speed machining steel Good finish.
General Mild Steel	(3B)	070M20	448-594	235	208	7861	12.4	✓	✓	✓	✓✓	(116-179)	–		Cold Drawn	Gen. Purpose M.S. for light stress uses, easily bendable.
Weldable Structural Steel		BS 4360 ref. 43C	430-540	275	207	7861	12.0	✓✓	✓	✓	✓✓	–	27 @ 0°C		Hot Finished	Commonly used for rolled hollow sections.
Weldable Structural Steel		BS 4360 ref. 50C	490-620	355	207	7861	12.0	✓✓	✓	✓	✓✓	–	27 @ –15°C		Hot Finished	Commonly used for rolled hollow sections.
Light Duty Hardenable	(16)	605M36	695-933	605-846	210	7833	12.4	✓✓	✓	✓	✓	201-352	28-50		Hardened & Tempered	
Medium Duty Hardenable	(19)	709M40	753-976	600-880	213	7861	11.9	✓✓	✓	✓	✓	201-375	22-50		Hardened & Tempered	
Heavy Duty Hardenable	(24)	817M40	823-1550	690-1127	213	7889	11.2	✓✓	✓	✓	✓	248-444	9-50		Hardened & Tempered	
Medium Duty, Case Hardenable	(351)	635M15	738-849		208	7889	12.2	✓✓	✓	✓	✓✓	207 Max.	22 Min.		Hardened & Tempered	
Heavy Duty, Case Hardenable	(36A)	655M13	957		208	7889	11.8	✓	✓	✓	✓✓	223-255	35 Min.		Carborized Refined & Hardened	Not suitable for small parts.
Free Machining	(58M)	303S41	540-695	232-278	193	7910	17.5	×	×	×	✓✓	183 Max.			Annealed	Cold work hardened, not heat treatment.
Marine Stainless	(58J)	316S16	630	300 Approx.	204	7972	17.0	✓	✓	✓	✓	183 Max.			Annealed	Cold working only. Very high corrosion resistance.
Stabilized Weldable	(58B)	321S12	490-650	195-310	201	7916	16.0	✓✓	✓✓	✓✓	✓✓	183 Max.			Annealed	Cold working only. Can be used up to 700 °C
'Silver Steel'		BS 1407: 1970				7889	12.5	×	×	×	×	(230)				
Ground Flat Stock		BS 4659: 1971 BO 1	200 Approx.	179 Approx.				×	×	×	×	(229)				
Grey (Flake) Cast Iron		BS 1452: 1990	180-220		97-131	7200-7300	12.2	×	✓	✓	✓	170-290				Very hard, brittle cast with little expansion.
Spheroidal Cast Iron		BS 2789 : 1985	370-420		172	7114	11.5	×	✓	✓	✓✓	140-190				Malleable more elastic cast iron (than above).

* Lower values are generally for untreated strip, tube etc., whilst the higher values relate to heat treated components e.g. high tensile bolts

** Mechanical properties quoted for through-hardening steels vary according to 'ruling sections' used in the tests (see BS 970 : Part 1 for data)

STEEL STRIP

THICK (mm)	0.1	0.12	0.16	0.2	0.25	0.3	0.4	0.5	0.6	0.8	1.0	1.2	1.6	2.0
WIDTHS FOR ALL THESE (mm)				5.0	10	12.5	15	20						

STEEL SHEET

THICK (mm)	0.6	0.8	1.0	1.2	1.6	2.0	2.5	3.0
SWG (approx.)	24	22	20	18	16	14	12	10

LENGTHS x WIDTHS FOR ALL THESE:
2 m x 1 m and 2.5 m x 1.25 m

METALS 2.1.3

Ferrous metals: Stock – Rounds

STEEL ROUND (Weight: 10 mm Round = 0.617 Kg/m)

BRIGHT: SUPER FREECUTTING STEEL

(BS 970: 1955: En 1A)
BS 970: 1991: 220M07/230M07 — Colour code: Green

Size (mm dia.)															
2	2.5	3	4	5	6	6.5	7	7.5	8	9	10	11	12	13	14
15	16	17	18	19	20	22	24	25	26	28	30	32	35	36	38
40	42	45	46	48	50	52	55	56	58	60	65	70	75	80	85
90	100	105	110	120	125	130	140	150							

BRIGHT: PRECISION GROUND SUPER FREECUTTING STEEL

(BS 970: 1955: En 1A)
BS 970: 1991: 220M07/230M07 — Colour code: Green

Size (mm dia.)														
4	6	8	10	11	12	15	16	18	20	25	30	35	40	50

BRIGHT: LEADED FREECUTTING STEEL

(BS 970: 1955: En 1A)
BS 970: 1991: 220M07/230M07 + lead — Colour code: Magenta

Size (mm dia.)															
3	3.5	4	5	6	6.5	7	7.5	8	9	10	11	12	13	14	15
16	17	18	19	20	22	24	25	26	28	30	32	35	36	38	40
45	48	50	55	60	65	70	75	80	85	90	100				

BRIGHT: '20' CARBON STEEL

(BS 970: 1955: En 1A)
BS 970: 1991: 070M20 — Colour code: Red/Blue

Size (mm dia.)															
3	4	5	6	6.5	7	8	9	10	11	12	13	14	15	16	17
18	19	20	22	24	25	26	27	28	30	32	33	35	36	38	39
40	42	45	48	50	52	55	56	60	65	70	75	80	85	90	95
100	105	110	115	120	125	130	140	150	160	180	190	200			

BLACK: ¾% NICKEL CHROMIUM CASE HARDENING STEEL

(BS 970: 1955: En 351)
BS 970: 1991: 635M15 — Colour code: Yellow/Green

Size (mm dia.)															
25	28	32	35	40	45	50	55	60	65	70	75	80	85	90	95
100	105	110	115	120	125	130	135	140	150	160	170	180	190	200	

SILVER STEEL ROUNDS BS 1407 : 1970 (Usually supplied in 330 mm lengths)

Size (mm dia.)															
2	2.5	3	3.5	4	4.5	5	5.5	6	6.5	7	7.5	8	8.5	9	9.5
10	11	12	13	14	15	16	17	18	19	20	21	22	23	24	25
26	27	28	30												

NOTE: Stock tables on this and the following page reproduced by kind permission of Macreadys Glynwed Ltd. Pentonville Road London N19 NE.

METALS 2.1.4

Ferrous metals: Stock – Hexagon and flats

STEEL SQUARES (Weight: 10 mm Square = 0.784 Kg/m)

BRIGHT: SUPER FREECUTTING STEEL																
(BS 970: 1955: En 1A) BS 970: 1991: 220M07/230M07																Colour code: Green
Size (mm sq.)	5	6	7	8	10	12	14	15	16	18	20	22	25	30	32	40
Size (mm sq.)	45	50	55	60	65											

BRIGHT: '20' CARBON STEEL																
(BS 970: 1955: En 3B) BS 970: 1991: 070M20																Colour code: Red//Blue
Size (mm sq.)	4	6	8	10	12	13	14	15	16	18	20	22	25	30	32	35
Size (mm sq.)	40	45	50	55	60	65	70	75	80	90	100					

STEEL HEXAGONS (Weight: 10 mm Hexagon = 0.679 Kg/m)

BRIGHT: SUPER FREECUTTING STEEL																
(BS 970: 1955: En 1A) BS 970: 1991: 220M07/230M07																Colour code: Green
Size (mm A/F)	5	5.5	6	7	8	10	11	12	13	14	15	16	17	18	19	20
Size (mm A/F)	22	24	25	27	30	•32	35	36	41	46	50	55	6	65	70	75

BRIGHT: 1½ % MANGANESE MOLYBDENUM STEEL Hardened and Tempered to 'T' Condition									
(BS 970: 1955: En 16T) BS 970: 1991: 605M36									Colour code: White
Size (mm A/F)	13	17	19	22	24	30	32	36	40

BRIGHT STEEL FLATS (Weight: 20 × 10 Flat = 1.57 Kg/m)

t *WIDTHS (W) and THICKNESSES (t) shown in the table below*
W

Flats are normally in material grades; 1) BS 970/070M20 (En 3B), 2) BS 970/060M15 (En 32B), 3) General (non BS) grades

Thickness	Width (W) mm																										
(t) mm	10	12	15	16	20	25	30	32	35	40	45	50	55	60	65	70	75	80	90	100	110	125	130	140	150	160	200
1.5	√		√		√	√																					
2	√				√	√																					
3	√	√	√	√	√	√	√	√		√		√			√			√									
4			√		√	√	√																				
5	√	√	√	√	√	√	√	√		√	√	√	√		√					√							
6	√	√	√	√	√	√	√	√	√	√	√	√	√	√	√	√	√	√	√	√		√	√	√		√	
8			√		√	√	√	√	√	√	√	√		√			√					√					
10		√	√	√	√	√	√	√	√	√	√	√	√	√	√	√	√	√	√	√	√	√	√	√	√	√	√
12				√	√	√	√	√	√	√	√	√	√	√	√	√	√	√	√	√	√	√	√	√	√	√	√
16					√	√	√	√	√	√	√	√	√	√	√	√	√	√	√	√	√	√	√		√	√	
20						√	√	√	√	√	√	√	√	√	√	√	√	√	√	√	√	√	√		√	√	√
25							√	√	√	√	√	√	√	√	√	√	√	√	√	√	√	√	√		√	√	√
30									√	√	√	√	√	√	√	√		√	√	√	√	√			√	√	
35											√	√				√	√										
40											√	√	√	√	√	√	√	√	√	√	√	√				√	
50															√	√		√	√	√	√	√				√	

METALS 2.1.5

Ferrous metals: Hollow sections – Construction, selection and use

TYPICAL APPLICATIONS: All types of small to medium load bearing structure, test rigs, machine frames, safety barriers, machine guards and beds, trailer chassis, materials handling equipment, container and coachbuilding frames.

DEFINITIONS

Straight steel members of uniform closed hollow section throughout where the wall thickness is small compared with the overall section dimensions.

CONSTRUCTION

These are of hot-rolled, seam welded construction form typically from BS 4360 grade 43C or 50C steel, the latter having higher tensile and yield stresses. They are supplied in a semi-finished state in standard lengths coated with a rust-preventing red oxide primer. 43C grades have no colour coding, 50C grades are marked in blue. Dimensional tolerances of sections and thickness are closely controlled and outer surfaces are flat and smooth.

NOTES ON SELECTION AND USE

RHS or CHS (Rectangular or Circular Hollow Sections) provide general purpose structural members with low bending and torsional characteristics at relatively low weight. All RHS and CHS are weldable and lend themselves to applications where the framework or structure is exposed to view, their clean appearance requiring nothing more than a finish paint coating. Where exposed to a corrosive environment, open ends should be capped and drain holes provided for the effects of condensation. If an all welded structure is specified, care must be taken to prevent distortion and 'burning through' of thin sections. Where grinders are used to clean up welds avoid cutting into the metal, especially on corners. If the structure is to be bolted, then through holes must be strengthened to prevent the section crushing as the bolt is tightened. Under no circumstances must sections be used as fluid/gas pressure or transport pipes or be used as a medium for reinforcing concrete. For applications where there is permanent exposure to external conditions, RHS and CHS can be supplied in weather resistant grades of steel (prefixed WR). However, particular care must be taken when welding some of these grades due to their high phosphorous content.

REFERENCES

BS 970 : Specification for wrought steels for mechanical and allied engineering purposes

BS 4360 : 1990 Specification for weldable structural steels (See also BS EN 10025)

BS 4848: Specification for hot-rolled structural steel sections (See also BS 4)

BS 5135 : 1984 Specification for arc welding of carbon and carbon manganese steels.

BS 6323 : Specification for seamless and welded steel tubes for automobile, mechanical and general engineering purposes

BS 6363 : 1983 Specification for welded cold formed steel structural hollow sections

METALS 2.1.6

Ferrous metals: Hollow sections – Round, square and rectangular

STEEL SECTIONS

Tolerances ± 1% of the section size.

Straightness – Maximum variation at centre-span is 1/600 of any lengths.

Lengths – All sections shown are supplied in lengths of 7.5m and 10.0m except for those marked * which are in lengths of 6.0m.

FIG. A. CIRCULAR

Outside Diameter D	Thickness t	Mass m	Sectional Area A	2nd Moment of Area I	Radius of gyration r	Section modulus Z = I/y	Torsional moment of inertia J	Torsional modulus C
mm	mm	kg/m	cm^2	cm^4	cm	cm^3	cm^4	cm^3
*21.3	3.2	1.43	1.82	0.77	0.650	0.72	1.54	1.44
33.7	2.6	1.99	2.54	3.09	1.10	1.64	6.19	3.67
	3.2	2.41	3.07	3.60	1.08	2.14	7.21	4.28
	4.0	2.93	3.73	4.19	1.06	2.49	8.38	4.97
48.3	3.2	3.56	4.53	11.6	1.60	4.80	23.2	9.59
	4.0	4.37	5.57	13.8	1.57	5.70	27.5	11.40
	5.0	5.34	6.80	16.2	1.54	6.69	32.3	13.40
60.3	3.6	4.51	5.74	23.5	2.02	7.78	46.9	15.6
	4.0	5.55	7.07	28.2	2.00	9.34	56.3	18.7
	5.0	6.82	8.69	33.5	1.96	11.10	67.0	22.2
76.1	3.2	5.75	7.33	48.8	2.54	12.8	97.6	25.6
	4.0	7.11	9.06	59.1	2.55	15.5	118.0	31.0
	5.0	8.77	11.20	70.9	2.52	18.6	142.0	37.6
88.9	3.2	6.76	8.62	79.2	3.03	17.8	158	35.6
	4.0	8.38	10.70	96.3	3.00	21.7	193	43.3
	5.0	10.30	13.20	116.0	2.97	26.2	233	52.4

FIG. B SQUARE

Size D × D	Thickness t	Mass M	Sectional Area A	2nd Moment of Area I	Radius of gyration r	Section modulus z = I/y	Plastic Modulus S	Torsional moment of of inertia J	Torsional modulus C
mm	mm	kg/m	cm^2	cm^4	cm	cm^3	cm^3	cm^4	cm^3
* 20 × 20	2.0	1.12	1.42	0.76	0.73	0.76	0.95	1.22	1.07
	2.6	1.39	1.78	0.88	0.70	0.88	1.15	1.44	1.23
30 × 30	2.6	2.21	2.62	3.49	1.11	2.33	2.88	5.56	3.30
	3.2	2.65	3.38	4.00	1.09	2.67	3.37	6.44	3.75
50 × 50	3.2	4.66	5.94	21.6	1.91	8.62	10.4	33.8	12.4
	4.0	5.72	7.28	25.5	1.87	10.20	12.5	40.4	14.5
	5.0	6.97	8.88	29.6	1.83	11.90	14.9	47.6	16.7
70 × 70	3.6	7.46	9.50	69.5	2.70	19.9	23.6	108	28.7
	5.0	10.10	12.90	90.1	2.64	25.7	31.2	142	36.8
100 × 100	4.0	12.0	15.3	234	3.91	46.8	54.9	361	68.2
	5.0	14.8	18.9	283	3.87	56.6	67.1	439	81.9
	6.3	18.4	23.4	341	3.81	68.2	82.0	533	97.9

FIG. C RECTANGULAR

Size D × B	Thickness t	Mass M	Sectional Area A	2nd Moment of Area I		Radius of gyration r		Section modulus Z = I/y		Torsional of inertia J	Torsional modulus C
				x–x	y–y	x–x	y–y	x–x	y–y		
mm	mm	kg/m	cm^2	cm^4	cm^4	cm	cm	cm^3	cm^3	cm^4	cm^3
50 × 50	2.6	3.03	3.86	12.4	5.45	1.79	1.19	4.96	3.63	12.1	5.90
	3.2	3.66	4.66	14.5	6.31	1.77	1.16	5.82	4.21	14.2	6.81
80 × 40	3.2	5.67	7.22	58.10	19.10	2.84	1.63	14.50	9.56	46.1	16.10
	4.0	6.97	8.88	69.60	22.60	2.80	1.59	17.40	11.30	55.1	18.90
100 × 50	3.2	7.18	9.14	117	39.10	3.58	2.07	23.5	15.60	93.3	26.40
	4.0	8.86	11.30	142	46.70	3.55	2.03	28.4	18.70	113.0	31.40
	5.0	10.90	13.90	170	55.10	3.50	1.99	34.0	22.00	135.0	37.00

Fig. A

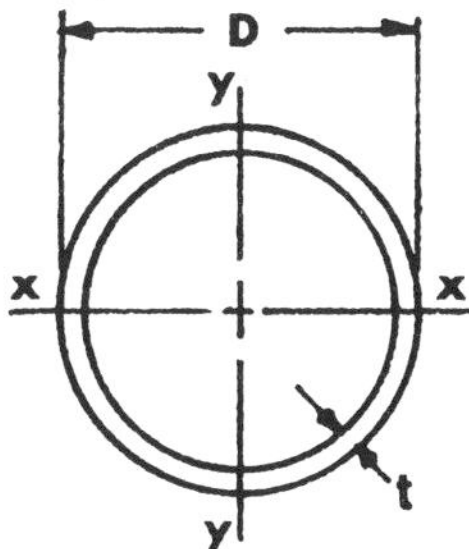

Fig. B

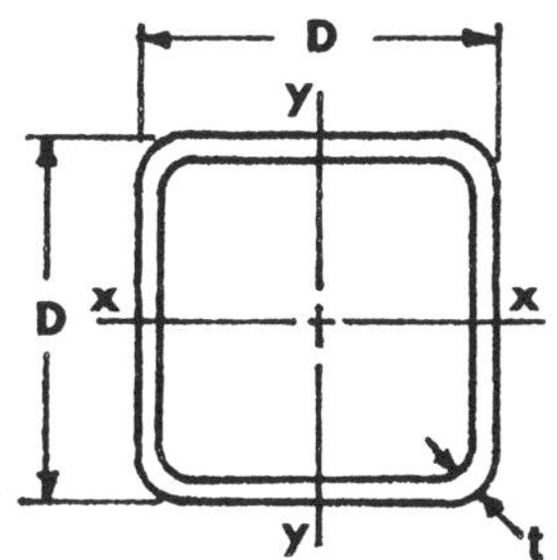

Fig. C

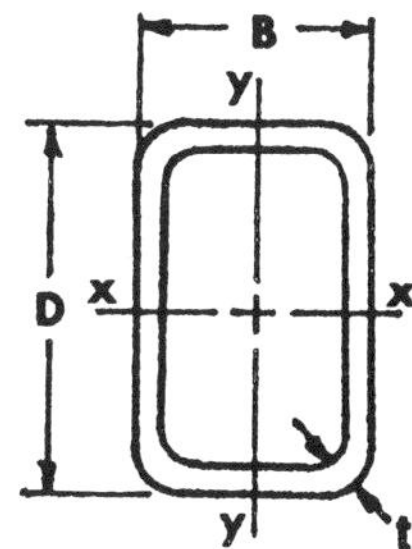

METALS 2.1.7

Ferrous metals: Open sections – Construction, selection and use

TYPICAL APPLICATIONS: All types and sizes of load bearing structure, bridges, building frames, process plant construction, ship and offshore rig building, cranes, storage and materials handling, vehicle chassis and trailers, test rigs, masts and pylons, piers and jetties.

DEFINITIONS:

Straight steel members of uniform open section throughout where flange and web thicknesses are small compared with the overall section dimensions.

CONSTRUCTION

These are of hot-rolled seamless construction from BS 4360 steel, complying with grades 43 (A to E inclusive), 50 (B and C) and 55 (C and E). All sections are supplied in a semi-finished state in standard lengths coated with a rust-preventing red-oxide primer. Dimensional tolerances are closely controlled and outer surfaces are flat and smooth.

NOTES ON SELECTION AND USE

Joists, channels and angles provide general purpose structural members with high strength properties at relatively low cost. All can be easily welded, bolted or riveted and lend themselves to applications where structural integrity is the highest priority, such as frameworks for small industrial buildings, process plant structures and loadbearing test rigs. The 'I' section joist is the most widely adaptable for all types of loading including direct tension, shear, bending and torsion, although for larger work reference should be made to BS 4 for 'universal' beams and columns. The joist sections have taper flanges which, while increasing their second moment of area, require taper washers to be used when bolting directly through the flanges. Channel sections are particularly useful for uprights and baseplates and when two are bolted back to back provide very strong 'I' sections. Angles are general purpose sections, often used for ties and bracing, and when two are bolted back to back form strong 'T' sections. To avoid brittle fracture when welded structures are specified, for extreme environmental conditions or where shock loading is likely, the requirements of BS 4360 for materials and BS 449 for construction must be followed. Note that welded work, although often easier to do, is often not as easy to modify or transport as a bolted structure.

REFERENCES

BS 4 :	Structural steel sections Part 1 : 1980 Specification for hot-rolled sections
BS 449 :	Specification for the use of structural steel in building (See also BS 5950) Part 2 : 1969 Metric units
BS 4360 : 1990	Specification for weldable structural steels
BS 4848 :	Specification for hot-rolled structural steel sections (See also BS 4)
BS 5950 :	Structural use of steelwork in building (See also BS 449)

METALS 2.1.2

Ferrous metals: Table of properties

JOISTS

To BS 4 : Part 1 where marked *
NOTE: Flanges have five degree taper

Designation		Depth of section D	Width of section B	Thickness		Area of section	2nd Moment of Area		Radius of gyration		Section modulus		Plastic modulus	
Nominal size	Mass per metre			Web t	Flange T		Axis x–x	Axis y–y	Axis x–x	Axis y–y	Axis x–x	Axis y–y	Axis x–x	Axis y–y
mm	kg	mm	mm	mm	mm	cm²	cm⁴	cm⁴	cm	cm	cm³	cm³	cm³	cm³
178 × 102	21.54 *	117.8	101.6	5.3	9.0	27.4	1519	139.2	7.44	2.25	170.9	27.41	193.0	44.48
152 × 89	17.09 *	152.4	88.9	4.9	8.3	21.8	881.1	85.98	6.36	1.99	115.6	19.34	131.0	31.29
127 × 76	13.36 *	127.0	76.2	4.5	7.6	17.0	475.9	50.18	5.29	1.72	74.94	13.17	85.23	21.29
102 × 64	9.65 *	101.6	63.5	4.1	6.6	12.3	217.6	25.30	4.21	1.43	42.84	7.97	48.98	12.91
76 × 76	12.65	76.2	76.2	5.1	8.4	16.3	158.6	52.03	3.12	1.78	41.62	13.60	48.84	22.51

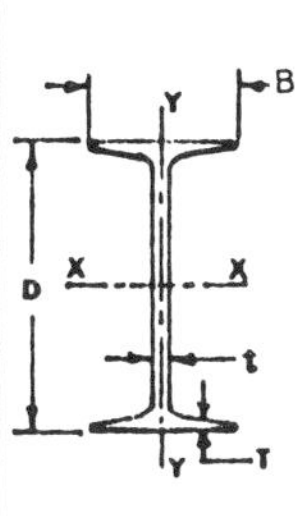

CHANNELS

To BS 4 : Part 1
NOTE: Flanges have five degree taper

Designation		Depth of section D	Width of section B	Thickness		Dim	Area of section	2nd Moment of Area		Radius of gyration		Section modulus		Plastic modulus	
Nominal size	Mass per metre			Web t	Flange T	c_y		Axis x–x	Axis y–y	Axis x–x	Axis y–y	Axis x–x	Axis y–y	Axis x–x	Axis y–y
mm	kg	mm	mm	mm	mm	cm	cm²	cm⁴	cm⁴	cm	cm	cm³	cm³	cm³	cm³
178 × 89	26.81 *	177.8	88.9	7.6	12.3	2.76	34.15	1753	241.0	7.16	2.66	197.2	39.29	229.6	75.44
127 × 64	14.90 *	127.0	63.5	6.4	9.2	1.94	18.98	482.5	67.23	5.04	1.88	75.99	15.25	89.4	29.31
102 × 51	10.42	101.6	50.8	6.1	7.6	1.51	13.28	207.7	29.10	3.95	1.48	40.89	8.16	48.8	15.71
76 × 38	6.70	76.2	38.1	5.1	6.8	1.19	8.53	74.14	10.66	2.95	1.12	19.46	4.07	23.4	7.76

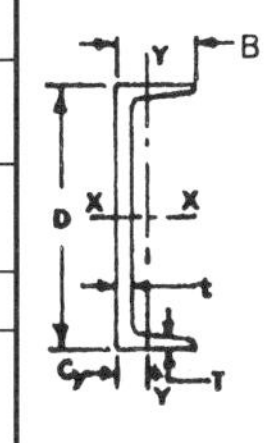

EQUAL ANGLES

To BS 4848 : Part 4

Designation		Mass per metre	Area of section	Dimension	2nd Moment of Area	Radius of gyration	Section modulus	Plastic modulus
Size A	Thickness t			c	Axis x–x, y–y	Axis x–x, y–y	Axis x–x, y–y	Axis x–x, y–y
mm	mm	kg	cm²	cm	cm⁴	cm	cm³	cm³
100 × 100	15	21.9	27.9	3.02	249	2.98	35.6	64.77
60 × 60	10	8.69	11.1	1.85	34.9	1.78	8.41	0.32
40 × 40	6	3.52	4.48	1.20	6.31	1.19	2.26	4.13
25 × 25	5	1.77	2.26	0.80	1.20	0.73	0.71	1.30

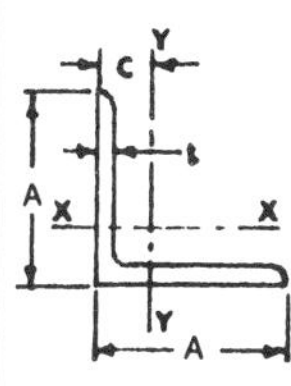

UNEQUAL ANGLES

To BS 4848 : Part 4

Designation		Mass per metre	Area of section	Dimension		2nd Moment of Area		Radius of gyration		Section modulus		Plastic modulus	
Size A × B	Thickness t			c_x	c_y	Axis x–x	Axis y–y	Axis x–x	Axis y–y	Axis x–x	Axis y–y	Axis x–x	Axis y–y
mm	mm	kg	cm²	cm	cm	cm⁴	cm⁴	cm	cm	cm³	cm³	cm³	cm³
125 × 75	12	17.8	22.7	4.31	1.84	354	95.5	3.95	2.05	43.2	16.9	77.36	31.42
100 × 65	10	12.3	15.6	3.36	1.63	154	51.0	3.14	1.81	23.2	10.5	41.91	19.41
80 × 60	8	8.34	10.6	2.55	1.56	66.3	31.8	2.50	1.73	12.2	7.16	22.17	13.08
65 × 50	8	6.75	8.60	2.11	1.37	34.8	17.7	2.01	1.44	7.93	4.89	14.40	8.94

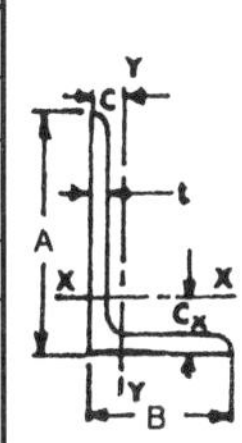

Note: Reference should be made to BS 449 for material grades where section thicknesses used are in excess of 20mm

SUPPLIERS

METALS: Ferrous metals

COMPANY	ADDRESS	TELEPHONE	FAX
Barworth Flockton Ltd	Ecclesfield SHEFFIELD S30 3XH	0742 468291	0742 454230
British Bright Bar Ltd	Bloomfield Road Tipton DUDLEY W Midlands DY4 9EP	021-520 8141	021-520 8929
Ductile Cold Mill (Glynwed Steels)	Jubilee Works Charles Street WILLENHALL W Midlands WV13 1HP	0902 366941	0902 633274
Goodfellow Advanced Materials A Division of Goodfellow Metals Ltd	The Science Park CAMBRIDGE CB4 4DJ	0223 420631	0223 420639
Kiveton Park Steel & Wire Works Ltd	Kiveton Park SHEFFIELD S Yorks S31 8NQ	0909 770252	0909 772949
Lee Bright Bars	P O BOX 54 Meadow Hall SHEFFIELD S Yorks S9 1HU	0742 437272	0742 431277
Longmore Brothers, Glynwed Steels Ltd	Springfield Steel Works Mill Street Darlaston WEDNESBURY W Midlands WS10 8TJ	021-526 4122	021-526 3027
Macreadys Glynwed Steels Ltd	Paynes Lane RUGBY Warks CV21 2UW	0788 542191	0788 540259
Rotherham Engineering Steels	PO BOX 50 Aldwarke Lane ROTHERHAM S60 1DW	0709 382141	0709 826363
Stockbridge Engineering Steels	Stockbridge SHEFFIELD S Yorks S30 5JA	0742 882361	0742 885033

USEFUL ADDRESSES

METALS: Ferrous metals

COMPANY	TELEPHONE
British Independent Steel Producers Association 5 Cromwell Road LONDON SW7 2HX	071 581 0231
Institute of Materials 1 Carlton House Terrace LONDON SW1Y 5DB	071 839 4071
Metal Finishing Association 10 Vyse Street BIRMINGHAM B18 6LT	021 236 2657
METCOM Mechanical & Metal Trades Confederation Savoy Tower Renfrew Street GLASGOW G2 3BZ	041 332 0826
Stainless Steel Fabricators Association 77 Renfrew Street GLASGOW G2 3BZ	041 332 0826
Steel Castings Research Trade Association 7 East Bank Road SHEFFIELD S2 3PT	0742 728647

METALS 2.1.9

Aluminium alloys: Forms, processes, selection and use

TYPICAL APPLICATIONS: Cladding, structures, castings, forgings for aircraft, extrusions for window frames, yacht fittings, fabricated frames and chassis for motor transport, sand cast and die cast automotive parts, ship superstructures, lightweight building frames.

DEFINITION

A non-ferrous metal whose major component is aluminium.

FORMS AND PROCESSES

Common forms of supply are: bar, tube, plate, sheet strip, extrusion and powder and ingots for casting. For semi-finished forms (eg. tube) the alloy is available as *non-heat treated* or *heat treated* and within these two states several intermediate conditions are available with a universal code letter designation system for each. Aluminium alloys can be sand or die cast, forged, rolled, pressed, extruded, drawn and formed at a relatively low cost compared with steels due to their lower melting point. For most applications no additional surface protection is needed as a natural oxidic layer builds up on the surface. Where appearance or other needs dictate, anodic (anodising) protection can be given. Most of these alloys can suffer fast, localised corrosion if in direct contact with dissimilar metals (see Appendix C).

NOTES ON SELECTION AND USE

The elastic stiffness of a structural aluminium alloy is about one third that of an equivalent steel member but it is approaching one third of its weight, so presenting the designer with considerable energy saving over steel if the product being designed has to move or be moved. Its high resistance to corrosion without any additional surface protection is a significant engineering gain over ferrous materials, which may also be a cost advantage because there is no need for post-fabrication surface coatings. Initial semi-finished material costs are high and products should therefore be designed to avoid waste material, unnecessary bulk and post-machining and finishing. In this context, a rapidly growing technique is the use of extrusions, often with complex cross-sections which, when cut off a length, offer the solution to hitherto expensive fabrications. Examples of this cost effective design approach can be seen from deck fittings on yachts to the outer casings of electric motors. Where there is design complexity in all three dimensions, then die-casting offers cost advantages over fabrication.

For extremely high strength (eg. aircraft parts) forgings can be used which, when properly designed, minimise both material used and at the same time lower the risk of damage arising from stress concentrations commonly found in fabricated parts. Fastening with bolts, screws and rivets is easy and cheap, but care is needed to avoid local overstressing and corrosion from contact with different metals. Most aluminium alloys are weldable, but it is important to select correct material and rod grades where structural or 'life or limb' products are concerned. All alloys can be bonded and in many applications requiring lightweight, high stiffness materials, composite sections are made using aluminium alloy skins, honeycombs or foams in conjunction with other materials such as wood, paper and plastics.

REFERENCES

BS 1470 : 1987 Spec. for wrought aluminium & al. alloys for general engineering purposes: plate sheet & strip
BS 1471 : 1972 Spec. for wrought aluminium & aluminium alloys for general engineering purposes – drawn tube
BS 1472 : 1972 Specification for wrought aluminium & aluminium alloys for general engineering purposes – forging stock and forgings
BS 1473 : 1972 Specification for wrought aluminium & aluminium alloys for general engineering purposes – rivet, bolt and screw stock
BS 1474 : 1987 Specification for wrought aluminium & aluminium alloys for general engineering purposes – bars, extruded round tube and sections
BS 1490 : 1988 Spec. for aluminium and aluminium alloy ingots and castings for general engineering purposes

ALUMINIUM ALLOYS – TABLE OF FORMS AND PROPERTIES

For stress/strain calculations, the modulus of elasticity of these alloys is 69-70 GN/m. Note that UTS only is given for strength, this is because the elastic limit for aluminium alloys is not clearly defined. Most suppliers will provide a value for a proof stress for a particular material if requested. The table shows old and new specification numbers as well as the equivalent ISO ref. to assist those familiar with the traditional methods of designation. These old numbers must not, in any way, be confused with letter / number system for defining CONDITION. Please refer to the table overleaf for full details of heat-treatment conditions, and always contact suppliers if in doubt. Stock sizes of material commonly available are also shown overleaf and it should be noted that aluminium extrusions are often a cost-effective solution to a design problem, even if they have to be specially made.

SPECIFICATION No.			FORMS OF MATERIAL AVAILABLE								CONDITION						WELDABILITY		STRENGTH		DENSITY	APPLICATIONS
SPEC. (BS) Ref. No.	Old BS Ref.	ISO Ref.	Plate Sheet and Strip BS 1470	Drawn Tube BS 1471	Forging Stock BS 1472	Forgings BS 1472	Rivet Stock For Forging BS 1473	Bolt and Screw Forging Stock BS 1473	Bars Extruded Tube and Section BS 1474	Wire BS 1475	Letter/number grades relating to heat-treated and non-heat-treated states (see overleaf for details) ▨ = common stock material						Inert Gas Arc (MIG or TIG)	Resistance (Spot, seam flash and stud)	Ultimate Tensile (Varies with condition) MN/m² MIN.	MAX.	Kg/m³	Aluminium and its alloys can be used across a wide range of applications providing it is correctly specified. CONTACT SUPPLIERS IF IN DOUBT.
1080A	1A	Al 99.8	√							√	M	O		H4		H8	Excel.	Good	90	125		Excellent corrosion resistance
1050A	1B	Al 99.5	√	√	√	√	√		√	√		O		H4		H8	Excel.	V/good	55	135		Good corrosion resistance
1200	1C	Al 99.0	√	√					√		M	O	H2	H4	H6	H8	Excel.	V/good	70	150	2710	Cheapest low strength grade
3103	N3	Al Mn1	√							√		O	H2	H4	H6	H8	Excel.	Excel.	90	195		Low strength/good formability
5251	N4	Al Mg2	√	√	√	√			√	√	M	O	H3		H6		V/good.	Excel.	160	275	2690	Marine panelling & structures
5154A	N5	Al Mg3.5	√	√	√	√	√		√	√		O	H2	H4			V/good.	Excel.	215	325		Good all round applications
5083	N8	Al Mg4.5 Mn	√	√	√	√			√		M	O	H2	H4			Excel.	Excel.	280	–	2660	Shipbuilding, road and rail uses
6063	H9	Al Mg Si		√	√	√			√	√			TB	TF			V/good.	V/good.	100	140		Architectural eg window frames
2031	H12	Al Cu2 Ni1 Mg Fe Si			√	√							TB	TF			–	–	310	–		General engineering forgings
2041A	H15	Al Cu4 Si Mg	√	√	√	√	√	√	√	√			TB	TF			Poor	Excel.	245	440		High strength with excellent weldability* but poor resistance
CLAD 2014A	H(C)15	Al Cu4 Si Mg	√										TB	TF					245	440		to corrosion. * Resistance only
2618A	H16	Al Cu2 Mg1.5 Fe1 Ni1			√	√								TF			–	–	430	–		High strength forgings
6061	H20	Al Mg1 Si Cu		√				√	√	√			TB	TF			V/good.	V/good.	190	–		Good machinability
6082	H30	Al Si1 Mg Mn	√	√	√	√	√	√	√			O	TB	TF			V/good.	V/good.	115	295	2700	Vehicles, bridges, cranes

ORDERING: STATE SPECIFICATION NO. FOLLOWED BY BS NO. AND REQUIRED CONDITION
e.g. *" ROLLED SHEET 2mm x 1000mm x 2000mm SPEC. TO 3123 / BS 1470 / H4 "*

STOCK CONDITIONS (SHOWN THUS ▨ ABOVE) ARE GENERALLY AVAILABLE FROM SUPPLIERS, BUT CONFIRMATION SHOULD BE OBTAINED BEFORE ORDERING

METALS 2.1.11

Aluminium alloys: Table of heat treatment conditions

The following conditions may be specified for aluminium alloys to enhance properties such as: strength, formability, and corrosion-resistance. Material forms such as special extrusions and forgings will not have a 'stock condition' specified, and it is therefore important to make the correct selection. For instance, where it is a choice between 'TB' or 'TF' (see alloys 2031 to 6061 overleaf) TB gives better corrosion resistance but TF is a more stable condition.

LETTER GRADE	MATERIAL CONDITION
M	As manufactured. Material which acquires some temper from shaping processes in which there is no special control over thermal treatment or amount of strain hardening.
O	Annealed. Material which is fully annealed to obtain the lowest strength condition.
H1, H2 H3, H4 H5, H6 H7, H8	Strain hardened. Material subjected to the application of cold work after annealing (or hot forming) or to a combination of cold work and partial annealing / stabilizing in order to secure the specified mechanical properties. The designations are in ascending order of tensile strength.
TB	Solution heat-treated and naturally aged. Material which receives no cold work after solution heat treatment except as may be required to flatten or straighten it. Properties of some alloys in this temper are unstable.
TD	Solution heat-treated, cold-worked and naturally aged.
TE	Cooled from an elevated temperature shaping process and precipitation-treated.
TF	Solution heat-treated and precipitation-treated.
TH	Solution heat-treated, cold-worked and then precipitation-treated.

METALS 2.1.12

Aluminium alloys: Sizes of standard sections

STANDARD SIZES OF MEDIUM STRENGTH GENERAL PURPOSE SECTIONS

FLAT BARS

Width (mm)	Thickness (mm) 1.6	2.5	3	4	6	10	12	16	25
10			√		√				
12		√	√	√	√	√			
16		√	√	√	√	√			
20		√	√	√	√				
25	√	√	√	√	√	√	√	√	
30		√	√	√	√	√	√		
40		√	√	√	√	√	√		
50			√	√	√	√	√		
60			√		√	√	√		
80			√		√	√	√		√
100			√		√	√	√	√	√
120					√	√		√	
160					√	√		√	
200						√		√	
250						√		√	

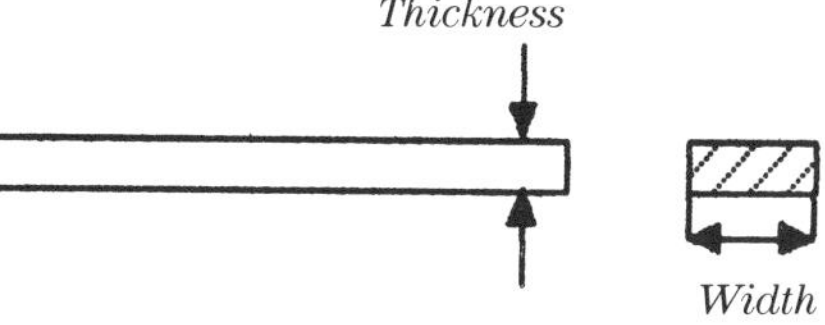

EQUAL ANGLES

Leg (mm)	Thickness (mm) 1.6	3	6	10
10		√		
12	√	√		
16		√		
20	√	√		
25	√	√	√	
30	√	√		
40		√	√	
50		√	√	√
60		√	√	
80		√	√	√
100		√	√	

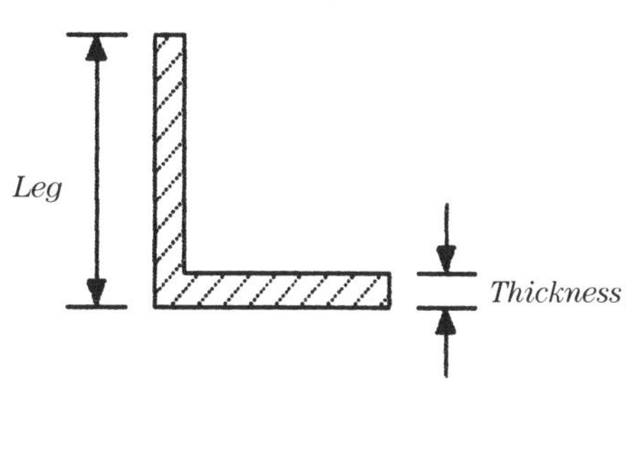

ROUND AND SQUARE BAR

Size (mm)	●	■	Size (mm)	●	■	Size (mm)	●	■
3	√	√	28	√	√	110	√	
4	√	√	30	√	√	120	√	√
5	√	√	32	√		130	√	
6	√	√	35	√		140	√	
7	√		40	√	√	160	√	√
8	√	√	45	√		180	√	
9	√		50	√	√	200	√	√
10	√	√	55	√				
12	√	√	60	√	√			
14	√		65	√				
16	√	√	70	√				
18	√		75	√				
20	√	√	80	√	√			
22	√		90	√				
25	√	√	100	√	√			

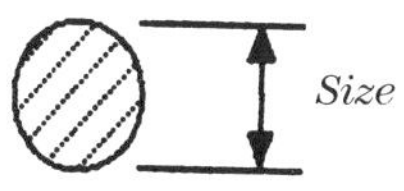

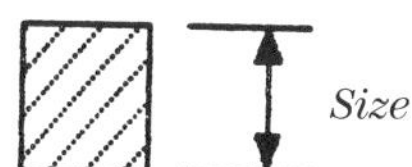

NOTE: Flats and angles are typically 6063, 6082 MAT

NOTE: Bar is typically 6063, 6082, 5083 MAT

SUPPLIERS

METALS: Aluminium alloys

COMPANY	ADDRESS	TELEPHONE	FAX
Alcan High Duty Extrusions Ltd	Lillyhall WORKINGTON Cumbria CA14 4JY	0900 2581	0900 66541
Aluminium Corporation Ltd	Dolgarrog CONWY Gwynedd LL32 8JH	0492 660211	0492 660703
Ano-Coil Ltd	Chippenham Drive Kingston MILTON KEYNES Bucks MK10 0AN	0908 75642	0908 643956
Banbury Aluminium	Southam Road BANBURY Oxfordshire OX16 7SN	0295 264444	0295 271244
BKL Extrusions Ltd	Factory Centre Kings Norton BIRMINGHAM W Midlands B30 3HF	021-458 2055	021-433 4000
E & E Kaye Ltd	Queensway ENFIELD Middlesex EN3 4SS	081 804 1601	081 804 8424
Goodfellow Advanced Materials A Division of Goodfellow Metals Ltd	The Science Park CAMBRIDGE CB4 4DJ	0223 420631	0223 420639
Hoogovens Aluminium UK Ltd	Prudential Buildings 5 St Philips Place Colmore Road BIRMINGHAM W Midlands B3 2PW	021-236 5777	021-233 3176
Ormiston Wire	1 Fleming Way Worton Road ISLEWORTH Middx TW7 6EW	081-569 7287	081-569 8601
Sapa Ltd	Sawpit Industrial Estate Tibshelf DERBY DE5 5NQ	0773 872761	0773 874389

USEFUL ADDRESSES

METALS: Aluminium alloys

ADDRESS	TELEPHONE
Aluminium Extruders Association Broadway House Calthorpe Road Fiveways BIRMINGHAM B15 1TN	021 456 1103
Aluminium Federation Ltd Broadway House Calthorpe Road Fiveways BIRMINGHAM B15 1TN	021 456 1103
Aluminium Stockholders Association P O BOX 111 Todd Road ST HELENS Merseyside WA9 1JD	0744 23051
British Non-Ferrous Metals Federation 10 Greenfield Crescent BIRMINGHAM B15 3AU	021 456 3322

PLASTICS 2.2.1

Plastics: Forms, processes, selection and use

TYPICAL APPLICATIONS: *Thermoplastics* – Advertising signs, plumbing and water pipes, guttering, window frames, domestic appliances, motor car interior and exterior parts, cable insulation, waterproof sheeting, clothing, furnishings, electrical and mechanical components. Thermosets – Boat hulls, car bodies, domestic and industrial working surfaces, adhesives, high voltage and high temperature electro-mechanical parts, electrical and thermal insulation materials, aerospace structural parts, storage tanks and vessel liners, gas and electrical enclosures.

DEFINITIONS

Thermoplastic: A plastics material capable of being formed and reformed repeatedly by heating and cooling without any change in its properties.
Thermosetting: A plastics material which, after forming cannot be reformed by heating without a change in its properties.

FORMS AND PROCESSES

Both types are supplied either as a raw material (granules, powders, liquids) or in a semi-finished form (sheet, rod, film, etc.). They can be filled, reinforced or laminated with a wide range of materials and are usually available in a variety of colours. Common methods of making finished products include: extrusion, injection moulding, sheet thermoforming, compression and transfer moulding, hand layup, blow moulding, casting and fabrication.

NOTES ON SELECTION AND USE

All plastics creep to some extent under the influence of temperature and/or stress. Thermosetting materials generally creep the least and have higher strength and dimensional stability than thermoplastics, but are also more expensive. Manufacturing times are fastest for thermoplastics components and, unlike thermosets, factory scrap can be recycled. Plastics can give off harmful fumes during moulding and if exposed to excessive heat. Electrical insulation, corrosion resistance, low weight and low coefficients of friction are properties common to most plastics. A broad division can be drawn for thermoplastics between 'bulk' and 'engineering' applications, the former covering such things as: packing, advertising signs and textiles and the latter including mechanisms, casings, seals and joints. Note that many engineering uses are in low mass, high value, products where the plastic often replaces traditional iron or aluminium castings or sheet metal work. The advantage of plastics mouldings is that they require little or no additional machining or protective coating. Thermosetting plastics are commonly used to create 'composite' materials such as GRP (glass reinforced plastics) where the glass may be in the form of continuous fibres, chopped strand or particles (see also 2.3.1). Several other types of reinforcement are available including carbon fibre which, when used properly, can increase the strength of the plastic to that of some structural metals. Metallic particles may be added to plastic for moulding to screen out the effects of electro-magnetic induction (EMI) on electronic products. The specification and performance of plastics and composite materials often varies between manufacturers and therefore detailed data on properties, based on approved test methods should be obtained from suppliers before final selection is made.

REFERENCES

BS 1755 : Glossary of terms used in the plastics industry
BS 2782 : Methods of testing plastics Parts 0–11 (1976–92)
BS 4618 : Recommendations for the presentation of plastics design data
BS 7008 : Aquisition and presentation of comparable data for basic properties of plastics
BS 7010 : 1988 Code of practice for a system of tolerances for the dimensions of plastics mouldings
ISO/TR 8244 – 1988 Plastics – Phenolic resins – Basis for classification

PLASTICS 2.2.2

Plastics: Table of plastics properties and forms of supply

No.	PROPERTIES OF PLASTICS MATERIALS * INDICATES A RELATED STANDARD SEE BELOW	Familiar Names	Chemical Abbreviation	Density kg/m³	Young's Modulus GN/m² @ 20 °C	Proof Stress (Max) MN/m² @ 20 °C	Impact Strength (Relative scale where: 0 = Very brittle, 10 = Very tough)		Heat Distortion Temp. (max.) @ 5 MN/m²	Average Water Absorption (3 mm thick for 24 hours)	Chemical Attack U = unaffected SA = strong acid	Solvent Attack U = unaffected SS = some solvents	Max. coefficient of linear expansion μm/(mK)	Available in: R = raw form SF = semi-finished	Mouldability and Effect of Sunlight: E = excellent G = good F = fair B = bad	
No.	MATERIAL			ρ	E	σ	@ −20 °C	@ +20 °C	°C	of vol			α		Mouldability	Sunlight
	THERMOPLASTICS:															
1	Acrylic	PERSPEX	PMMA	1200	3.1	76	0.2	0.4	95	0.35	SA	SS	90	R/SF	E	G
2	Acrylonitrile/ Butadiene/Styrene	CYCOLAC	ABS	1000	2.8	62	2.0	8.0	107	0.2	SA	SS	130	R	G	F
3	Cellulose Acetate Butyrate		CAB	1220	1.4	48	0.5	4.5	108	2.2	SA	SS	170	R/SF	E	G
4	Nylon 11	MARANYL	N	1100	–	60	1.0	1.2	155	0.4	SA	SS	150	R	G	B
5	Nylon 66	MARANYL	N	1150	1.5	84	0.7	1.5	182	0.9	SA	U	150	R/SF	G	B
6	Polytetrafluoroethylene	FLUON	PTFE	2200	0.6	41	1.7	2.7	121	0	U	U	200	R/SF	F	E
7	Polyacetal	DELRIN	PA	1400	2.8	69	1.0	1.0	169	0.12	SA	U	80	R	G	F
8	Polyethylene (LD)	POLYTHENE	LDPE	900	0.24	16	No Break	No Break	50	0.01	SA	SS	180	R/SF	E	B
9	Polypropylene	PROPATHENE	PP	900	1.0	38	0.25	4.0	110	0.01	SA	U	110	R	E	F
10	Polystyrene	LUSTREX	PS	1000	3.5	84	0.15	0.35	113	0.2	SA	SS	80	R/SF	E	B
11	Polyvinylchoride	DARVIC	PVC	1400	2.4	59	0.7	2.0	74	0.5	U	SS	50	R/SF	F/G	F/G
12	Polycarbonate	MAKROLON	PC	1200	2.2	66	8.0	10.0+	143	0.3	U	SS	70	R/SF	G	F
13	Polyethylene (HD)	POLYTHENE	HDPE	970	1.0	38	1.0	8.0	80	0.010	S/A	U	130	R/SF	G	B
	THERMOSETTING:															
14	Epoxides (see also 2.3.2)	ARALDITE	ER	3000	4.1	84	0.2	0.6	299	BAD	U	U	90	R	E	F
15	Melamine Formaldehyde	MELAMINE	MF	1500	9.0	90	0.15	0.25	205	0.3	SA	U	40	R/SF	E	F
16	Phenol Formaldehyde (filled)	BAKELITE	PF	1400	8.4	58	0.15	0.4	127	1	SA	U	45	R	F/G	F
17	Polyester (glass filled) (see also 2.3.2)	FIBRE-GLASS	GRP	1500	12.0	120	8.0	10.0	175	–	S/A	SS	36	R	G	F/G
18	Polyester (dough)	BEETLE	DMC	2000	14.0	70	2.0	4.0	230	0.15	U	SS	34	R	G	B
19	Urea formaldehyde (filled)		UF	1500	10.4	90	0.15	0.25	138	0.8	SA	U	27	R/SF	E	F

* SELECTED STANDARDS MAKING SPECIFIC REFERENCE TO MATERIALS IN THIS TABLE AS FOLLOWS:

MATERIAL	*STANDARD*
1	BS 3990, 4305, 6340 6747 7015, 7253
2	BS 4935, 5255, 5391, 5392
3	BS 1524
5	BS 4928, 5409
6	BS 6564, 4375, 5106, 6974, BS Aero 2G210, Aero M57
8, 13	BS 3412, 4928, 6234, 7344
9	BS 5139, 4991, 4928, 4881, 5254, 7303
10	BS 1493, 3126, 3837, 6203
11	BS 2571, 1763, 2571, 3757, 3869, 2739, 4023, 4808, 6346
12	BS 6005
15	BS EN 438
17	BS 3532, 4549, 4928, 4994 (SEE ALSO 2.3.2), EN 2377

SUPPLIERS

PLASTICS

COMPANY	ADDRESS	TELEPHONE	FAX
Akzo Chemicals Ltd Akzo Plastics Division	1–5 Queens Road Hersham WALTON ON THAMES Surrey KT12 5NL	0932 247891	0932 231204
B P Chemicals Ltd BP Polyolefins (UK) Division	Bo'ness Road GRANGEMOUTH FK3 9XH		
Cabot Plastics Ltd	Gate Street DUKINFIELD Cheshire SK16 4RU	061 330 5051	
CIBA-Geigy Plastics & Addtives Co Plastics Division	Hinxton Road Duxford CAMBRIDGE CB2 4QA	0223 832121	0223 838404
Dow Chemical Co. Ltd	Hayes Road Sully PENARTH South Glamorgan CF6 2YB	0446 737151	0446 743424
Du Pont Polymer Products Dept	Maylands Avenue HEMEL HEMPSTEAD Herts HP2 7DP		
Evode Plastics Ltd	Wanlip Road SYSTON Leicestershire LE7 8PD	0533 696752	0533 692960
Hoechst UK Ltd Polymers Division	Stafford Park 12 TELFORD Shropshire TF3 3BJ	0952 292747	0952 292383
ICI Chemical Polymers Ltd	PO Box 54 Wilton MIDDLESBROUGH Cleveland TS6 8JA	0642 45144	
Polypenco Ltd	PO Box 56 83 Bridge Road East WELWYN GARDEN CITY Herts AL7 1LA	0707 321221	0707 327581
Vitacom Ltd	Bank Street Clayton MANCHESTER M11 4AS	061 223 3241	061 655 3618
Zotefoams Ltd	675 Mitcham Road CROYDON CR9 3AL	081-684 3622	081-684 7571

USEFUL ADDRESSES

PLASTICS

ADDRESS	TELEPHONE
British Plastics Federation 5 Belgrave Square LONDON SW1X 8PD	071 235 9483
Plastics and Rubber Institute 11 Hobart Place LONDON SW1W 0HL	071 245 9555
Plastics Machinery Distributors Association Down House Broomhill Road LONDON SW18 4JQ	081 874 3299
British Rigid Urethane Foam Manufacturers Assoc. 206 Corn Exchange Hanging Ditch MANCHESTER M4 3BQ	061 835 1031
RAPRA Technology Ltd Shawbury SHREWSBURY SY4 4NR	0939 250383

OTHER MATERIALS 2.3.1

Miscellaneous metals and non-metals: Forms, processes, selection and use

TYPICAL APPLICATIONS: **Copper** – electrical conductors; **Brass** – electric switch parts; **Phosphor bronze** – plain bearings; **Natural rubber** – tyre treads; **Synthetic rubber** – cable sheathing; **Carbon-fibre** – aircraft structures; **Wood** – structural members for building; **Glass** – domestic glazing; **Ceramics** – high voltage insulators; **Cement** – civil engineering construction.

FORMS AND PROCESSES

Non-ferrous metals and alloys such as **brass** and **phosphor bronze** are available as ingots, sheets, wires, bars and tubes, the latter being especially economic for the manufacture of bearings and bushes. In some of the traditional areas of use for these materials their high relative cost means that in recent years they have been replaced by plastics. **Rubbers**, both natural and synthetic, are available normally in sponge or solid sheet or tube (hose) form, in a variety of hardnesses. Raw synthetic material for moulding is available, but it has a short shelf life. **Carbon fibre reinforced plastics** are supplied either in the form of raw materials or as pre-impregnated sheets for shaping and curing by the user. **Wood** is supplied in a variety of forms and mouldings and where predictable, structural performance is needed, pre-fabricated plywood structures can be made to order. **Glass** is made in fibres, sheets, rods and tubes and can be annealed, treated and coated to improve performance. **Cement** can be supplied raw or in the form of concrete products such as slabs, bricks and pre-cast, reinforced sections.

NOTES ON SELECTION AND USE

Copper and copper-based materials are widely used as high conductors of heat and electricity and for water piping in heating installations. Areas of technology such as solar heating and underwater engineering are providing new applications, replacing those lost to plastics materials.

Lead. High density, resistance to radiation and use as an additive give lead unique advantages over other materials, but in areas such as weather protection it is being replaced by plastic and bitumen compounds.

Natural rubbers are still chosen for their superior properties such as elasticity, resilience, fatigue and chemical and thermal resistance even though they are being replaced by synthetics in less exacting applications.

Synthetic rubbers may be compounded for a variety of duties and are now used widely where environmental and chemical resistance is required including hosing and cabling and large sheeting applications.

Carbon fibres are relatively new as reinforcing materials, but nevertheless their outstanding ability to offer high-strength, low-weight advantages to structures has brought them into use in products ranging from sports goods to high performance cars. Care must be taken with suppliers because different manufacturing methods create wide variations in strength and quality. Finished products must also be protected from harsh environments.

Wood must be properly cut and dried to ensure good long-term properties and, where high structural integrity is needed, must be carefully inspected and tested beforehand. High structural performance and long life can now be achieved with modern laminating and jointing processes.

Glass is available as sheet, rod, tube, and fibre and can be reinforced, toughened, tinted and coated.

Ceramics, although once only used as insulating mediums, are now being more widely applied in areas of high mechanical and thermal stress, and can be supplied in semi-finished forms for machining into precision components.

REFERENCES

See facing table

OTHER MATERIALS 2.3.2

Rubber, composites, glasses and ceramics: Table of useful properties

NON FERROUS METALS

MATERIAL	GRADE OR TYPE	DENSITY	YOUNG'S MODULUS	TENSILE STRENGTH	APPLICATIONS NOTES	RELATED BS No.
		Kg/m^3	GN/m^2 (GPa)	MN/m^2 (MPa)		
COPPER	Pure	8900	124	400	Electrical wiring and high conducting components	BS 2870 to BS 2875 BS 6931
BRASS	Cu-Zn 70/30	8400	110	400	Marine and electrical parts	
PHOSPHOR BRONZE	Spring Temper	8800	110	800	Non-corrosive springs, switch parts, sleeve bushes	
LEAD	Pure	11000	14	40	Additive for metals, roof covering	BS 1178 BS 3332

POLYMERS AND RUBBER

MATERIAL	GRADE OR TYPE	DENSITY	YOUNG'S MODULUS	TENSILE STRENGTH	APPLICATIONS NOTES	RELATED BS No.
		Kg/m^3	GN/m^2 (GPa)	MN/m^2 (MPa)		
RUBBER	Natural (601 RHD)	900	0.05	20	Tyre treads, bridge bearings, elastic machine mountings	BS 1154 BS 903
RUBBER	Natural (351 RHD)	900	0.01	20	Rubber bands, sheeting, gaskets, abrasion resistant sheathing	BS 1154 BS 903
RUBBER	Synthetic 'Neoprene'	1250	0.01	24	Radiator hose, drive belts. Water and weather resistant.	BS 2752
RUBBER	Synthetic 'Hypalon'	1200	0.01	21	Sheeting, cable covers, acid hoses. Outstanding weather resistance	BS 6374 Aero 131, 136
RUBBER	Synthetic 'Nitrile'	1000	0.005	15	Oil resistant seals, gaskets, fabrics. Poor weathering.	BS 2751
STRUCTURAL FOAM	Polyphenylene oxide	900	1.7	32	Car fascia panels, typewriter and television cabinets	

COMPOSITES

MATERIAL	GRADE OR TYPE	DENSITY	YOUNG'S MODULUS	TENSILE STRENGTH	APPLICATIONS NOTES	RELATED BS No.
		Kg/m^3	GN/m^2 (GPa)	MN/m^2 (MPa)		
CARBON FIBRE + EPOXY	Continuous filament	1550	170	1500	Aircraft structural components, high performance car parts	
WOOD	White Pine	400	7	6 *	Doors, window frames, carpentry	
WOOD	English Oak	720	12	10 *	Furniture, panelling, specialist work	
PLYWOOD	Douglas Fir	560	12	6 *	Roof trusses and other building structures, cladding, panelling	BS 5268 BS EN 313

* Parallel to grain and in dry condition

GLASSES AND CERAMICS

MATERIAL	GRADE OR TYPE	DENSITY	YOUNG'S MODULUS	TENSILE STRENGTH	APPLICATIONS NOTES	RELATED BS No.
		Kg/m^3	GN/m^2 (GPa)	MN/m^2 (MPa)		
GLASS	Borosilicate	2200	65	55	Glass fibre, chemical and high temperature ware	BS 2598, BS 3496, 3691, 3749
GLASS	Soda/Lime/Silica	2500	70	50	Domestic and commercial glazing work	BS 952
GLASS	Lithium/ al. silicate	2500	85	120	High voltage and high temperature insulation	BS 4495 BS 1902 : Part 6 BS 3779
CEMENT	Portland	2200	45	3.4 (20) **	Civil engineering and general construction	BS 12 BS EN 196

** ( ) in compression

SUPPLIERS

OTHER MATERIALS

COMPANY	ADDRESS	TELEPHONE	FAX
COPPER AND COPPER BASED ALLOYS:			
Delta Extruded Metals Co Ltd	Greets Green Road WEST BROMWICH W Midlands B70 9ER	021-553 6188	021-553 6505
Goodfellow Metals Ltd	The Science Park CAMBRIDGE CB4 4DJ	0223 420631	0223 420639
RUBBERS (Natural):			
James Walker & Co Ltd	Lion Works WOKING GU22 8AP	0483 757575	0483 755711
RUBBERS (Synthetic):			
Arnew Park Rubber Ltd	Maybrook Road Castlevale Industrial Estate Minworth SUTTON COLDFIELD B76 8AX	021-351 3155	021-313 1192
James Walker & Co Ltd	Lion Works WOKING GU22 8AP	0483 757575	0483 755711
Victaulic Industrial Polymers	St Peters Road HUNTINGDON Cambridgeshire PE18 7DS	0480 411333	0480 50430
CARBON FIBRES:			
Fibreforce Composites Ltd	Fairoak Lane Whitehouse Ind Est RUNCORN WA7 3DU	0928 701515	0928 713572
WOOD:			
D W Archer Ltd	17–19 Rose Kiln Lane READING RG2 0JW	0734 866877	
Meyer Montague Ltd	New Docks SOUTHAMPTON	0703 229341	0703 334252
GLASS AND CERAMICS:			
The English Glass Co Ltd	Scudamore Road LEICESTER LE3 1UG	0533 871371	0533 312077
Morgan Matroc Ltd	St Peters Road Rugby WARWICKSHIRE CV21 3QR	0788 542166	0788 79787

USEFUL ADDRESSES

OTHER MATERIALS

ADDRESS	TELEPHONE
British Bronze and Brass Ingot Manufacturers Assoc. 136 Hagley Road BIRMINGHAM B16 9PN	021 454 4141
British Non-Ferrous Metals Federation 10 Greenfield Crescent BIRMINGHAM B15 3AU	021 456 3322
British Cement Association Wexham Springs SLOUGH SL3 6PL	0753 662727
Copper Development Association Orchard House Mutton Lane POTTERS BAR Herts EN6 3AP	0707 50711
Glass and Glazing Federation 44–48 Borough High Street LONDON SE1 1XB	071 403 7177
British Glass Manufacturers' Confederation Northumberland Road SHEFFIELD S10 2UA	0742 686201
Society of Glass Technology 20 Hallam Gate Road SHEFFIELD S10 5BT	0742 663168
Plastics and Rubber Institute 11 Hobart Place LONDON SW1W 0HL	071 245 9555
RAPRA Technology Ltd Shawbury SHREWSBURY SY4 4NR	0939 250383
TRADA Timber Research and Development Association Chiltern House Stocking Lane Hughenden Valley HIGH WYCOMBE Bucks HP14 4ND	024024 3091

Notes

SECTION 3 – FASTENERS

THREADED FASTENERS 3.1.1

Nuts, bolts, screws and washers: Construction, selection and use

TYPICAL APPLICATIONS: All types of engineering assembly ranging from precision miniature instruments to large scale civil and structural engineering. Usually where repair, modification or maintenance is anticipated. Especially high usage in automobile assembly, storage and materials handling equipment and petrochemical plant.

DEFINITIONS:

Bolt: A normally hexagon headed fastener with a circular section shank which has a 'v' thread for part of its length. **Screw:** A fastener with a variety of heads which is threaded all along the length of its shank. **Socket-headed screw:** A fastener with, typically, a hexagon socket set into a cap, countersunk, or button head. **Machine screw:** A screw fastener whose head has either a straight or recessed screwdriver slot. **Self-tapping screw:** A single component fastener which cuts its own thread when driven into a pre-made hole. **Washer:** An annular disc which is placed under a nut to distribute the load when it is tightened.

CONSTRUCTION: Most fasteners are made of low or medium carbon steel by machining (bright) or forging (black) with threads either cut or rolled. Corrosion resistance may be provided by zinc plating or galvanising. Materials such as stainless steels, bronzes and brasses may be specified for extreme environments. High performance fasteners are made from high tensile and alloy steels and these may be specially machined to reduce local stresses and increase fatigue-resistance.

NOTES ON SELECTION AND USE

The plain hexagon nut and bolt is the commonest engineering fastener and is supplied in a very wide range of standard sizes. Thread forms are almost universally standardized to ISO (metric) with 'UNC' and 'UNF' still used alongside metric in the USA. The fit between threads on nut and bolt is closely toleranced during manufacture and therefore if threads are to be coated or plated afterwards, wider clearances must be specified to the sizes given in the relevant standard. Allow sufficient space between nuts or bolt heads for easy spanner access. Socket-headed screws are often selected for a higher degree of precision or where space is limited. Machine screws are generally used where a flush fit is needed but where lower tightening torques are acceptable. Self-tapping screws are ideal for fast assembly of thin section material onto thicker structures where there is little or no rear access. Plain washers are standard for all bolted fixtures, with spring, crinkle (avoid these in soft materials where they may induce local failure) or tab washers being used to prevent loosening due to shock or vibration. Locking of the fastener may also be done by locknuts, castellated nuts, elastic stop nuts and spring nuts. Threads may also be coated with a locking adhesive. Load bearing members should apply forces to bolt shank not thread. Correct fastener selection should be based on: simplicity, minimising types and quantity, defining materials and finish, assessment of static and dynamic stresses. Check Aerospace standards (EN series) for specialist; high strength, low weight, low stress concentration fastening systems. General strength estimates may be made using the minor diameters shown in the table, but the relevant standard must be used for accurate work as other details concerning root dimensions need to be taken into account. All nuts and bolts can be supplied in a number of strength grades which are also listed in the standards. *'BS EN' (European) standards are now published which are* generally *similar to the current BS/ISO standard but are* not *exact equivalents.*

REFERENCES

BS 856: 1969 (1989)	Specification for wing nuts
BS 1936:	Specification for undercuts and runouts for screw threads
BS 2470: 1973 (1988)	Specification for hexagon socket screws and wrench keys. Inch series.
BS 3382:	Specification for electroplated coatings on threaded components
BS 3643:	ISO metric screw threads
BS 3692: 1967 (ISO 272)	Specification for ISO metric precision hexagon bolts, screws and nuts. Metric units
BS 4168:	Hexagon socket screws and wrench keys: Metric series
BS 4174: 1972	Specification for self-tapping screws and metallic drive screws
BS 4183: 1967	Specification for machine screws and machine screw nuts: Metric series
BS 6104:	Mechanical properties of fasteners (see also BS EN 20898)
BS 6105: 1981	Specification for corrosion – resistant stainless steel fasteners
BS 6322:	Tolerances for fasteners
BS EN 20225: 1992	Fasteners – Symbols and designation of dimensions
BS EN 20273: 1992	Fasteners – Clearance holes for bolts and screws
BS EN 20898: –	Mechanical properties of fasteners
BS EN 24014 to 24018: 1992	Hexagon head bolts and screws
BS EN 24032 to 24036: 1992	Hexagon nuts

THREADED FASTENERS 3.1.2

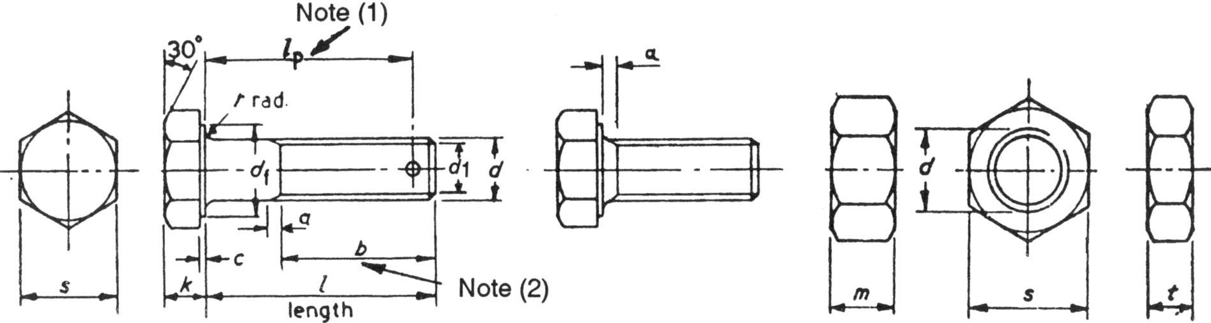

Hexagon head bolt, washer faced *Hexagon head screw, washer faced* *Normal thickness nut.* *Thin nut*

A full bearing head is available without washer face.

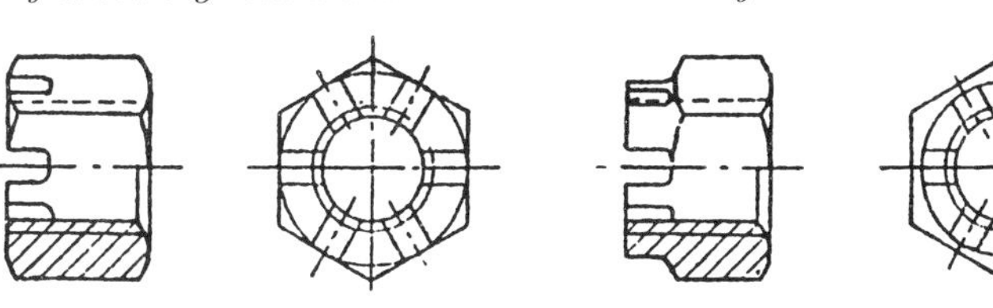

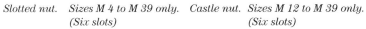

Slotted nut. Sizes M 4 to M 39 only. (Six slots) *Castle nut. Sizes M 12 to M 39 only. (Six slots)*

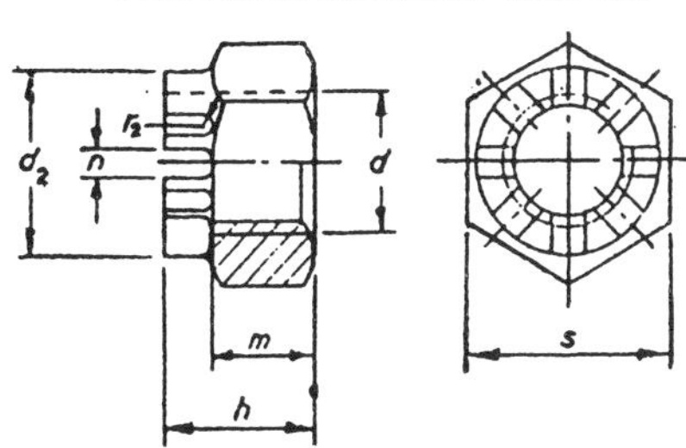

Castle nut. Sizes M 42 to M 68 only. (Eight slots)

($l \leq 125$, $b = 2d + 6$) ($125 < l \leq 200$, $b = 2d + 12$) ($200 < l$, $b = 2d + 25$)

$a = 2\frac{1}{2}$ x Pitch r_2 min. = 0.25n min.

Nominal lengths available; 5, 6, 8, 10, 12, 14, 16, 20, 25, 30 . . . All dimensions in millimetres

All sizes shown in brackets are non-preferred.

TABLE OF NUT AND BOLT DIMENSIONS:- (See BS 3692 for full range)

Nominal size & thread dia. d	Pitch of thread coarse pitch series	Diameter of unthreaded shank d max	min	Width across flats s max	min	Height of head k max	min	Radius under head r max	min	Diameter of washer face d_f max	min	Thickness of normal nut m max	min	Thickness of thin nut t max	min	Thickness h max	min	Diameter d_2 max	min	Minor* Diameter d_1
M 1.6	0.35	1.6	1.46	3.2	3.08	1.225	0.975	0.2	0.1	—	—	1.30	1.05	—	—	—	—	—	—	1.221
M 2	0.4	2.0	1.86	4.0	3.88	1.525	1.275	0.3	0.1	—	—	1.60	1.35	—	—	—	—	—	—	1.567
M 2.5	0.45	2.5	2.36	5.0	4.88	1.825	1.575	0.3	0.1	—	—	2.00	1.75	—	—	—	—	—	—	2.013
M 3	0.5	3.0	2.86	5.5	5.38	2.125	1.875	0.3	0.1	5.08	4.83	2.40	2.15	—	—	—	—	—	—	2.459
M 4	0.7	4.0	3.82	7.0	6.85	2.925	2.675	0.3	0.2	6.55	6.30	3.20	2.90	—	—	5	4.70	—	—	3.242
M 5	0.8	5.0	4.82	8.0	7.85	3.650	3.35	0.35	0.2	7.55	7.30	4.00	3.70	—	—	6	5.70	—	—	4.134
M 6	1	6.0	5.82	10.0	9.78	4.15	3.85	0.4	0.25	9.48	9.23	5.00	4.70	—	—	7.5	7.14	—	—	4.917
M 8	1.25	8.0	7.78	13.0	12.73	5.65	5.35	0.6	0.4	12.43	12.18	6.50	6.14	5.0	4.70	9.5	9.14	—	—	6.647
M 10	1.5	10.0	9.78	17.0	16.73	7.18	6.82	0.6	0.4	16.43	16.18	8.0	7.64	6.0	5.70	12	11.57	—	—	8.376
M 12	1.75	12.0	11.73	19.0	18.67	8.18	7.82	1.1	0.6	18.37	18.12	10.00	9.64	7.0	6.64	15	14.57	17	16.57	10.106
(M 14)	2	14.0	13.73	22.0	21.67	9.18	8.82	1.1	0.6	21.37	21.12	11.00	10.57	8.0	7.64	16	15.57	19	18.48	11.835
M 16	2	16.0	15.73	24.0	23.67	10.18	9.82	1.1	0.6	23.27	23.02	13.00	12.57	8.0	7.64	19	18.48	22	21.48	13.835
(M 18)	2.5	18.0	17.73	27.0	26.67	12.215	11.785	1.1	0.6	26.27	26.02	15.00	14.57	9.0	8.64	21	20.48	25	24.48	15.294
M 20	2.5	20.0	19.67	30.0	29.67	13.215	12.785	1.2	0.8	29.27	28.80	16.00	15.57	9.0	8.64	22	21.48	28	27.48	17.294
(M 22)	2.5	22.0	21.67	32.0	31.61	14.215	13.785	1.2	0.8	31.21	30.74	18.00	17.57	10.0	9.64	26	25.48	30	29.48	19.294
M 24	3	24.0	23.67	36.0	35.38	15.215	14.785	1.7	1.0	34.98	34.51	19.00	18.84	10.0	9.64	27	26.48	34	33.38	20.752
(M 27)	3	27.0	26.67	41.0	40.38	17.215	16.785	1.7	1.0	39.98	39.36	22.00	21.48	12.0	11.57	30	29.48	38	37.38	23.752
M 30	3.5	30.0	29.67	46.0	45.38	19.26	18.74	1.7	1.0	44.98	44.36	24.00	23.48	12.0	11.57	33	32.38	42	41.38	26.211
(M 33)	3.5	33.0	32.61	50.0	49.38	21.26	20.74	1.7	1.0	48.98	48.36	26.00	25.48	14.0	13.57	35	34.38	46	45.38	29.211
M 36	4	36.0	35.61	55.0	54.26	23.26	22.74	1.7	1.0	53.86	53.24	29.00	28.48	14.0	13.57	38	37.38	50	49.38	31.67
(M 39)	4	39.0	38.61	60.0	59.26	25.26	24.74	1.7	1.0	58.86	58.24	31.00	30.38	16.0	15.57	40	39.38	55	54.26	34.67
M 42	4.5	42.0	41.61	65.0	64.26	26.26	25.74	1.8	1.2	63.76	63.04	34.00	33.38	16.0	15.57	46	45.38	58	57.26	37.129
(M 45)	4.5	45.0	44.61	70.0	69.26	28.26	27.74	1.8	1.2	68.76	68.04	36.00	35.38	18.0	17.57	48	47.38	62	61.26	40.129
M 48	5	48.0	47.61	75.0	74.26	30.26	29.74	2.3	1.6	73.76	73.04	38.00	37.38	18.0	17.57	50	49.38	65	64.26	42.587
(M 52)	5	52.0	51.54	80.0	79.26	33.31	32.69	2.3	1.6	—	—	42.00	41.38	20.0	19.48	54	53.26	70	69.26	46.587
M 56	5.5	56.0	55.54	85.0	84.13	35.31	34.69	3.5	2.0	—	—	45.00	44.38	—	—	57	56.26	75	74.26	50.046
(M 60)	5.5	60.0	59.54	90.0	89.13	38.31	37.69	3.5	2.0	—	—	48.00	47.38	—	—	63	62.26	80	79.26	54.046
M 64	6	64.0	63.54	95.0	94.13	40.31	39.69	3.5	2.0	—	—	54.00	53.26	—	—	66	65.26	85	84.13	57.505
(M 68)	6	68.0	67.54	100.0	99.13	43.31	42.69	3.5	2.0	—	—	54.00	53.26	—	—	69	68.26	90	89.13	61.505

Note (1): Bolts with split pin holes available, dimension 'l' must be stated. Nominal hole and split pin sizes to be agreed with manufacturer.

Note (2): Shortest length designated a bolt is when 'l' = 'b', less than this is called a screw.

*When making stress calculations refer to BS 3692 App D and BS 3643 for detail.

THREADED FASTENERS 3.1.3

Hexagon socket screws: Details and table of sizes

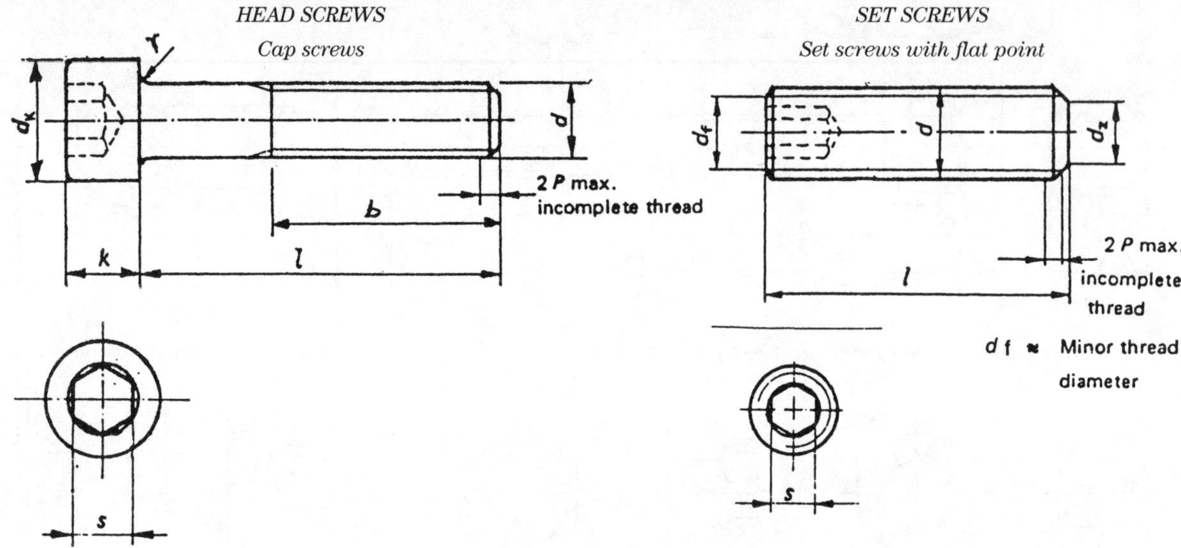

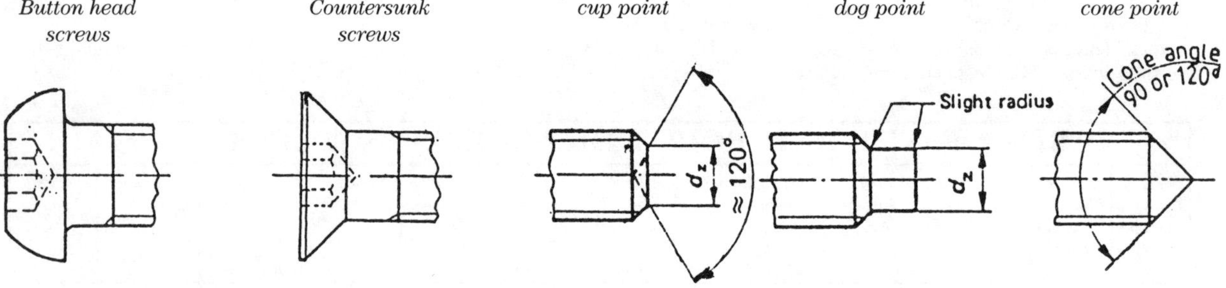

M3–M16 M3–M20

Limited sizes available

Head screws available in lengths ranging from $l = d$ to $10d$. Set screws available in lengths ranging from $l = \frac{3}{4}d$ to $5d$

Nominal lengths available; 2.5, 3, 4, 5, 6, 8, 10, 12, 16, 20, 25, 30, 35, 40 . . .

Dimensions in millimetres

THREAD SIZE d		M 1.6	M 2	M 2.5	M3	M 4	M 5	M 6	M 8	M 10	M 12	M 16	M 20	M 24
THREAD DIAMETER d	max.	1.6	2	2.5	3	4	5	6	8	10	12	16	20	24
	min.	1.46	1.86	2.36	2.86	3.82	4.82	5.82	7.78	9.78	11.73	15.73	19.67	23.67
HEAD DIAMETER d_k	max. (Plain)	3	3.8	4.5	5.5	7	8.5	10	13	16	18	24	30	36
	max. (Knurled)	3.14	3.98	4.68	5.68	7.22	8.72	10.22	13.27	16.27	18.27	24.33	30.33	36.39
	min.	2.86	3.62	4.32	5.32	6.78	8.28	9.78	12.73	15.73	17.73	23.67	29.67	35.61
PITCH P		0.35	0.4	0.45	0.5	0.7	0.8	1.0	1.25	1.5	1.75	2.0	2.5	3.0
k	max.	1.6	2	2.5	3	4	5	6	8	10	12	16	20	24
	min.	1.46	1.86	2.36	2.86	3.82	4.82	5.70	7.64	9.64	11.57	15.57	19.48	23.48
r	min.	0.1	0.1	0.1	0.1	0.2	0.2	0.25	0.4	0.4	0.6	0.6	0.8	0.8
s (Head screws)	nominal	1.5	1.5	2	2.5	3	4	5	6	8	10	14	17	19
s (Set screws)	nominal	0.7	0.9	1.3	1.5	2.0	2.5	3.0	4.0	5.0	6.0	8.0	10.0	12.0
b	min.	0.8	1.0	1.5	2.0	2.5	3.5	4.0	5.5	7.0	8.5	12.0	15.0	18.0
d_z	max.	0.8	1.0	1.5	2.0	2.5	3.5	4.0	5.5	7.0	8.5	12.0	15.0	18.0
	min.	0.55	0.75	1.25	1.75	2.25	3.2	3.7	5.2	6.64	8.14	11.57	14.57	17.57

THREADED FASTENERS 3.1.4

Machine screws: Details and table of sizes

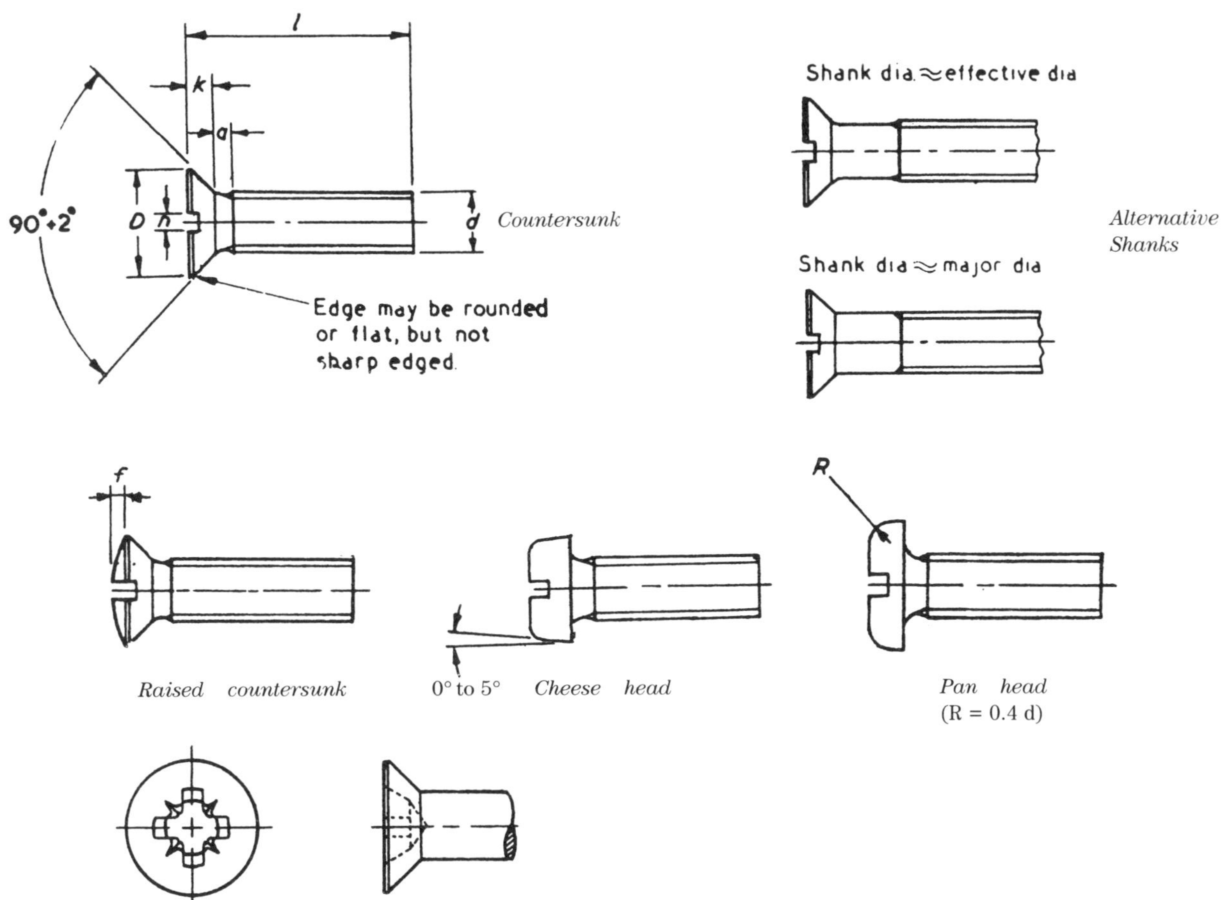

Recessed Heads available (Not suitable for very small screws)

Machine screws available in lengths ranging from l = d to 10d
Nominal lengths available; 1.5, 2, 2.5, 3, 4, 5, 6, 8, 10, 12, 14, 16, 20 . . .

Dimensions in millimetres

d	**Head diameter D**						**Head height k**						**f**	**a**	
Nominal size and thread diameter	**Plain/Raised Countersunk**		**Cheese Head**		**Pan Head**		**Plain/Raised Countersunk**		**Cheese Head**		**Pan Head**		**Height of raised portion**	**Width of slot**	
	Max.	Min.	Max.	Min.	Max.	Min.	Max.	Min.	Max.	Min.	Max.	Min.	Nom. (0.25d)	Max.	Min.
M 1	2.20	1.76	2.00	1.75			0.60	0.48	0.70	0.56	–	–	0.25	0.45	0.31
M 1.2	2.64	2.14	2.30	2.05			0.72	0.60	0.80	0.66			0.30	0.50	0.36
(M 1.4)	3.08	2.52	2.60	2.35			0.84	0.72	0.90	0.76			0.35	0.50	0.36
M 1.6	3.52	2.86	3.00	2.75			0.96	0.84	1.00	0.86			0.40	0.60	0.46
M 2	4.40	3.50	3.80	3.50			1.20	1.08	1.30	1.16			0.50	0.70	0.56
(M 2.2)	4.84	3.88	4.00	3.70			1.32	1.20	1.50	1.36			0.55	0.80	0.66
M 2.5	5.50	4.45	4.50	4.20	5.00	4.70	1.50	1.38	1.60	1.46	1.50	1.36	0.60	0.80	0.66
M 3	6.30	5.25	5.50	5.20	6.00	5.70	1.65	1.50	2.00	1.86	1.80	1.66	0.75	1.00	0.86
(M 3.5)	7.35	6.12	6.00	5.70	7.00	6.64	1.93	1.75	2.40	2.26	2.10	1.96	0.90	1.00	0.86
M 4	8.40	7.04	7.00	6.64	8.00	7.64	2.20	2.00	2.60.	2.46	2.40	2.26	1.00	1.20	1.06
(M 4.5)	9.00	7.85	8.00	7.64	9.00	8.64	2.25	2.03	3.10	2.92	2.70	2.56	1.10	1.20	1.06
M 5	10.00	8.75	8.50	8.14	10.00	9.64	2.50	2.25	3.30	3.12	3.00	2.86	1.25	1.51	1.26
M 6	12.00	10.50	10.00	9.64	12.00	11.57	3.00	2.70	3.90	3.72	3.60	3.42	1.50	1.91	1.66
M 8	16.00	14.00	13.00	12.57	16.00	15.57	4.00	3.60	5.00	4.82	4.80	4.62	2.00	2.31	2.06
M 10	20.00	17.50	16.00	15.57	20.00	19.48	5.00	4.50	6.00	5.82	6.00	5.82	2.50	2.81	2.56
M12	24.00	21.00	18.00	17.57			6.00	5.40	7.00	6.78			3.00	3.31	3.06
(M 14)	28.00	24.50	21.00	20.48			7.00	6.30	8.00	7.78			3.50	3.31	3.06
M 16	32.00	28.00	24.00	23.48			8.00	7.20	9.00	8.78			4.00	4.37	4.07
(M 18)	36.00	31.50	27.00	26.48			9.00	8.10	10.00	9.78			4.50	4.37	4.07
M 20	40.00	35.00	30.00	29.48			10.00	9.00	11.00	10.73			5.00	5.37	5.07

THREADED FASTENERS 3.1.5

Self-tapping screws: Details and table of sizes

THREAD TYPES

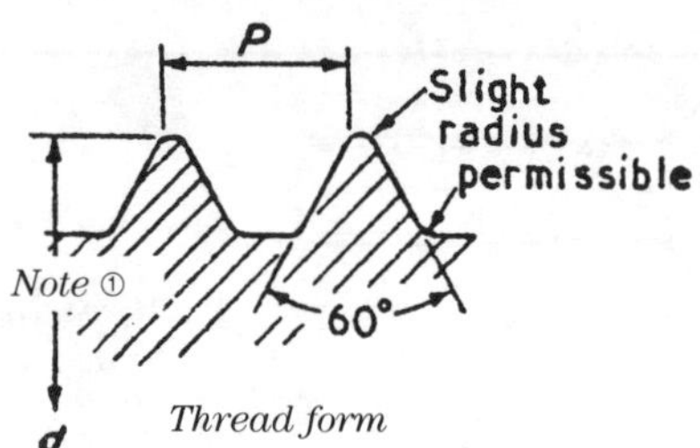

Thread form

Thread forming

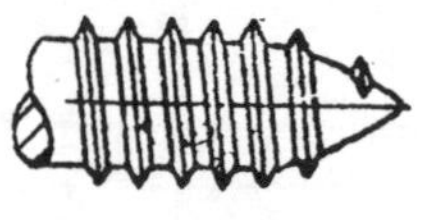
Type AB

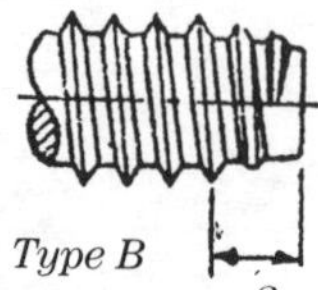
Type B
≈ 2p

Thread cutting

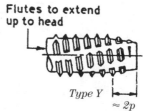

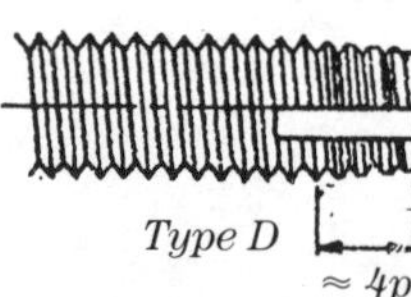
Type D
≈ 4p

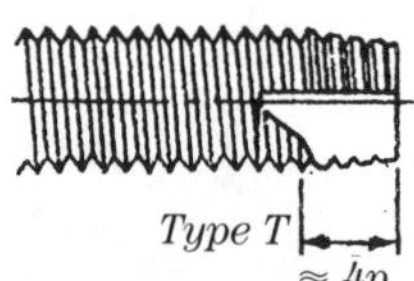
Type T
≈ 4p

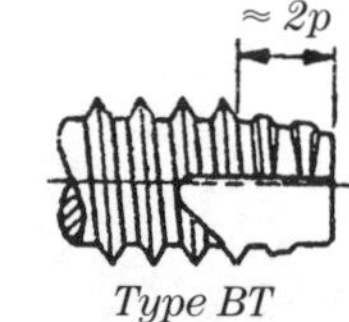
≈ 2p
Type BT

Flutes to extend up to head

Type Y
≈ 2p

HEAD TYPER

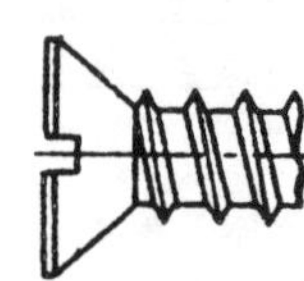

Countersunk

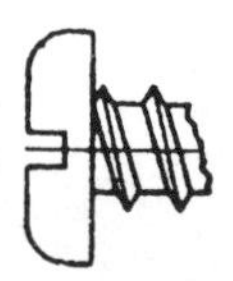
Pan

Slotted Mushroom

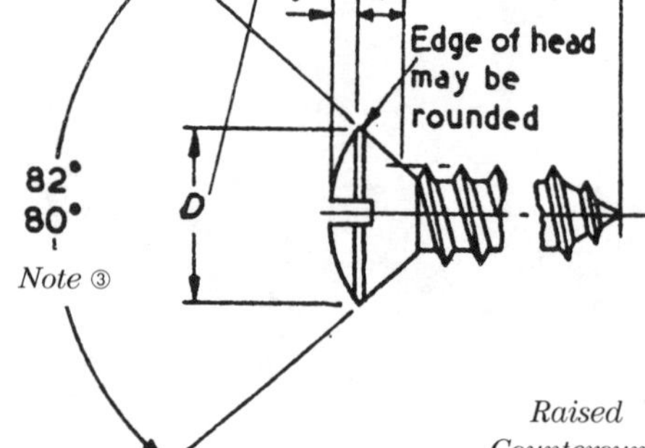

Raised Countersunk

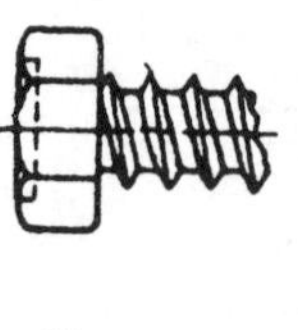
Hexagon

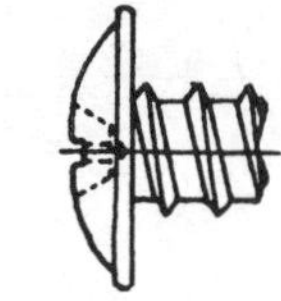
Recessed Flange

Nominal lengths available: 4.5, 6.5, 9.5, 13, 16, 19, 22, 25, 32, 38, 45, 50 . . .

Dimensions in millimetres

Screw size (No.)	Pitch P		Major diameter d ①			Diameter of head D ②		Depth of head k ②	Height of raise f	Width across flats S	
	Types AB, B BT & Y	Types D & T	Types AB, B & BT	Type Y	Types D & T	Max.	Min.	ref.	nom	Max.	Min.
2	0.79		2.24			4.37	3.73	1.30	0.64		
4	1.07	0.53	2.90	2.95	2.84	5.71	4.95	1.70	0.84	5.0	4.82
6	1.27	0.64	3.53	3.58	3.51	7.09	6.20	2.11	1.02	5.5	5.32
8	1.41	0.71	4.22	4.27	4.17	8.43	7.42	2.54	1.22	7.0	6.78
10	1.59	0.79	4.80	4.88	4.83	9.78	8.64	2.95	1.40	8.0	7.78
12	1.80		5.46	5.54		11.13	9.88	3.35	1.60	8.0	7.78
14	1.80	0.91	6.25	6.35	6.35	12.88	11.48	3.89	1.83	10.0	9.78
16	2.12	1.07	8.00		7.94	16.13	14.43	4.85	2.29	13.0	12.73

THREAD	USES	NOTES
Type AB	Light sheet, plastics, metal clad and resin impregnated plywood.	Mushroom Flange and Hexagonal Heads unavailable in long in long lengths. Unavailable in size 2.
Type B	Same as AB, + heavy plate, non-ferrous cast.	Mushroom Flange and Hexagonal Heads unavailable in long lengths.
Type BT/Y	Same as B, + asbestos and composites.	Y only available in Recess Countersunk and Pan Heads. Both unavailable in size 2.
Type D/T	Aluminium zinc and lead die-cast, sheet steel, cast iron brass, plastics.	Approximately standard Machine Screw thread. Both unavailable in size 2.

NOTES: ① Thread diameters for guidance only. Diameters may be exceeded after coating.
② Head diameter and depth are for guidance and apply only to countersunk and raised countersunk heads. For other head forms consult BS 4174.
③ Head angle is Nom. 80°, compared with 90° on Machine Screws.

Some dimensions are converted from imperial, and are subject to rounding errors.

THREADED FASTENERS 3.1.6

Flat, spring and crinkle washers: Details and table of sizes

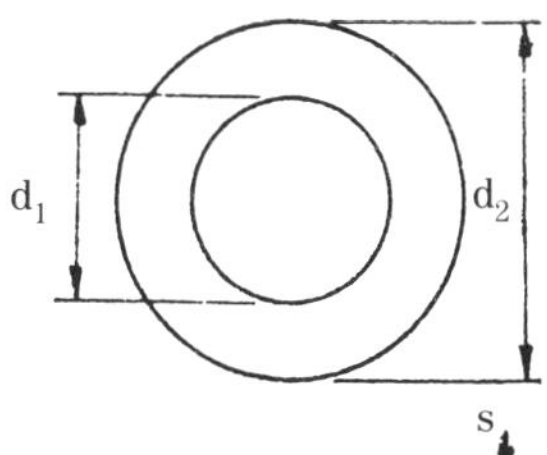

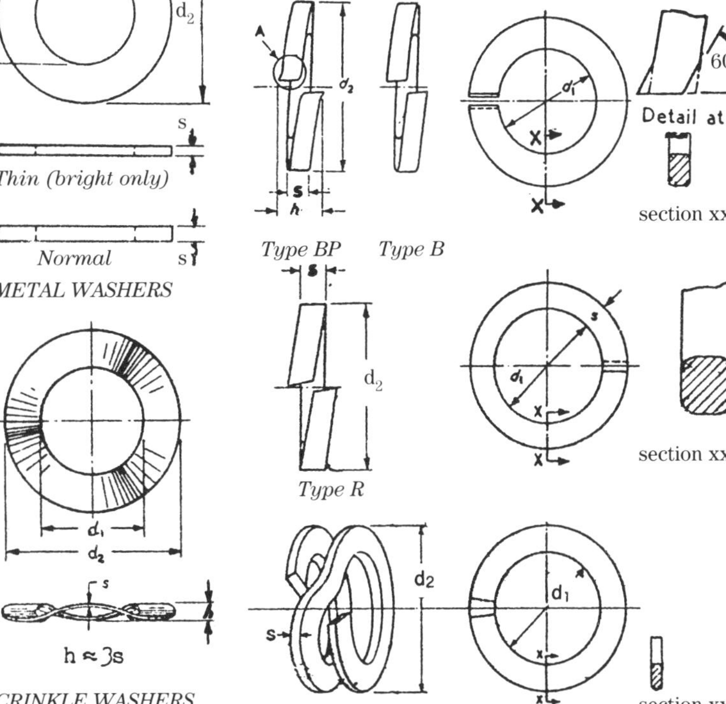

Type D

Types A, B and BP h = 2s; Type D h = 5s

SPRING WASHERS

CRINKLE WASHERS

Nominal size and thread diameter d	Inside Diameter d_1		Outer Diameter d_2	Thickness s
	Max.	Min.	Max.	Min.
M 1.6	1.8	1.7	3.7	0.16
M 2	2.3	2.2	4.6	0.16
(M 2.2)	2.5	2.4	5.2	0.16
M 2.5	2.8	2.7	5.8	0.16
M 3	3.32	3.2	6.4	0.16
(M 3.5)	3.82	3.7	6.9	0.20
M 4	4.42	4.3	8.1	0.28
M 5	5.42	5.3	9.2	0.30
M 6	6.55	6.4	11.5	0.40
M 8	8.55	8.4	15.0	0.40
M 10	10.68	10.5	19.6	0.55
M 12	13.18	13.0	22.0	0.55
(M 14)	15.18	15.0	25.5	0.55
M 16	17.18	17.0	27.8	0.70
(M 18)	19.21	19.0	31.3	0.70
M 20	21.21	21.0	34.7	0.70

METAL WASHERS

Nom. size of bolt or screw	Inside diameter d_1		Outside diameter d_2			Thickness s		
	nom *l*		normal	large	black X. large	normal	thin	black X. large
	Min.	max.	nom.	nom.	nom.	nom.	nom.	nom.
M 1.0	1.1	1.25	2.5	–	–	0.3	–	–
(M 1.2	1.3	1.45	3.0	–	–	0.3	–	–
(M 1.4)	1.5	1.65	3.0	–	–	0.3	–	–
M 1.6	1.7	1.85	4.0	–	–	0.3	–	–
M 2	2.2	2.35	5.0	–	–	0.3	–	–
(M 2.2)	2.4	2.55	5.0	–	–	0.5	–	–
M 2.5	2.7	2.85	6.5	–	–	0.5	–	–
M 3	3.2	3.4	7	–	–	0.5	–	–
(M 3.5)	3.7	3.9	7	–	–	0.5	–	–
M 4	4.3	4.5	9	10.0	–	0.8	–	–
(M 4.5)	4.8	5:0	9	–	–	0.8	–	–
M 5	5.3	5.5	10	12.5	15	1.0	0.8	1.6
M 6	6.4	6.7	12.5	14	18	1.6	0.8	2
(M 7)	7.4	7.7	14	–	21	1.6	0.8	2
M 8	8.4	8.7	17	21	24	1.6	1.0	2
M 10	10.5	10.9	21	24	30	2.0	1.25	2.5
M 12	13	13.4	24	28	36	2.5	1.6	3
(M 14)	15	15.4	28	30	42	2.5	1.6	3
M 16	17	17.4	30	34	48	3.0	2.0	4
(M 18)	19	19.5	34	37	54	3.0	2.0	4
M 20	21	21.5	37	39	60	3.0	2.0	5
(M 22)	23	23.5	39	44	66	3.0	2.0	5
M 24	25	25.5	44	50	72	4.0	2.5	6
(M 27)	28	28.5	50	56	81	4.0	2.5	6
M 30	31	31.6	56	60	90	4.0	2.5	8
(M 33)	34	34.6	60	66	99	5.0	3.0	8
M 36	37	37.6	66	72	108	5.0	3.0	10
(M 39)	40	40.6	72	77	117	6.0	3.0	10

Sizes shown in brackets are non-preferred

SPRING WASHERS

Nominal size and thread diameter d	Inside diameter d_1 types A, B & BP		Inside diameter d_1 type D		Outside dia. d_2 types B & BP	Outside dia. d_2 type A	Outside dia. d_2 type D	Thickness s types B & BP	Thickness s type A	Thickness s type D
	max.	min.	max.	min.	max.	max.	max.	nom.	nom.	nom.
M 1.6	1.9	1.7	–	–	3.5	–	–	0.4	–	
M 2	2.3	2.1	2.4	2.1	4.3	–	4.4	0.5	–	0.5
(M 2.2)	2.5	2.3	2.6	2.3	4.7	–	4.8	0.6	–	0.6
M 2.5	2.8	2.6	2.9	2.6	5.0	–	5.5	0.6	–	0.7
M 3	3.3	3.1	3.6	3.3	6.1	5.5	6.2	0.8	1	0.8
(M 3.5)	3.8	3.6	4.1	3.8	6.6	6.0	7.5	0.8	1	0.8
M 4	4.35	4.1	4.6	4.3	7.55	6.95	8.0	0.9	1.2	0.8
M 5	5.35	5.1	5.6	5.3	9.15	8.55	9.8	1.2	1.5	0.9
M 6	6.4	6.1	6.6	6.3	11.7	9.6	12.9	1.6	1.5	1
M 8	8.55	8.2	8.8	8.4	14.85	12.75	15.1	2	2	1.2
M 10	10.6	10.2	10.8	10.4	18.0	15.9	18.2	2.2	2.5	1.2
M 12	12.6	12.2	12.8	12.4	21.0	17.9	20.2	2.5	2.5	1.6
(M 14)	14.7	14.2	15.0	14.5	24.1	21.1	25.4	3	3	1.6
M 16	16.9	16.3	17.0	16.5	27.3	24.3	27.4	3.5	3.5	2
(M 18)	19.0	18.3	19.0	18.5	29.4	26.4	29.4	3.5	3.5	2
M 20	21.1	20.3	21.5	20.8	33.5	30.5	31.9	4	4.5	2
(M 22)	23.3	22.4	23.5	22.8	35.7	32.7	35.9	4	4.5	2.5
M 24	25..3	24.4	26.0	25.0	39.8	35.7	39.4	5	5	3.25
(M 27)	28.5	27.5	29.5	28.0	43.0	38.9	44.0	5	5	3.25
M 30	31.5	30.5	33.0	31.5	48.0	43.9	49.5	6	6	3.25
(M 33)	34.6	33.5	36.0	34.5	55.1	47.0	52.5	6	6	3.25
M 36	37.6	36.5	40.0	38.0	58.1	52.1	60.5	6	7	3.25
(M 39)	40.8	39.6	43.0	41.0	61.3	55.3	63.5	6	7	3.25

Dimensions in millimetres

SUPPLIERS

THREADED FASTENERS: Nuts, bolts, screws and washers

COMPANY	ADDRESS	TELEPHONE	FAX
Abmore Engineering Co. Ltd	Bill Quay Warehouses Shields Road GATESHEAD Tyne & Wear NE10 0QE	091 469 7721	091 438 6771
Atlas Bolt (Darlaston) Ltd a div of Armstrong Fastenings Ltd	PO Box 6 Station Street Darlaston WEDNESBURY WS10 8UL	021-526 4951	021-526 4575
The Bolt & Nut Co (Tipton) Ltd	Park Lane East TIPTON W Midlands DY4 8RF	021-522 2353	021-522 2304
Cooper and Turner	Templeborough Works Sheffield Road SHEFFIELD S Yorks S9 1RS	0742 560057	0742 445529
Delta Precision Ltd	Millmarsh Lane Brinsdown ENFIELD Middlesex EN3 7XE	081 805 8088	081 364 7285
Deltight International Ltd	Unit 9 Satellite Ind Park Neachalls Lane Wednesfield WOLVERHAMPTON WV11 3PQ	0902 307776	0902 307855
Fastener Technique Ltd	Hever Road EDENBRIDGE Kent TN8 5EA	0732 864266	0732 866726
Forest Fasteners, a Div of Armstrong Fastenings Ltd	Treforest Industrial Estate PONTYPRIDD Mid Glamorgan CF37 5YG	0443 841663	0443 841141
Holo-Krome Ltd	Kingsway West DUNDEE Tayside DD2 4TB	0382 623455	0382 621196
Lanarkshire Bolt Ltd	Burnbank HAMILTON Strathclyde ML3 0QU	0698 284444	
RotaBolt Ltd	5 Peartree Business Pk Peartree Lane DUDLEY W Midlands DY2 0UW	0384 214442	0384 455186
Wragg (Bolts & Nuts) Ltd, Arnold	Stannington Road Stannington SHEFFIELD S Yorks S6 6AG	0742 331155	0742 331169

USEFUL ADDRESSES

THREADED FASTENERS

ADDRESS	TELEPHONE
British Turned Parks Manufacturers Association 136 Hagley Road BIRMINGHAM B16 9PN	021 454 4141
British Industrial Fasteners Federation Blundell House Torrington Avenue COVENTRY CV4 9GU	0203 466496

Notes

SECTION 4 – JOINING PROCESSES

WELDING 4.1.1

Pressure and fusion welding: Forms, processes, selection and use

TYPICAL APPLICATIONS: All types of engineering where a permanent joint is needed. Especially high usage in automotive and shipbuilding, petrochemical plant, pipelines, pressure vessels, civil and structural engineering, prefabricated components, heating and ventilating plant.

DEFINITION: An operation in which two or more parts are united, by means of heat, pressure, light or sound or a combination of these, in such a way that there is continuity in the nature of the material between the joined parts.

FORMS AND PROCESSES: Welds generally take the form of fillet, butt, plug, seam or spot joints between similar or dissimilar materials. They form a permanent bond which is load bearing and, if continuous, is as resistant to pressure as the parent material. Welding methods may be divided into: **pressure** ('solid phase') i.e. spot and hammer welding, and **fusion** ('liquid phase') i.e. arc and gas welding.

NOTES ON SELECTION AND USE:

The process selected must be metallurgically suited to the material being joined, must be capable of meeting size and shape demands of the joint, and must be economically feasible. Products to be welded should be designed to prevent metal distortion and defects, to allow access for the man or machine doing the welding, and to permit ease of quality control. Process choice is affected by the class of product to be welded and these can be grouped into three classes: **Components** are often small and can be moved to the process which may be a permanent installation handling them in batches or on a flowline basis. 'Solid phase' processes such as spot and flash welding are often used. **Structures** are usually large and often remote from basic services and require the welding process to be moved to them so portable manual or semi-automatic arc welding equipment is commonly used. **Semi-finished products** such as tubes and sections are made in factory conditions using permanent installations and often employing a continuous weld process such as resistance seam arc and electronic beam welding. Good welding is rarely a low cost method of joining metal unless quantity is high and quality can be maintained. Lack of forethought in design, inadequate joint preparation and unskilled use of chosen welding methods are all factors which commonly lead to weld failure. As well as mechanical considerations, good weld design includes fully specifying materials and test methods. These methods may be destructive and/or non-destructive, must comply with national or international standards and testing must be done by qualified personnel.

REFERENCES:

BS 499 :	Welding terms and symbols
BS 638 :	Arc welding power sources, equipment and accessories
BS 709 : 1983	Methods of destructive testing fusion welded joints and weld metal in steel
BS 1723 :	Brazing
BS 2633 : 1987	Specification for Class I arc welding of ferritic steel pipework for carrying fluids
BS 3923 :	Methods for ultrasonic examination of welds
BS 4870 :	Specification for approval testing of welding procedures
BS 4871 :	Spec. for approval testing of welders working to approved welding procedures
BS 4872 :	Spec. for approval testing of welders when welding procedure approval is not required
BS 5135 : 1984	Specification for arc welding of carbon and carbon manganese steels
BS 6944 : 1988	Spec. for flash welding of butt joints in ferrous metals (excl. pressure piping applications).
BS 6990 : 1989	Code of practice for welding on steel pipes containing process fluids or their residuals
BS 7009 : 1988	Application of real-time radiography to weld inspection
PD 6493 : 1991	Guidance on some methods for the derivation of acceptance levels for defects in fusion welded joints
BS EN 25817 : 1992	Arc-welded joints in steel-quality levels
BS EN 288	Specification and approval of welding procedures for metallic materials
BS EN 28167 : 1992	Specification for projections for resistance welding
BS 4219 : 1990	Specification for welding primers and weld-through sealants
BS 4570 : 1985	Specification for fusion welding of steel castings
BS EN 24063 : 1992	Welding, brazing, and soldering, nomenclature of processes and symbolic references on drawings (etc).
BS 4515 : 1984	Specification for welding of steel pipelines on land and offshore
BS EN 287	Approval testing of welders for fusion welding

Selecting a process

DIAGRAM SHOWING: ROOT, FUSION PENETRATION, WELD JUNCTION AND ZONES OF TYPICAL WELDS:

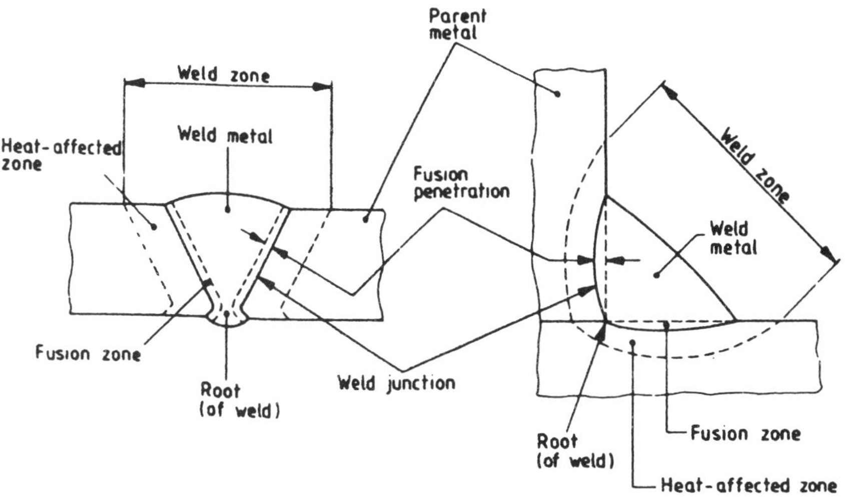

TABLE SHOWING THICKNESS RANGE FOR WELDING PROCESSES (LOG SCALE)

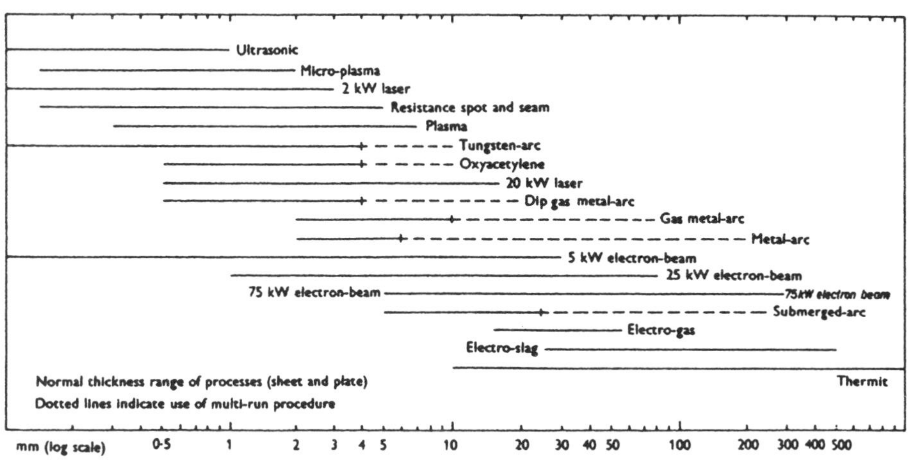

TABLE OF MAIN PROCESSES FOR DIFFERENT SHAPES OF JOINT

Process	Sheet & plate	Large pipe & cylinders	Butts: Tubes	Butts: Bar	Attach-ments	Fillets or T joints
Plasma	△	△	△			
Resistance spot	△	△			△	
Resistance seam	△	△			△	
Tungsten-arc	△	△	△		△ a	△ a
Oxyacetylene	△	△	△			
Gas metal-arc	△	△	△		△ a	△
Metal-arc	△	△	△		△ a	△
Cored wire	△	△				△
Submerged-arc	△ b	△				△
Electro-gas	△ c					△
Electro-slag	△					△
Electro-beam	△	△	△ d	△ d	△	△
Flash			△	△	△	
Friction			△	△	△	
Resistance butt			△	△		
Diffusion			△	△	△	△
Projection					△	△
Tungsten-arc spot					△	
Gas metal-arc spot					△	
Thermit				△		△

KEY TO TABLE:

- a Light gauge only
- b Mainly in flat position
- c Mainly in vertical position
- d Work revolved under fixed welding station

These tables are from 'Welding Process Technology' by P.T. Houldcroft with kind permission of Cambridge University Press.

WELDING 4.1.3

Numerical list of processes

The following is a guide to the most common welding, brazing and soldering processes. For detailed descriptions of these and other related subjects, refer to **BS 499 : Part 1 Welding terms and symbols.**

NUMERICAL INDICATION OF PROCESS (Complying with ISO 4063)

No.	Process	No.	Process
1	**Arc welding**	47	Gas pressure welding
11	Metal-arc welding without gas protection	48	Cold welding
111	Metal-arc welding with covered electrode	**7**	**Other welding processes**
112	Gravity arc welding with covered electrode	71	Thermit welding
113	Bare wire metal-arc welding	72	Electroslag welding
114	Flux cored metal-arc welding	73	Electrogas welding
115	Coated wire metal-arc welding	74	Induction welding
118	Firecracker welding	75	Light radiation welding
12	Submerged arc welding	751	Laser welding
121	Submerged arc welding with wire electrode	752	Arc image welding
122	Submerged arc welding with s trip electrode	753	Infrared welding
13	Gas shielded metal-arc welding	76	Electron beam welding
131	MIG welding	77	Percussion welding
135	MAG welding: metal-arc welding with non-inert gas shield	78	Stud welding
136	Flux cored metal-arc welding with non-inert gas shield	781	Arc stud welding
14	Gas-shielded welding with non-consumable electrode	782	Resistance stud welding
141	TIG welding	**9**	**Brazing, soldering and braze welding**
149	Atomic-hydrogen welding	91	Brazing
15	Plasma arc welding	911	Infrared brazing
18	Other arc welding processes	912	Flame brazing
181	Carbon arc welding	913	Furnace brazing
185	Rotating arc welding	914	Dip brazing
2	**Resistance welding**	915	Salt bath brazing
21	Spot welding	916	Induction brazing
22	Seam welding	917	Ultrasonic brazing
221	Lap seam welding	918	Resistance brazing
225	Seam welding with strip	919	Diffusion brazing
23	Projection welding	923	Friction brazing
24	Flash welding	924	Vacuum brazing
25	Resistance butt welding	93	Other brazing processes
29	Other resistance welding processes	94	Soldering
291	HF resistance welding	941	Infrared soldering
3	**Gas welding**	942	Flame soldering
31	Oxy-fuel gas welding	943	Furnace soldering
311	Oxy-acetylene weldine	944	Dip soldering
312	Oxy-propane welding	945	Salt bath soldering
313	Oxy-hydrogen welding	946	Induction soldering
32	Air fuel gas welding	947	Ultrasonic soldering
321	Air-acetylene welding	948	Resistance soldering
322	Air-propane welding	949	Diffusion soldering
4	**Solid phase welding ; Pressure welding**	951	Flow soldering
41	Ultrasonic welding	952	Soldering with soldering iron
42	Friction welding	953	Friction soldering
43	Forge welding	954	Vacuum soldering
44	Welding by high mechanical energy	96	Other soldering processes
441	Explosive welding	97	Braze welding
45	Diffusion welding	971	Gas braze welding
		972	Arc braze welding

WELDING 4.1.4

Chart of derivation of processes

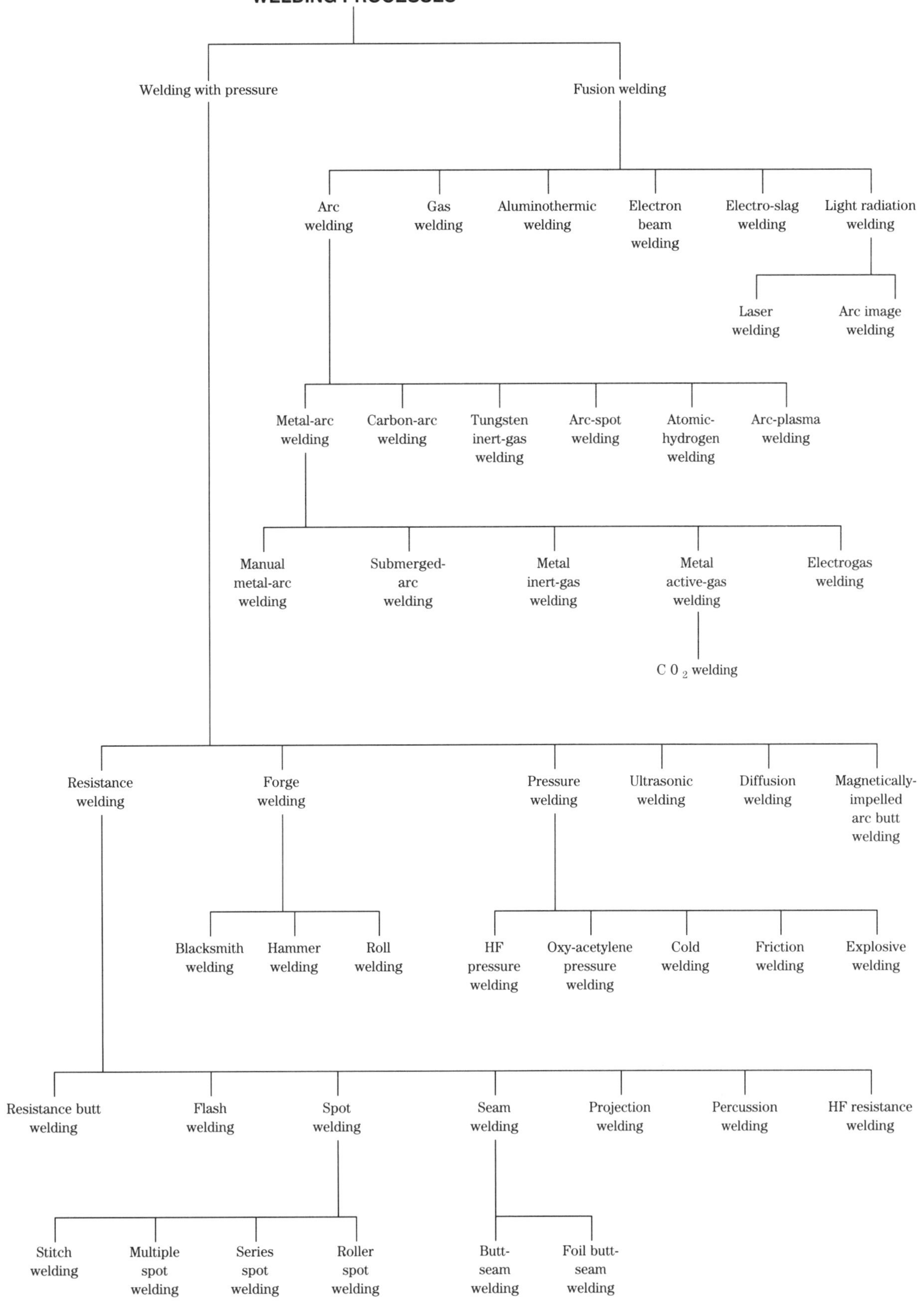

WELDING 4.1.5

Joints, weld types and weld preparation (1-10)

The following sketches show the sectioned appearance of the majority of weld types in common use and should be used as a guide to selection for the design of structures and components. Note that these are *not* drawing symbols, these are shown in BS EN 24063. Refer to section 10.2.1 for graphical presentation. (See also BS EN 27286 for *equipment* symbols).

Sketch BS 499 Part 1 fig 29. 1-10	Type of joint	Type of weld(s)	Preparation	Remarks
1 	Butt	Butt Compound	Close square	Full penetration
2 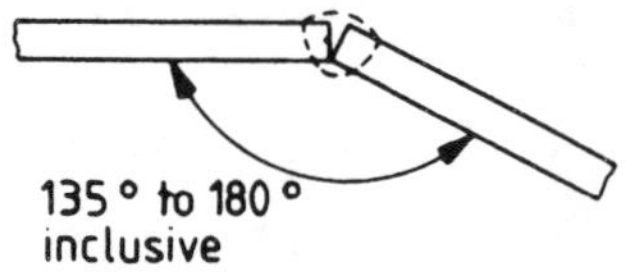 (135 ° to 180 ° inclusive)	Butt	Butt	Close square	Full penetration
3 	Butt	Butt	Raised edges	–
4 	Butt	Butt	Close square	Partial penetration
5 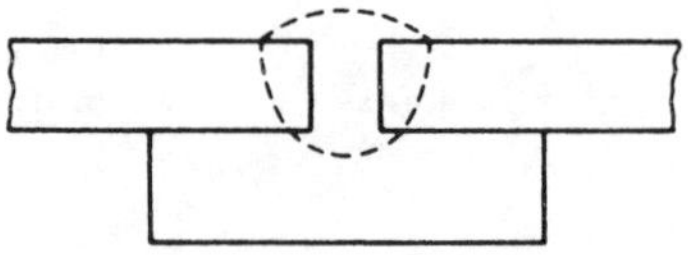	Butt	Butt	Open square with backing bar	Full penetration
6 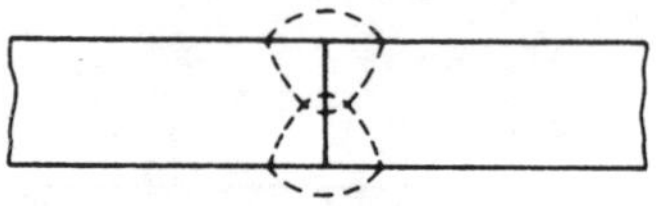	Butt	Butt	Close square	Full penetration Welded from both sides
7 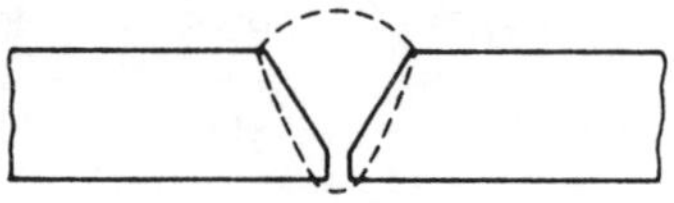	Butt	Butt	Single-V with root faces	Full penetration
8 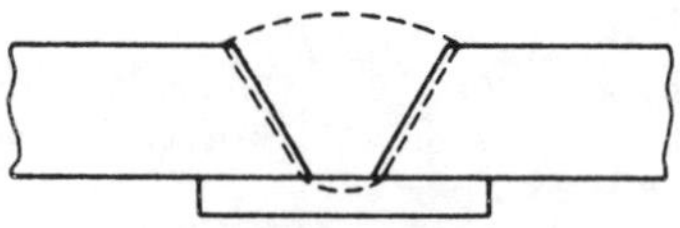	Butt	Butt	Single-V with backing strip	Full penetration
9 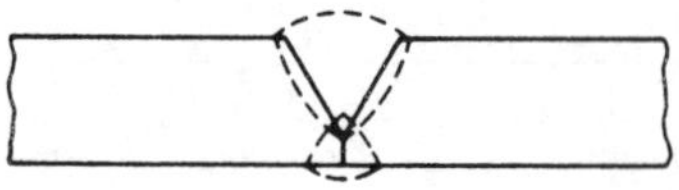	Butt	Butt	Single-V with root faces	Full penetration Sealing run used
10 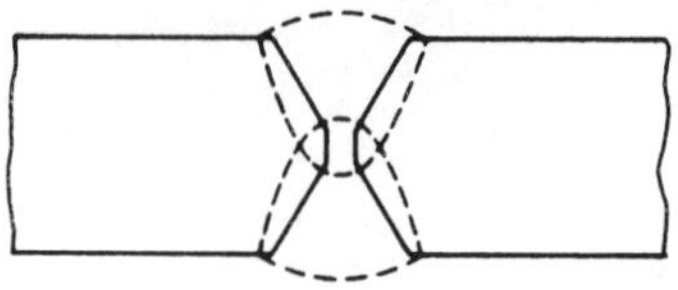	Butt	Butt	Double-V with root faces	Full penetration Welded from both sides

WELDING 4.1.5

Joints, weld types and weld preparation (11-19)

Sketch BS 499 Part 1 fig 29. 11-19	Type of joint	Type of weld(s)	Preparation	Remarks
11 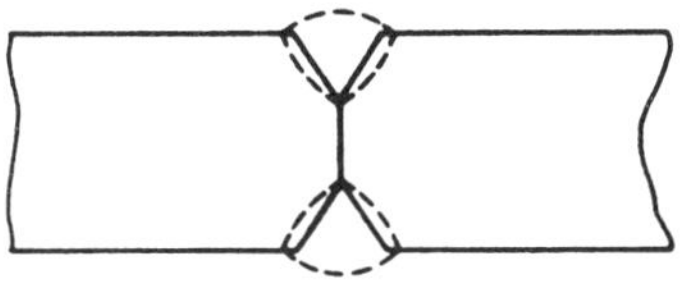	Butt	Butt	Double-V with wide or deep root faces	Partial penetration Welded from both sides
12 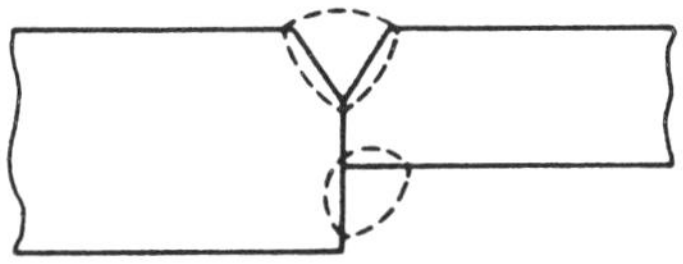	Butt	Butt and fillet	Single-V with wide or deep root faces	Partial penetration Welded from both sides
13 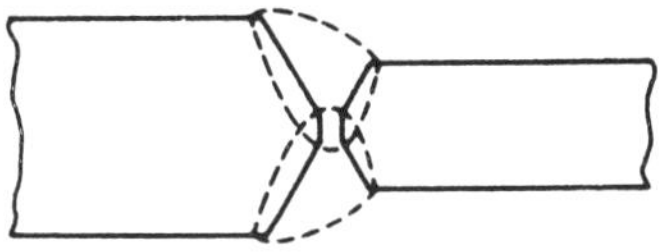	Butt	Butt	Double-V with root faces	Full penetration Welded from both sides
14 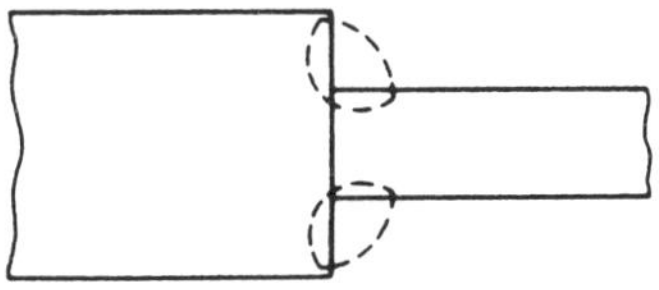	Butt	Fillet	Close square	Welded from both sides
15 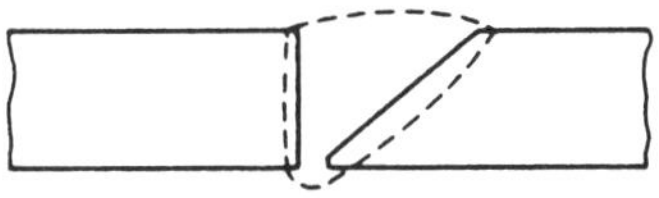	Butt	Butt		Full penetration
16 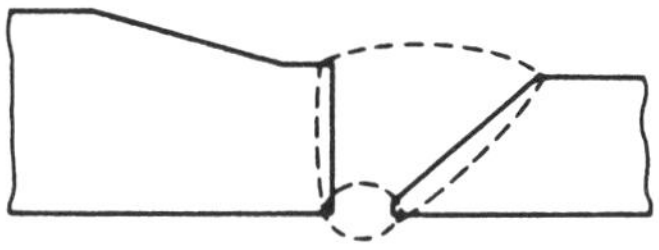	Butt	Butt	Single-bevel with root face. Thicker plate tapered	Full penetration Sealing run used
17 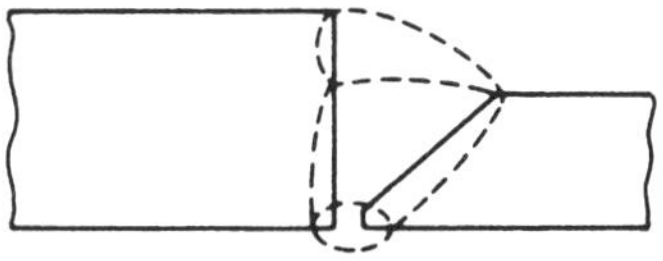	Butt	Compound of butt and fillet	Single-bevel with root face	Full penetration Sealing run used
18 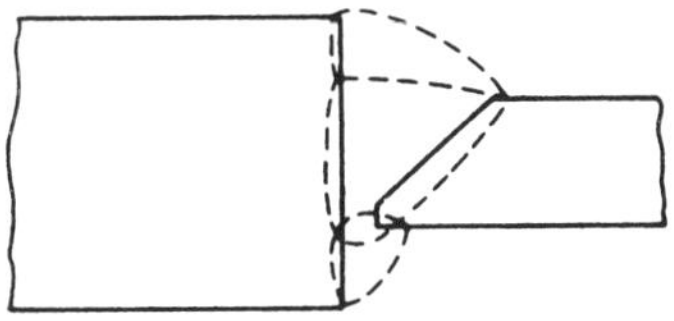	Butt	Compound of butt and fillet	Single-bevel with root face	Full penetration Welded from both sides
19 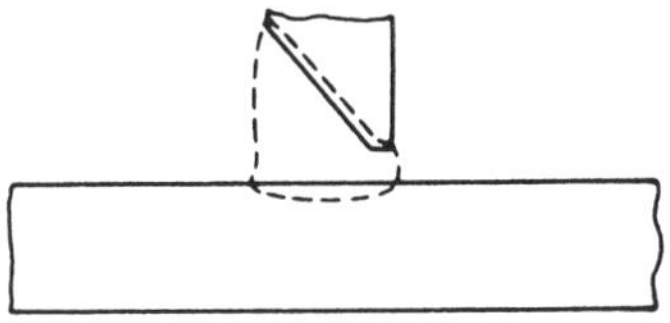	T	Butt	Single-bevel with root face	Full penetration

WELDING 4.1.5

Joints, weld types and weld preparation (20-27)

Sketch BS 499 Part 1 fig 29. 20-27	Type of joint	Type of weld(s)	Preparation	Remarks
20 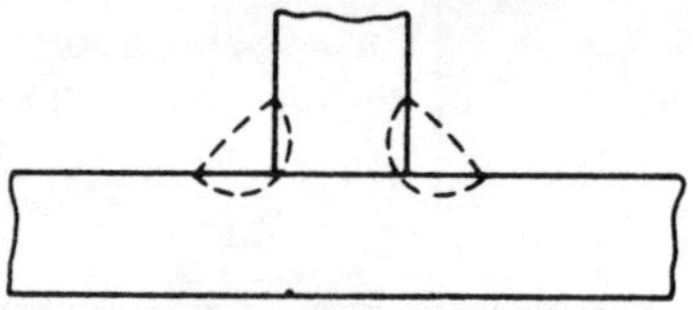	T	Fillet	Close square	Welded from both sides
21 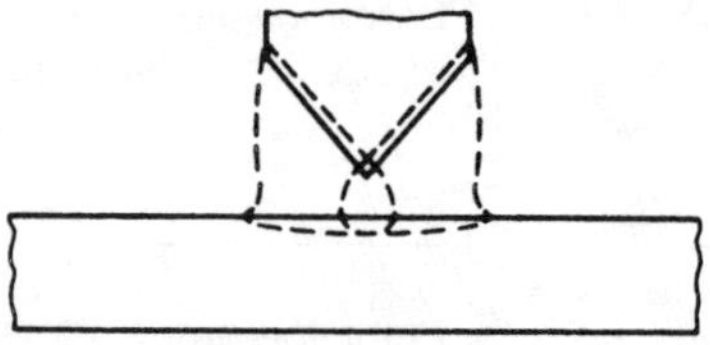	T	Butt	Double-bevel	Full penetration. Welded from both sides
22 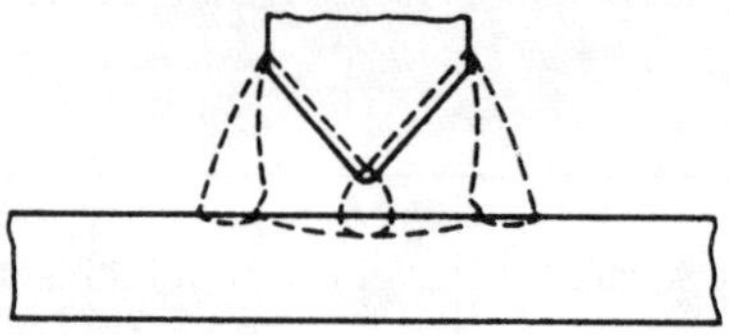	T	Compound of butt and fillets	Double-bevel	Full penetration Welded from both sides
23 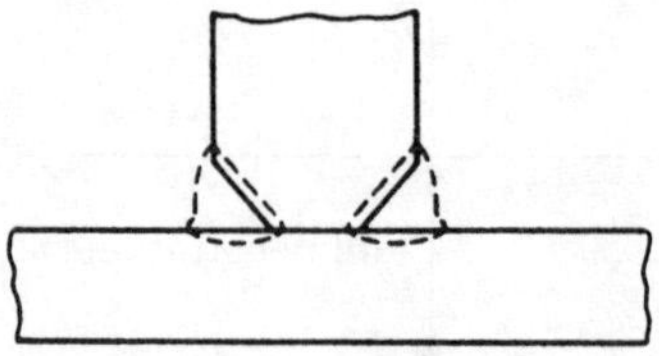	T	Butt	Double-bevel with wide or deep root face	Partial penetration Welded from both sides
24 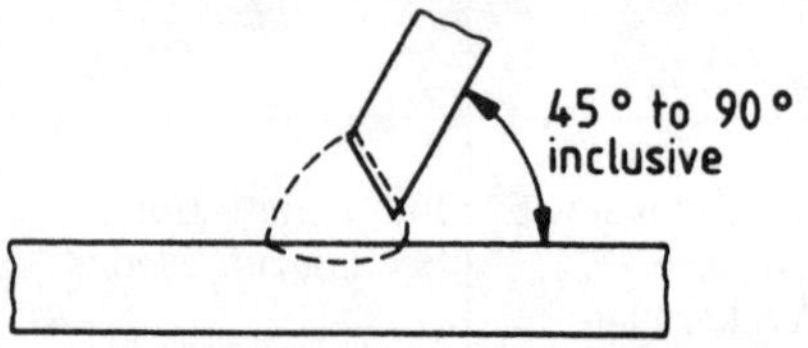 45° to 90° inclusive	T	Butt	Single-bevel	Full penetration
25 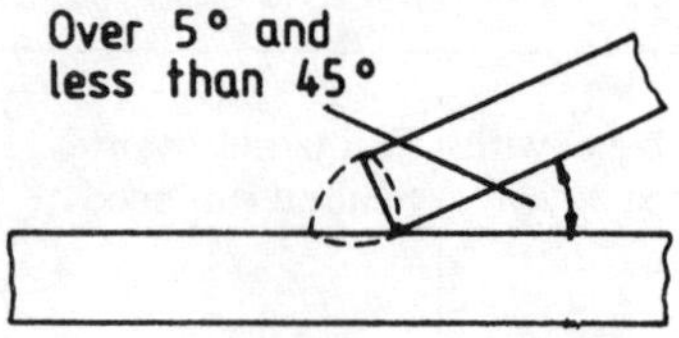 Over 5° and less than 45°	T	Fillet	Edge prepared as necessary	–
26 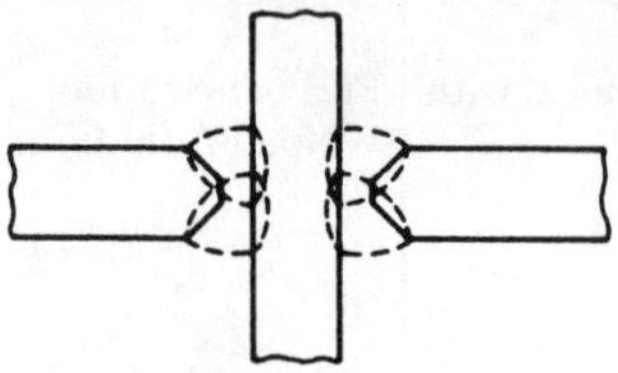	Cruciform	Butt	Double-bevel	Welded from both sides
27 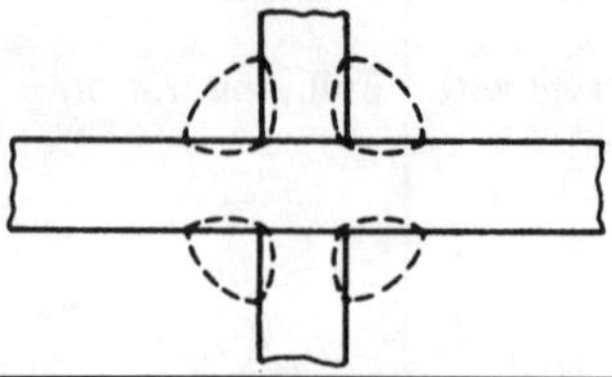	Cruciform	Fillet	Close square	Welded from both sides

WELDING 4.1.5

Joints, weld types and weld preparation (28-36)

Sketch BS 499 Part 1 fig 29. 28-36	Type of joint	Type of weld(s)	Preparation	Remarks
28 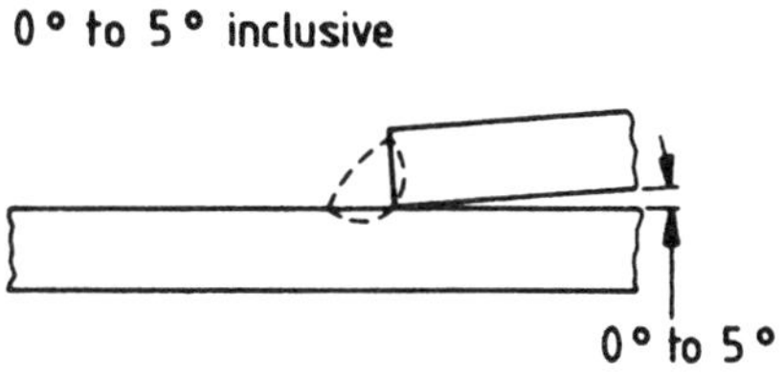 0° to 5° inclusive; 0° to 5°	Lap	Fillet	Square edge	–
29 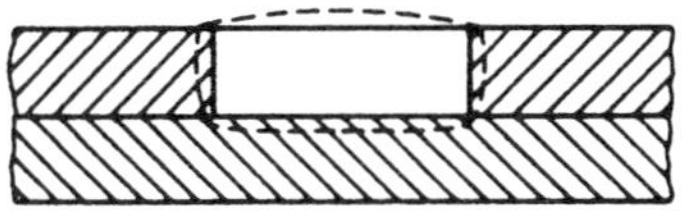	Lap	Plug	Hole(s) of any shape in one plate	–
30 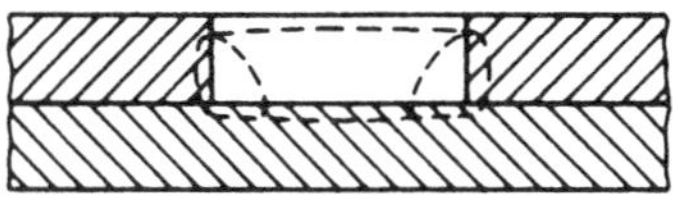	Lap	Fillet	Hole(s) of any shape in one plate	Welded all round
31 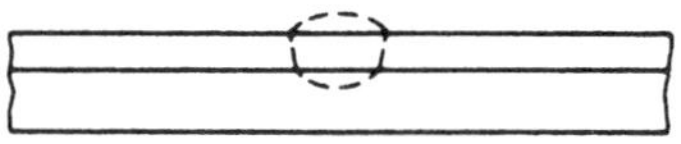	Lap	Fusion spot	None	–
32 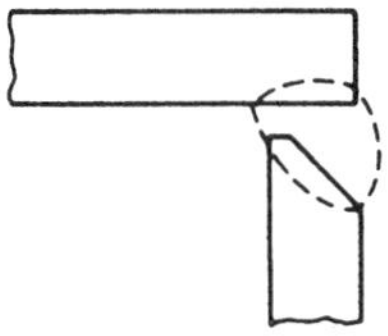	Corner	Butt	Single-bevel with root face	Full penetration
33 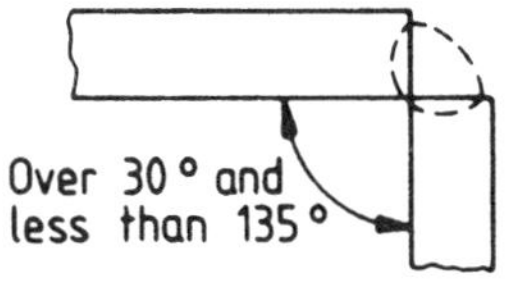 Over 30° and less than 135°	Corner	Fillet	Edges prepared as necessary	–
34 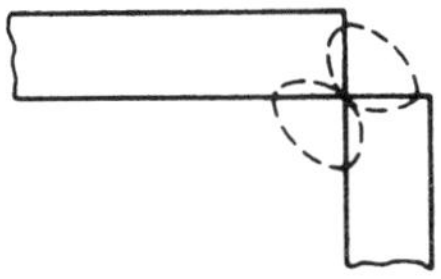	Corner	Fillets	Square edge	Welded from both sides
35 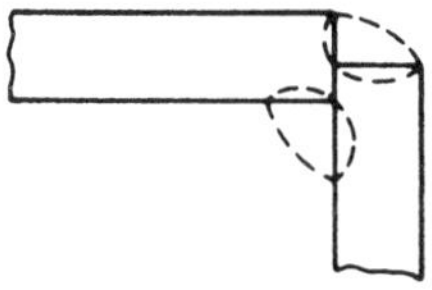	Corner	Fillets	Square edge	Partially lapped corner Welded from both sides
36 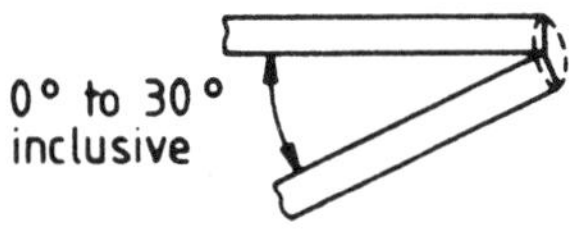 0° to 30° inclusive	Edge	Edge	Square edge	Edges fully covered

SUPPLIERS

WELDING: Welding Equipment and Consumables

COMPANY	ADDRESS	TELEPHONE	FAX
WELDING EQUIPMENT:			
Bullfinch Ltd	Diadem Works Kings Road BIRMINGHAM B11 2AJ	021-706 6301	021-707 0995
Efco Ltd	Forsyth Road Sheerwater WOKING GU21 5RZ	0483 726433	0483 773818
Murex Ltd	Hertford Road WALTHAM CROSS EN8 7RP	0992 710000	0992 715803
WELDING CONSUMABLES:			
British Alcan Wire Ltd	Brandon Way WEST BROMWICH W Midlands B70 8JJ	021-553 3191	021-553 5881
Johnson & Nephew (Ambergate) Ltd	Ambergate DERBY DE5 2HE	077 385 2396	077 385 6020
Johnson Wire Ltd	PO Box 14 Denby Dale Road WAKEFIELD W Yorks WF2 7BD	0924 375172	0924 379760
WELDING GASES:			
BOC Ltd	The Priestley Centre 10 Priestley Road The Surrey Research Park GUILDFORD GU2 5XY	0483 579857	0483 505211

USEFUL ADDRESSES

WELDING

ADDRESS	TELEPHONE
BEAMA Ltd Federation of British Electrotechnical and Allied Manufacturers Association 8 Leicester Street LONDON WC2H 7BN	071 437 0678
National Association of Arc Welding Equipment Repairers 74 Chester Road Castle Bromwich BIRMINGHAM B36 9BU	021 776 7474
Welding Institute Abington Hall CAMBRIDGE CB1 6AL	0223 891162
Welding Manufacturers Association 8 Leicester Street LONDON WC2H 7BN	071 437 0678
R A Farrar Professor of Welding Engineering Faculty of Engineering Southampton University Highfield SOUTHAMPTON Hants SO9 5NH	0703 593561

ADHESIVES 4.2.1

Adhesive bonding: Forms, processes, selection and use

TYPICAL APPLICATIONS: Fabrication in the aerospace, boat-building and automotive industries, electro-mechanical assemblies, building and construction, wood, plastic and metal structural joints, acid, solvent and corrosion free joints, non-conducting assemblies, sealing and packaging, DIY.

DEFINITIONS:

The joining of similar or dissimilar materials using natural or synthetic substances which form a rigid or semi-rigid interface without the use of mechanical fastening.

FORMS AND PROCESSES:

Adhesives are available as low or high viscosity liquids, pastes, mastics, films, tapes and powders, and may be supplied as single or multi-part systems (i.e. resin and powder, paste and liquid). Application can be by hand spreading, brushing, flowing, roll coating, spraying or contact. Setting agents are: heat, pressure, time, chemical catalyst, vulcanisation or reactivation. Final state after setting can be hard or soft, thin or thick film and the bond may be designed to be temporary or permanent.

NOTES ON SELECTION AND USE:

The first stage of selection is to assess arguments for or against the use of adhesives, and to do this some broad questions should be addressed: Is the joint to be loaded or not under working conditions? What type of joint is involved? What is the function of the joint? What are the service and environmental conditions? How long can the cure time be? Good joint design is crucial for successful adhesive bonding and it is unsatisfactory to use the rules that are applied for mechanical fastenings. Achieving even load distribution is an important factor in joint design. It should be noted that an excessive overlap on a common lap joint causes unwanted stress concentrations at the ends. Where the material to be bonded is flexible, there are more stresses than in rigid materials because of more local distortion under load. It is not necessarily true to assume that the thinner the adhesive line, the better the joint because the adhesives and the part to be joined must be considered in total, and in many instances a thick 'glue line' is of benefit. The advantages of adhesives over mechanical jointing include: ability to join dissimilar materials of a variety of forms and sizes including small and delicate shapes, the uniform distribution of stresses across the bond area, effective compensation for uneven or irregular surfaces, the fabrication of complex shapes and smooth profiles, reduction of joint weight, high damping and insulation capabilities and the potential for cost saving during product assembly. There are, however, disadvantages over mechanical methods: the length of time needed to reach working strength, the possibility of residual stresses building up where high curing temperatures are used, the need for pre- and post- assembly jigs and curing procedures, hazards of inflammability and toxicity, and the difficulties of adjusting or dismantling once a joint has set.

Almost without exception, all uncured adhesives require some safety precautions. In particular, there are inhalation risks from solvent-based adhesives and potential for skin damage from 'superglues' (ie cyanoacrylates). Some adhesives are highly inflammable in their uncured form. Strict control of storage and use to manufacturer's recommendations is essential. For bulk or production use, metering, dispensing and application equipment is available. Most adhesives present no safety risks after curing.

REFERENCES:

BS 745 : 1969 (1988) Specification for animal glue for wood (joiner's glue) (dry glue: jelly or liquid glue.)

BS 4071 : 1966 (1988) Specification for polyvinyl acetate (PVA) emulsion adhesives for wood.

BS 5350 : Methods of test for adhesives. Introduction, Groups A–H

BS 5442 : Classification of adhesives for construction

BS 6138 : 1989 Glossary of terms used in the adhesives industry

CP 3012 : 1972 Codes of practice for cleaning and preparation of metal surfaces

BS EN 301 : 1992 Adhesives, phenolic and aminoplastic for load bearing timber structures

BS EN 2243 Structural adhesives test methods

BS EN 204 : 1991 Classification of non-structural adhesives for joining of wood

BS 1203 : 1979 (1991) Specification for synthetic resin adhesives for plywood

BS 1204 : 1993 Specification for synthetic resin adhesives for wood

ADHESIVE SELECTION

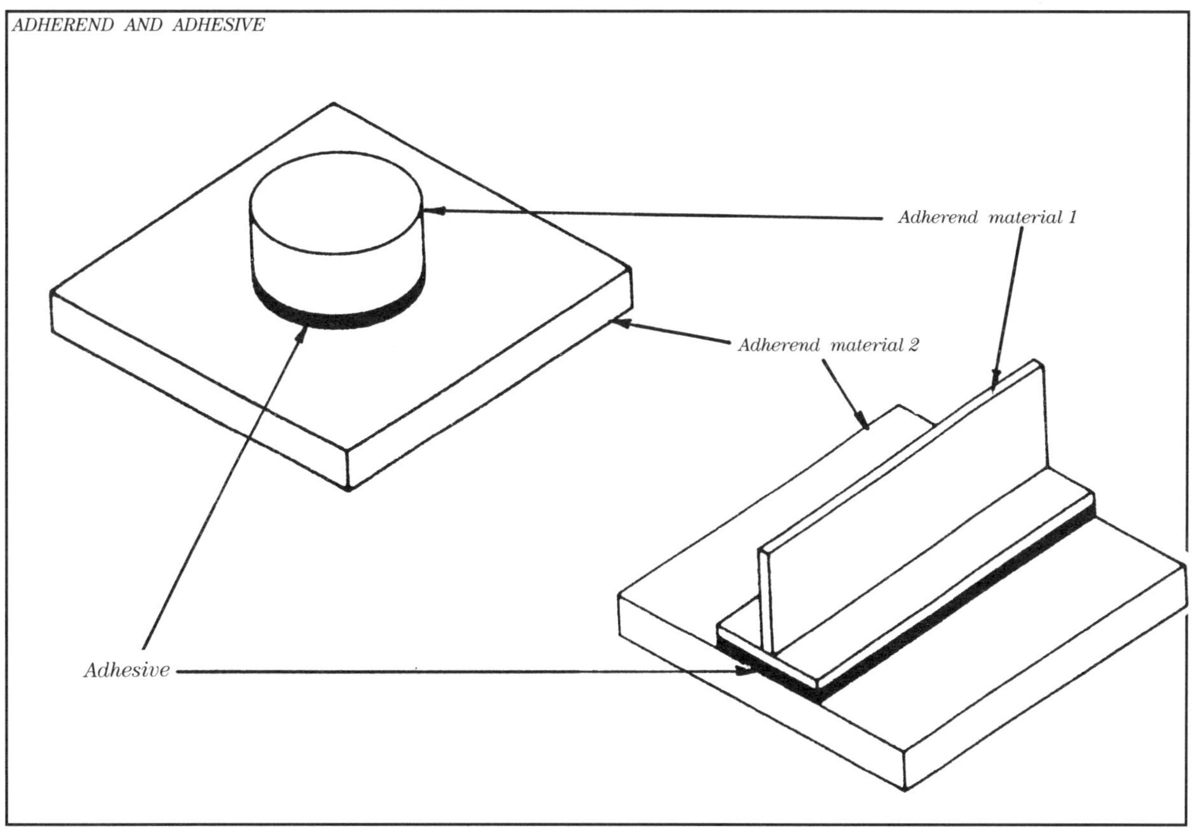

Illustrations from 'Adhesives in Engineering Design' © W.A. Lees

HOW TO USE THE FOLLOWING TABLES

Tables A and ***B*** overleaf list a range of *adherend materials* and the most compatible *adhesive types* for joining them successfully.

The *adhesive types* are given a small letter code: **a, b, c**, etc. and ***Table A*** lists those that are a **primary choice**, **secondary choice** or that should be **rejected** for a given adherend material.

A **'primary'** adhesive / adherend combination will function well, right up to the limit of the adhesive's capability.

'Secondary' indicates that performance may not be so predictable.

'Reject' here indicates a basic adherend / adhesive incompatibility which renders the adhesive unsuitable.

It should be appreciated, however, that an inherently high strength adhesive rated as a secondary on a given adherend may well produce a far stronger bond than a weak adhesive rated as primary for the same material.

A brief description of the main adhesive types is given on pages 58–59 and note that when deciding on compatibility it is essential that the '**special notes**' given in ***Table B*** are read carefully since special circumstances may eliminate some of the choices.

ADHESIVES 4.2.3

Table A
ADHESIVE / ADHEREND COMPATABILITY TABLE

Ref. No.	MATERIAL (Adherend)	ADHESIVE (See Table B) Reject	Secondary	Primary	Ref. No.	Special notes
1	Cellulose – board, paper, wood etc	cdosu	ghx	abefijklmnpqrtvwyz	1	23
2	Cementitious – concrete, mortar etc. including asbestos sheet	abcdehl mnorstuv	gx	fijkpqwyz	2	12, 23
3	Ceramic – ferrite, masonry, pottery	abcdsu	lmno	efghijkpqrtvwxyz	3	23
4	Fabric-cloth, felt	abcdelstuv	ghox	fijkmnpqrwyz	4	23
5	Friction materials	abcdosu	efhijkpqrtvwyz	glmnx	5	12, 23
6	Glass	abcdflmnsu	eghijkopqrtvwxyz	–	6	13
7	Leather	abcdghorsux	ejlmntvwz	fikpqy	7	23
8	Metals	abl	f	all but abfl	8	14
	PLASTICS					
9	ABS	abcdghjmnosuxz	fklqtv	eiprwy	9	15
10	poly Acetal	abchlmnosu	dfgkx	eijpqrtvwyz	10	16
11	poly Acrylate	abcghjlmnosuxz	dfkpq	eirtvwy	11	15
12	poly Alkyd	abchlmnosu	dfgkptvwx	eijqryz	12	16
13	poly Allyl phthalate	abchlmnosu	dfgkptvwx	eijqryz	13	16
14	poly Amide	abchosu	dfgijptvwyz	eklmnqrx	14	16
15	poly Amino	abchlmnosu	dfgkptvwx	eijqryz	15	16
16	poly Carbonate	abcdhlmnoqstuvw	efgj	ikprxyz	16	17
17	Epoxy (incl. fibre reinforced laminates)	abclmnosu	dfktv	eghijpqrwxyz	17	16
18	poly Ester (thermoset and reinforced laminates)	abclmnosu	dfijktv	eghpqrwxyz	18	16
19	poly Ethylene	abchlmnosu	defgkptvwx	ijqryz	19	18
20	poly Imide	abclmnosu	dftvw	eghijkpqrxyz	20	16
21	poly Methyl methacrylate (perspex®)	abcghjlmnosuxz	dfkpq	eirtvwy	21	15
22	Phenolic (including laminates)	csu	abdflmntv	eghijkopqrwxyz	22	16
23	poly Phenylene Oxide	abclmnosu	dfghktvx	eijpqrwyz	23	20
24	poly Propylene	abchlmnosu	defgkptvwx	ijqryz	24	18
25	poly Styrene (including foam)	abcghlmnosux	djkpqtvwz	efiry	25	19
26	poly Sulphone	abcdghklmnosux	efijpwyz	qrtv	26	20
27	poly Tetra-fluoroethylene (PTFE)	abchlmnosu	defgkptvwx	ijqryz	27	18
28	poly Vinyl Chloride (PVC)	abcdghlmnosux	fijkptvyz	eqrw	28	–
29	poly Urethane (Elastomers including foam)	abcdghjlmnosuxz	efikqtvwy	pr	29	18, 19, 23
	RUBBERS					
30	Butyl			eqr	30	21
31	Chloro-sulphonated polyethylene			eqrw	31	21
32	EPM			eqr	32	21
33	EPDM			eklpqr	33	21
34	Fluorinated and other speciality types			eqr	34	25
35	Chloroprene			eijnpqryz	35	21
36	Cyclized			eijnqryz	36	21
37	'Hard' Structural	Reject all but primaries indicated	Not applicable	eijnpqryz	37	21
38	Natural			epqr	38	21
39	NBR			eijnpqryz	39	21
40	Neoprene			eijknpqryz	40	21
41	Nitrile			ekqr	41	21
42	SBR			eijnpqryz	42	21
43	'Soft' non-structural			eijnpqryz	43	21
44	Silicone			–	44	20

Reproduced from 'Adhesives in Engineering Design' by W.A. Lees 1984, published by The Design Council.

ADHESIVES 4.2.4

Adhesive types and curing method
Table B ADHESIVE CODES

Adhesive type	Code	Sub-groups of main types	Code	Special notes (see Table A)
Amino	a	Cold-cured, two-part	a	26
	b	Heat-cured (or warmed), two-part	b	1, 26
Anaerobic	c	Cold-cured	c	2, 27
	d	Cold-cured plus accelerator	d	2
Cynanoacrylate	e	Cold-cured	e	3, 30
Emulsion / Latex	f	Cold-cured	f	26
Epoxide	g	Single part, liquid / paste form (always heat-cured)	g	4, 9
	h	Single part, tape or film form (always heat-cured)	h	4, 5, 9
	i	Two-part, cold-cured	i	8, 10, 28
	j	Two-part, heated to some degree	j	4, 8, 10
Hot melt	k	Always heat-activated	k	6, 32
Phenolic / resorcinolic	l	Cold-cured, two-part	l	26
	m	Heat-cured, two-part	m	1, 26
Phenolic (modified)	n	Heat-cured, two-part	n	1, 26
Plastisol	o	Always heat-cured	o	2, 4, 32
Polyurethane	p	Cold-cured, two-part	p	7
Solvent- borne rubbers	q	Cold and vulcanised	q	11, 29
Tape	r	Pressure sensitive	r	5
Toughened adhesives		**Acrylic-based**		
	s	Anaerobic, thermoplastic, cold-cured	s	2, 27
	t	Anaerobic, thermoplastic, cold-cured plus accelerator	t	2
	u	Anaerobic, thermoset, cold-cured	u	2, 27
	v	Anaerobic, thermoset, cold-cured plus accelerator	v	2
	w	Non-anaerobic, two-part, cold-cured – could be mixed	w	2, 11
		Epoxy-based		
	x	Single-part, liquid / paste form (always heat-cured)	x	2, 4, 9
	y	Two-part, cold-cured	y	8, 10
	z	Two-part, heated to some degree	z	4, 8, 10

SPECIAL NOTES TO TABLES

Some plastics, e.g. polyethylene, polypropylene, PTFE and silicone rubbers are particularly difficult to bond – except when used in co-axial (slip fitted or threaded) joints.

1 Hot presses are expensive. **2** Often used without rigorous surface preparation. **3** Plastics and rubber parts not normally cleaned and never with chlorinated solvent. **4** Inexpensive heating techniques available. **5** May need pre-shaping; curved surfaces difficult. **6** Equipment inexpensive. **7** Expensive equipment necessary. Severe physiological hazard. **8** Small volumes may be hand-mixed. **9** Physiological activity very low. **10** Possible physiological hazards. **11** Vapour extraction often needed. Some materials have hazardous flash points. **12** Resistance to cleavage and tensile forces low due to nature of adherend's surface. **13** Glass joints only reliable in dry environments. Otherwise, surface preparation or specialised adhesives necessary. UV curing adhesives are especially useful and will also bond some transparent plastics. **14** Most metal components will bond well in co-axial (slip-fitted or threaded) joint configurations – usually without rigorous surface preparation. However, this is not so for variants in lap and butt joints. Here performance depends on: basic metal or alloy; modulus; joint geometry; mode of loading and surface preparation. Steel alloys generally bond well and often, when toughened adhesives are used, do not require surface preparation. However, other common engineering metals and alloys can be difficult and surface preparation is often required to maximise performance. **15** Care – stressed plastic may crack. **16** Surface preparation may be needed. **17** Care – some forms particularly prone to sress cracking. **18** Requires special preparation for use in lap/butt joints. Rough or knurled surfaces usually acceptable for co-axial (slip-fitted) joints without chemical pre-treatment. **19** Some adhesives dissolve this plastic – take special care with the foam form. **20** Special problems – consult supplier. **21** Freshly cut, or lightly abraded, close fitting surfaces usually give the best result. **22** Butt joints are susceptible to damage and fail readily if abused. Extreme forms – such as bonded edges – must be avoided except in special circumstances eg honeycomb sandwich panels. **23** Care – absorption likely. **24** Apart from a few specialised adhesives (such as the polyimides – consult specialist supplier) – all conventional types decompose above this temperature. **25** Success depends on degree of modification – consult manufacturer. **26** A porous surface may be necessary. **27** Narrow bond lines may not cure properly. **28** Quick-cure versions are brittle. **29** High performance levels only from vulcanised systems. **30** Cyanoacrylates are brittle and readily degrade in warm wet conditions – particularly when metal surfaces involved. **31** Do not reject 'e' (cyanoacrylate) if: (a) it is a primary for both surfaces and, either (b) neither surface is metal or (c) one surface is a flexible rubber-based (30–43 inc) material. **32** Vapour extraction may be required.

ADHESIVES 4.2.5

Adhesive bonding: Acceptable and Unacceptable Practice in Joint Design

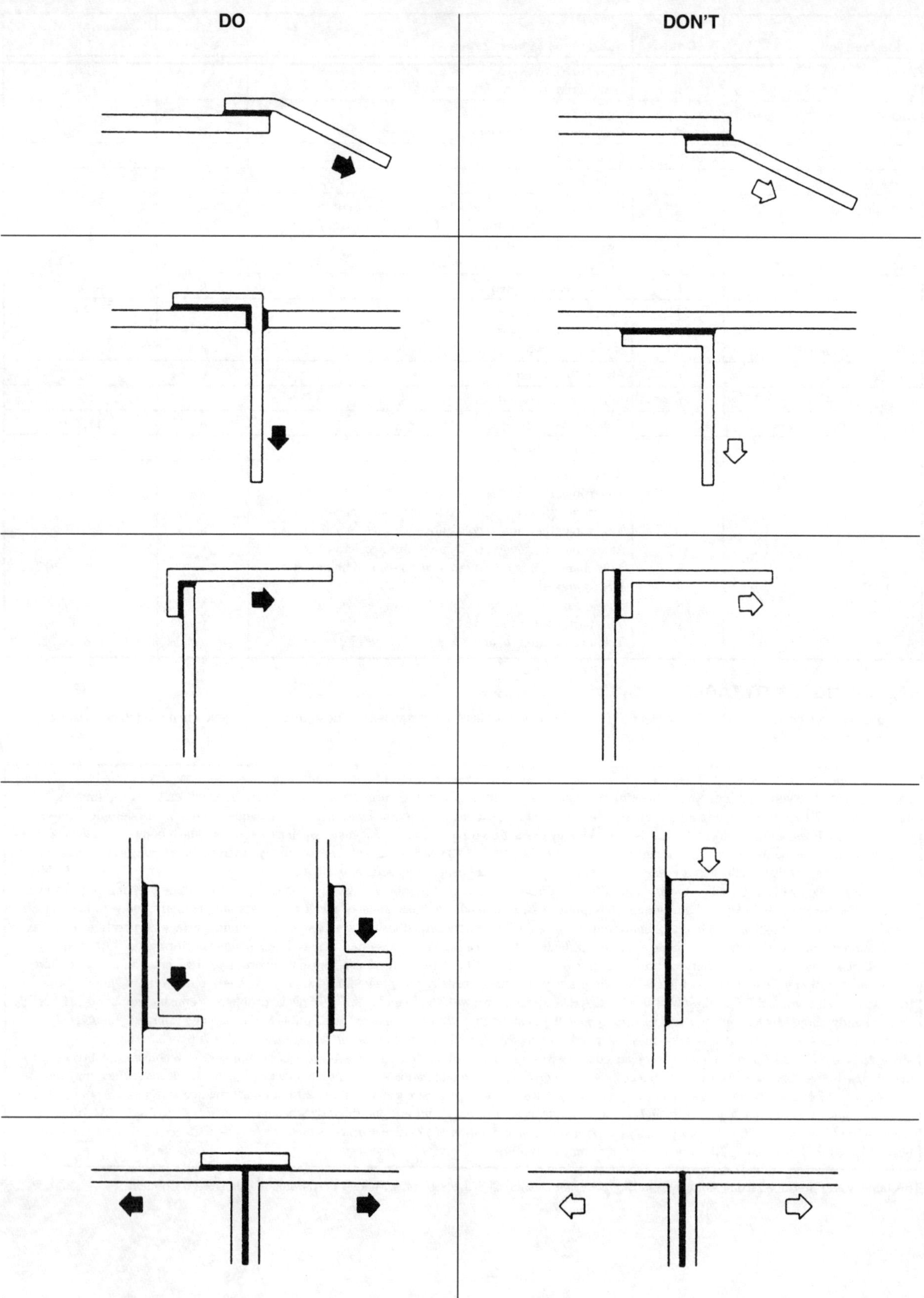

From 'Adhesives in Engineering Design' by W.A. Lees, Technical Director, Permabond Adhesives Ltd.

ADHESIVES 4.2.5

Adhesive bonding: Acceptable and Unacceptable Practice in Joint Design *(contd.)*

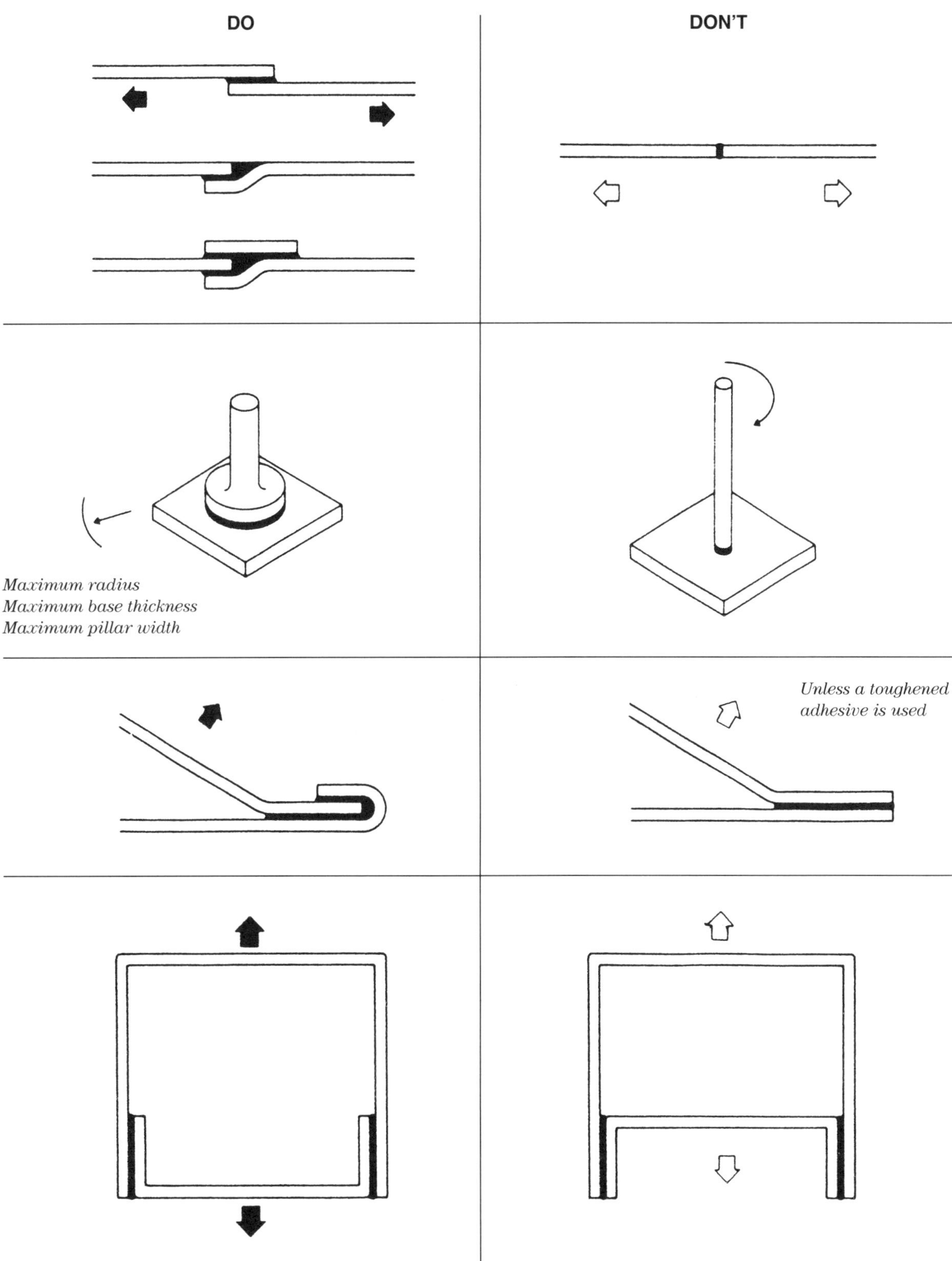

This structure is based on welding practice and does not favour the adhesive. By reversing the closing panel, the load in the joint becomes compressive and the left-hand box is 3–4 times stronger than that on the right.

From 'Adhesives in Engineering Design' by W.A. Lees, Technical Director, Permabond Adhesives Ltd.

GLOSSARY OF ADHESIVE TYPES

The following ten types of adhesives are commonly used in the mass production assembly industries.

Amino – These urea-formaldehyde adhesives come as water-based syrups or powdered solids for mixing with water. Curing requires heat and/or a catalyst., causing a polymerisation reaction to take place which produces water and the adhesive cures. These adhesives have few conventional engineering applications, being commonly used in the woodworking industry for bonding and lamination of wood and wood-associated materials. They are available in different viscosities, reaction speeds, etc. to suit a multiplicity of uses. However, they may not be used with metal without special primers, they almost invariably require at least one surface to be porous and will not fill large gaps successfully. Because of their high water content, pressure must be applied during curing. They form strong joints with wood.

Anaerobic – Often known by other terms such as 'sealants' and 'locking compounds', anaerobic adhesives are based on acrylic resins and characteristically set when in the presence of metal and the absence of atmospheric oxygen. This normally means that the adhesives only harden when the components, upon which they are being used, are assembled. Generally, the adhesives are used to lock, seal and retain all manner of turned, threaded and fitted parts. High viscosity variants are also used as gasketting materials in difficult situations.

Cyanoacrylates – These adhesives are also based on acrylic resins but unlike the anaerobic adhesives they harden – in thin films – because of the catalytic effect of surface moisture. Generally, hardening takes place in a few seconds and for this reason they are frequently used in the assembly of small plastic parts. They bond most types of rubber extremely well, but caution is needed when it is intended to use them in conjunction with metal components in warm moist conditions.

Emulsion – Emulsion adhesives are generally modest viscosity, milky white dispersions often – though not always – based on polyvinyl acetate with up to approximately 65 per cent solids content. To cure emulsion adhesives the water carrier is usually absorbed by at least one of the bonded surfaces (though evaporation can also play some part). Therefore at least one surface to be bonded by the adhesive must be absorbent. As water is removed, the dispersed plastic phase is forced into contact and congeals; the resulting film binds the surfaces together. Cure rate depends on the speed of water extraction. Normally, the cured adhesive film is completely thermoplastic but special acid catalysts, available for some formulations, will promote cross-links in the film to enhance environmental stability. Emulsion adhesives are extensively used in the woodworking and packaging industries, and have applications with fabrics and fabric-based components used in 'engineered' products, for example loud-speaker cones. They also bond ceramics well. They are normally used for relatively lightly-loaded materials – preferably in good environments. Heat accelerates their rate of degradation. These adhesives may corrode metal.

Epoxides – Primarily based on an epoxide resin and one of a variety of 'hardeners' the epoxide adhesives can be found in many different types of composition. Often, they are formulated to meet the specific requirements of individual applications. Very strong and versatile, they are most frequently used on the larger components for their viscous nature makes them unsuitable for more intricate work. This latter is increasingly being assembled with the aid of the anaerobic and cyanoacrylate adhesives. New single component epoxide adhesives have been developed which are cured by heating, and these, unlike the earlier materials, do not require to be mixed prior to use. Some have been found to be useful on small parts where they replace solder.

Flexon (Toughened Acrylic Adhesives) – These materials represent a new type of rubber modified adhesive, usually based on acrylic resins. They may be cured by any one of a number of mechanisms, but their principal feature is their characteristic 'toughness'. That is to say, their ability to withstand extremely severe shock, peel and cleavage forces. Generally, adhesives of this type are not too adversely affected by residual surface contamination. While industrial experience with these newer types is still relatively limited they are worthy of very careful consideration for they really do possess an outstanding performance particularly under severe environmental conditions.

Hot Melts – As their name implies Hot Melts are essentially based on thermoplastic mixes of waxy substances usually of the polyolefin type. In the solid form they may vary in nature from rigid substances to extremely flexible solids depending upon the exact nature of their composition. They are used in the molten form and bond rapidly as they cool. They may be used on almost any scale – small components being fixed in position by individual drops whereas tanks of the liquid adhesive may be used for coating large areas. It should be noted that Hot Melts are unsuitable for the assembly of load bearing structures.

continued. . .

ADHESIVES 4.2.6

Glossary of Adhesive Types *(contd.)*

Phenolic – Phenolic adhesives are based on phenol-formaldehyde resins. They are one of the earliest groups of structural adhesives to be developed. They come in a variety of forms but usually suffer the disadvantage that they often release quantities of water on curing. For this reason heated presses or jigged autoclaves are often required and their employment almost inevitably involves the use of capital equipment and some degree of procedural complexity. Despite this, they and the related resorcinol-formaldehyde resins remain popular wherever structural integrity must be maintained under severe environmental conditions.

Plastisols – The Plastisol adhesives are based on PVC dispersions which change from the liquid to the solid form on being heated. The change of state is caused by the PVC particles absorbing the liquid in which they are dispersed, congealing and forming a strong solid on cooling. Plastisols are particularly suitable for large scale work and for situations when their reaction mechanism can use a heat source which is primarily intended for another purpose. Typically, the stoving ovens found in the motor industry are frequently used in this manner. Plastisols may be used on any scale but in practice are not too convenient for the assembly of small components. Plastisols can carry substantial loads, but should not be used whenever the structural integrity of the assembly must be maintained by them.

Polyurethanes – Like the Epoxides the Polyurethane adhesives can be individually formulated to meet a wide variety of requirements. Nonetheless, their use almost invariably involves two components and generally specialised mixing equipment. Although they have a greater degree of susceptibility to moisture attack than the other structural adhesives, the Polyurethanes can be considered to be good durable load-bearing adhesives.

Rubber – Rubber adhesives are usually based on relatively simple solutions of a variety of rubbery polymers in a solvent. Evaporation of the solvent gives the desired bonding action. Rubber based adhesives are not suitable for use in loaded structures or in bad environments.

Tapes – Adhesives tapes are available in a wide variety of forms and types but almost invariably they are based on a pressure sensitive adhesive. While adequate for the bonding of small components they cannot be used to support heavy loads. However, the more durable versions can be relied upon to perform satisfactorily under environmental duress provided that they are only very lightly loaded.

Based on information in 'Kempe's Engineers Year-Book 1989', published by Morgan-Grampian Book Publishing Co. Ltd. and 'Adhesives in Engineering Design' © W.A.Lees 1984 published by The Design Council

SUPPLIERS

ADHESIVES: Adhesive bonding

COMPANY	ADDRESS	TELEPHONE	FAX
Adhesive & Sealants Ltd	Unit 33 Burlbutt Road Heathcote Ind Estate WARWICK CV34 6TD	0926 833367	0926 881469
Apollo Chemicals Ltd	Sandy Way Amington Industrial Estate TAMWORTH Staffs B77 4DS	0827 54281	0827 53030
Bostik Ltd	Ulverscroft Rd LEICESTER LE4 6BW	0533 510015	0533 531943
CIBA-Geigy Plastics & Additives Co	Hinxton Rd Duxford CAMBRIDGE CB2 4QA	0223 832121	
Cyanamid Aerospace Products	Abenbury Way Wrexham Industrial Estate WREXHAM Clwyd LL3 9UF	0978 661971	0978 660220
Dow Corning Ltd	Cardiff Road BARRY South Glamorgan CF6 7YL	0446 732350	
Evode Ltd	Common Road STAFFORD ST16 3EH	0785 57755	
ITW Devcon	Brunel Close Park Farm WELLINGBOROUGH Northants NN8 3QX	0933 675299	0933 675765
Loctite UK	Watchmead WELWYN GARDEN CITY Herts AL7 1JB	0707 331277	0707 330233
Permabond Adhesives Ltd	Woodside Road Eastleigh Hants SO5 4EX	0703 629628	0703 629629
Raychem Ltd	Faraday Road Dorcan SWINDON Wilts SN3 5HH	0793 528171	0793 482516

USEFUL ADDRESSES

ADHESIVES

ADDRESS	TELEPHONE
Adhesive Tape Manufacturers Association 44 Masons Hill BROMLEY Kent BR2 9EQ	081 464 0131
BASA British Adhesives and Sealants Association 33 Fellowes Way STEVENAGE Herts SG2 8BW	0438 358514
FeRFA: the Trade Federation of Specialist Contractors & Materials Suppliers to the Construction Industry 1st Floor 241 High Street ALDERSHOT Hants GU11 1TJ	0252 342072
Pressure Sensitive Manufacturers Association Sysonby Lodge Nottingham Road MELTON MOWBRAY Leicestershire LE13 0NU	0664 500055

Notes

SECTION 5 – BEARINGS

PLAIN BEARINGS 5.1.1

Sintered bronze bushes: Construction, selection and use

TYPICAL APPLICATIONS: Crankshafts for engines, gearbox shafts, pivots on earth-moving equipment, linkages, steering gear suspension systems, electric motor and dynamo shafts, instrument spindles, hinges, cranks and sliders.

DEFINITIONS:

A locality common to two members of a mechanism, so designed that the members may move relatively to each other and transmit force from one to another by sliding or rotating motion. The locality may be formed either from the parent material of one member of the mechanism, or be an addition with no moving parts in itself. Solid, plain and flanged bronze bushes are of seamless continuous cylindrical or annular shape.

CONSTRUCTION:

Solid bushes are typically tin/copper/graphite composition, compacted and sintered to provide a porous structure capable of retaining 25 to 30% by volume of lubricating oil. Split bushes or half bearings for automotive crankshafts have surface overlays of lead/tin or lead/tin/copper.

NOTES ON SELECTION AND USE:

Supplied normally as a machinable bush for finish boring or lapping on assembly or as a two part split bush for ease of location (e.g. on motor engine crankshafts). Journal bearings for carrying radial loads are by far the most common, often supplied as complete assemblies including housings ('plummer' or 'pillow' blocks) with replaceable liners. Internal surfaces often have grooves to assist in the distribution of lubricants, but the trend, especially in lightly loaded applications, is toward reducing the need for continuous lubrication. Many modern bearings are rated as dry (no lubricant required), pre-lubricated (marginal lubrication required) or as standard bushes (full lubrication needed). Flanged bushes have a surface at right angles to the axis to provide location and to serve as a light thrust bearing. High interference fits are needed with standard housings and as the bearing material has a low compressive strength, great care is essential during assembly. Lead-in chamfers are provided on the outer edges of bearings to prevent local damage and insertion tools are commonly specified to make assembly easier. Final checking of bores should be done with plug gauges. Maximum running temperature of housing should normally be below 60°C.

REFERENCES

BS 308 :	Engineering drawing practice
	Part 3 : 1990 Geometrical tolerancing. (ISO 1101/2, ISO 1101)
BS 3332 : 1987	Specification for white metal bearing alloy ingots
BS 4480 :	Plain bearings: metric series
	Part 1 : 1992 Sintered bronze bushes
BS 4500 :	ISO Limits and fits
	4500A and 4500B, Data sheets
BS 5983 :	Metric spherical plain bearings
BS 5600 :	Powder metallurgical material and products
BS Aero SP94	Specification for bronze oil-retaining bushes
BS 1098	Specification for jig bushes
BS EN 2285 to 2288	Lined aluminium and steel self-lubricating bushes (etc)

PLAIN BEARINGS 5.1.2

Sintered bronze bushes: Plain and flanged sizes, loading and tolerances

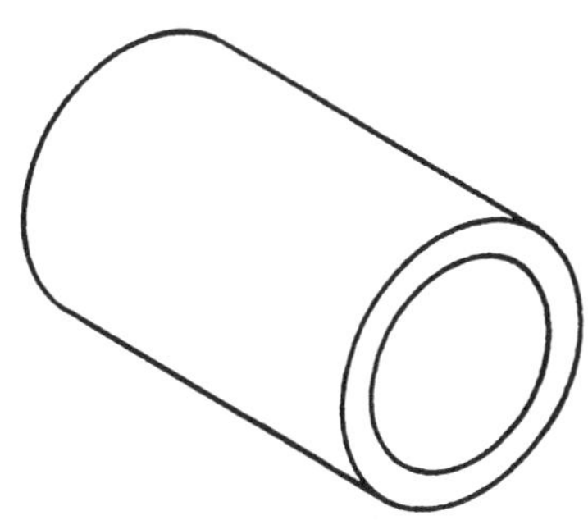
Plain bush

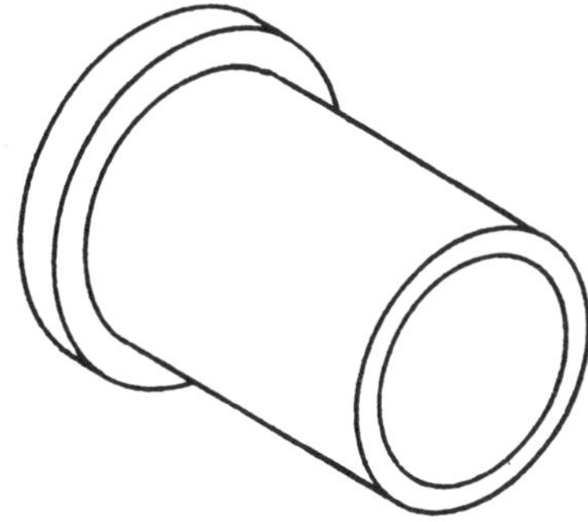
Flanged bush

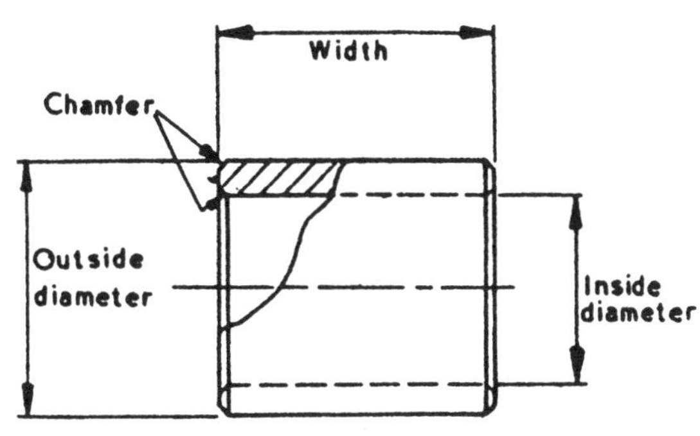

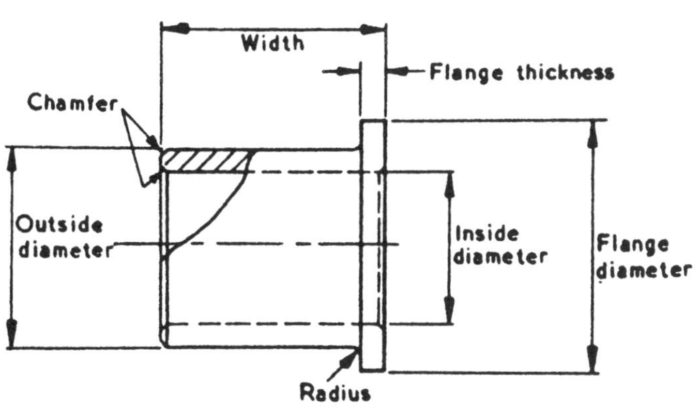

Inside dia.	Outside dia.	Plain bush Width	Flange bush Width	Flange dia.	Flange thickness
1	3	1- 2	2	5	1
1.5	4	1- 2	2	6	1
2	5	2- 3	3	8	1.5
2.5	6	2- 3	3	9	1.5
3	6	3- 4	4	9	1.5
4	8	3- 4- 6	3- 4- 6	12	2
5	9	4- 5- 8	4- 5- 8	13	2
6	10	4- 6-10	4- 6-10	14	2
7	11	5- 8-10	5- 8-10	15	2
8	12	6- 8-12	6- 8-12	16	2
9	14	6-10-14	6-10-14	19	2.5
10	16	8-10-16	8-10-16	22	3
12	18	8-12-20	8-12-20	24	3
14	20	10-14-20	10-14-20	26	3
15	21	10-15-25	10-15-25	27	3
16	22	12-16-25	12-16-25	28	3
18	24	12-18-30	12-18-30	30	3
20	26	15-20-25-30	15-20-25-30	32	3
22	28	15-20-25-30	15-20-25-30	34	3
25	32	20-25-30-35	20-25-30	39	3.5
28	36	20-25-30-40	20-25-30	44	4
30	38	20-25-30-40	20-25-30	46	4
32	40	20-25-30-40	20-25-30	48	4
35	45	25-35-40-50	25-35-40	55	5
38	48	25-35-45-55	25-35-45	58	5
40	50	30-40-50-60	30-40-50	60	5
42	52	30-40-50-60	30-40-50	62	5
45	55	35-45-55-65	35-45-55	65	5
48	58	35-50-70	35-50	68	5
50	60	35-50-70	35-50	70	5
55	65	40-55-70	40-55	75	5
60	72	50-60-70	50-60	84	6

MAXIMUM LOADS

Shaft velocity (V)	Maximum pressure on projected bearing area (P)
m/s	MN/m^2
Static	34.3
Slow and intermittent	20.6
0.125	13.7
0.25 to 0.50	3.53
0.50 to 0.75	2.35
0.75 to 1.00	1.77
over 1.00	1.77 / V

TOLERANCES FOR PLAIN BUSHES (see BS 4500)

Housing: H7
Fitted inside diameter of bearing: H7
Width: js13
Insertion pin: m5
Concentricity. The concentricity tolerance (see BS 308 : Part 1) of the outside diameter with respect to the inside diameter shall be IT9. The value of IT9 shall be that which applies to the outside diameter.

PLAIN BEARINGS 5.1.3

Wrapped bushes: Construction, selection and use

TYPICAL APPLICATIONS: Motor vehicle controls, linkages and suspensions, electric motor and dynamo spindles, mechanical handling equipment, high production industrial and consumer products, precision mechanisms, packaging machinery.

DEFINITION:

A locality common to two members of a mechanism, so designed that the members may move relatively to each other and transmit force from one to another by sliding or rotating motion. The locality may be formed either from the parent material of one member of the mechanism, or be an addition with no moving parts in itself. A wrapped bush is of cylindrical shape having a continuous split from one end to the other which closes when the bush is fitted into the housing.

CONSTRUCTION:

These are typically made from rolled material and either bi-metal, eg. copper alloy on steel backing, or composite, eg. PTFE/lead bearing surface combined with a bronze interlayer on a steel backing.

NOTES ON SELECTION AND USE

Forms of supply may be as dry bearings (no lubricant required), pre-lubricated (marginal lubrication required) or as standard (full lubrication required). The advantage of the wrapped bush is that it is designed to be self-retaining requiring no additional location and lending itself to high volume, cost-effective applications. Unlike split journal plain bushes on crankshafts, they cannot be used unless the shaft or spindle has a free end which can be fitted into them. Wrapped bushes are generally specified for medium load, low wear applications. Some types, typically in the standard range, can be finish machined on the internal bore on assembly. Other types, typically in the composite range, are supplied pre-finished. Housings and shaft tolerances must be specified exactly, cleanliness and care are essential during assembly. Lead-in chambers are provided on the outer edges of bearings to prevent local damage and insertion tools are commonly specified to make assembly easier. Final checking of bores should be done with plug gauges. Note that particular care with tolerances should be taken when housings are likely to expand under normal running conditions.

REFERENCES

BS 308 :	Engineering drawing practice Part 3 : 1990 Geometrical tolerancing (ISO 1101/2, ISO 1101)
BS 3332 : 1987	Specification for white metal bearing alloy ingots
BS 4480 :	Plain bearings: metric series Part 4 : 1979 Dimensions, tolerances and methods of checking wrapped bushes (ISO 3547)
BS 4500:	ISO Limits and fits 4500A and 4500B, Data sheets

PLAIN BEARINGS 5.1.4

Wrapped bushes: Sizes and tolerances

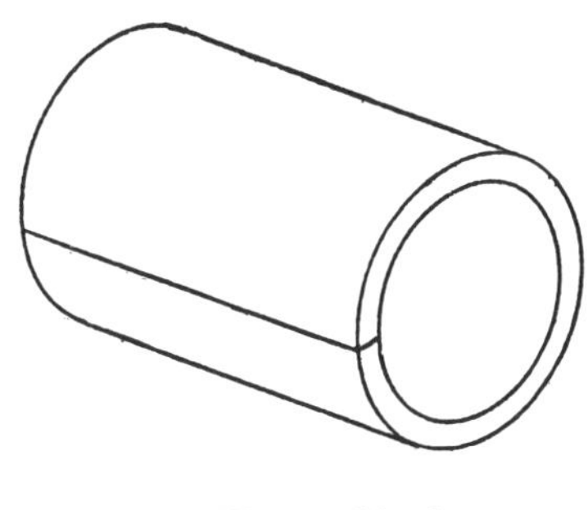

Wrapped bush

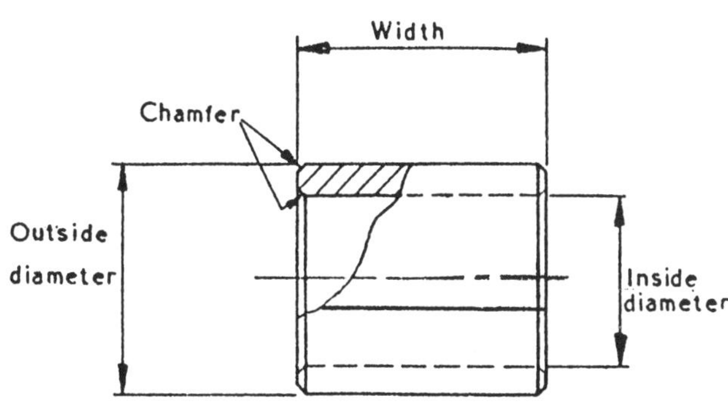

Note: As the split in the bush is normally open when supplied, no accurate measurenent of internal or external diameter can be made. Wall thickness, however, can be checked and BS 4480 should be referred to for recommended method.

Housing dia. *	Shaft diameter				
6	4.5	4			
7	5.5	5			
8	6.5	6			
9	7.5	7			
10	8.5	8			
11	9.5	9			
12	10.5	10			
13	11.5	11			
14	12.5	12			
15		13	12		
16		14	13		
17		15	14		
18		16	15		
19		17	16		
20		18	17		
21		19	18		
22		20	19		
		21	20		
24		22	21		
25		23	22		
26			23	22	
			24	23	
28			25	24	
30			27	26	
32			29	28	
34			31	30	
36			33	32	
38			35	34	
			36	35	
40			37	36	
42			39	38	
			41	40	
45			42	41	40
48			45	44	43
50			47	46	45
53			50	49	48
56				51	50
				52	51
60				53	52
				56	55

*** Housing diameter tolerances**
These should be H8, H7 or H6 according to machining facilities. A deviation from H may be necessary in the case of housings of high expansion or non-rigid material.

Housing diameters	**Width** tolerance on widths ± 0.25											
	5	10	15	20	25	30	40	50	60	70	80	100
6 and 7	x	x										
8 to 10		x	x									
11 to 15		x	x	x								
16 to 20			x	x	x							
21 to 25			x	x	x	x						
26 to 34				x	x	x	x					
36 to 48					x		x	x				
50 to 57					x		x		x			
60 to 67						x		x		x		

Tolerance on internal diameter of pre-finished bushes fitted into a rigid housing.

Housing diameter	Tolerance on internal diameter of bush	Coaxiality tolerance e
≤ 50	0.025	0.025
> 50 ≤ 80	0.035	0.030
> 80 ≤ 120	0.050	0.040
> 120 ≤ 150	0.070	0.050

PLAIN BEARINGS 5.1.5

Solid plastics bushes: Construction, selection and use

TYPICAL APPLICATIONS: Low speed moving parts in domestic and industrial appliances, motor vehicle linkages, hinges and catches, small boat tackle, rudder pivots, instrument spindles, electro-mechanical audio/visual and copying equipment, cameras, toys, clockwork mechanisms, materials handling and packaging machines, aerospace hinges, pivots and linkages.

DEFINITIONS:

A locality common to two members of a mechanism, so designed that the members may move relatively to each other and transmit force from one to another by sliding or rotating motion. The locality may be formed either from the parent material of one member of the mechanism, or be an addition with no moving parts in itself. Plain and flanged plastics bushes are of seamless, continuous cylindrical or annular shape.

CONSTRUCTION:

Both thermoplastic and thermosetting plastics are used, and these can be filled or unfilled. More common materials are: Epoxies, Phenolics, Polyesters, Polyamides (Nylons), Polyacetals (POM), and PTFE, although in theory most plastics will provide some kind of bearing surface. Performance can be greatly improved by the use of a small amount of oil or grease on some plastics, and sometimes a solid lubricant filler is added to the plastic compound during manufacture.

NOTES ON SELECTION AND USE:

Thermoplastic types are cheaper in quantity but may not be as dimensionally stable as thermosets and generally are limited to running at around or below 100°C. (PTFE is an exception since in its filled form it can run at temperatures up to 250°C.) Reinforced thermosets are superior for high load, high temperature, low speed applications. Some types of plastics bearings have good underwater wear resistance but care is needed to avoid materials which may swell in wet conditions. Plastics materials are heat retaining and therefore should not be used for bearings where heat build up may be a problem unless there is adequate ventilation or cooling. Advantages over metal bushes include: resistance to corrosion, resistance to chemicals, good damping and good electrical insulation. Great care is needed with interference fits and running clearances because of the wide range of material types available. Special methods are needed for the machining of plastics materials and the soft nature of their surfaces puts them at risk from accidental damage prior to or during assembly. Suppliers should always be consulted on the detailed assembly and running conditions for any particular material.

REFERENCES

BS 308 :	Engineering drawing practice Part 3 : 1990 Geometrical tolerancing (ISO 1101/2, ISO 1101)
BS 3332 : 1987	Specification for white metal bearing alloy ingots
BS 4480 :	Plain bearings: metric series Part 2 : 1974 Solid plastics bushes
BS 4500 :	ISO Limits and fits 4500A and 4500B, Data sheets

PLAIN BEARINGS 5.1.6

Solid plastics bushes: Plain and flanged – dimensions

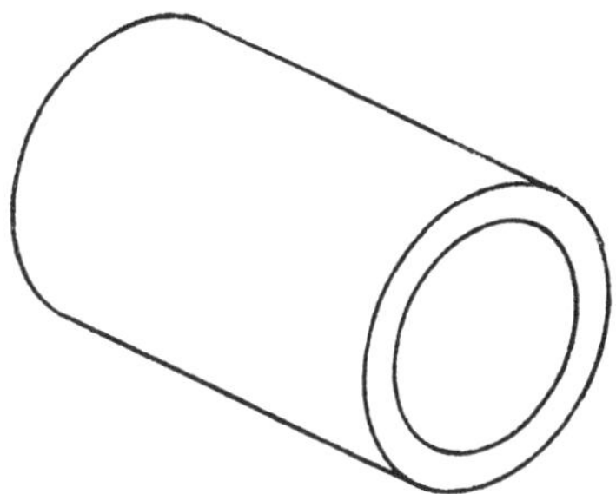

Plain bush

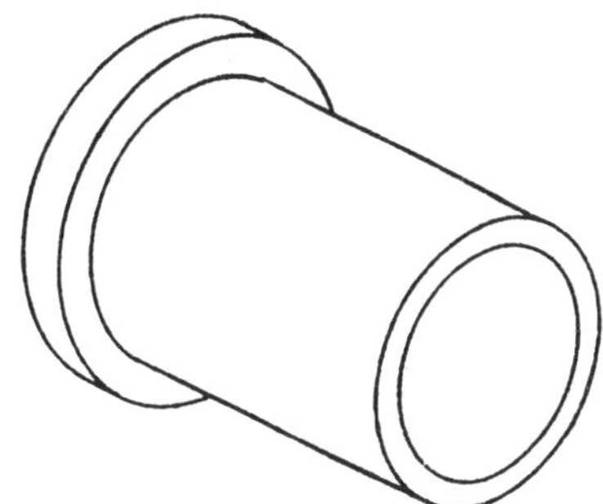

Flanged bush

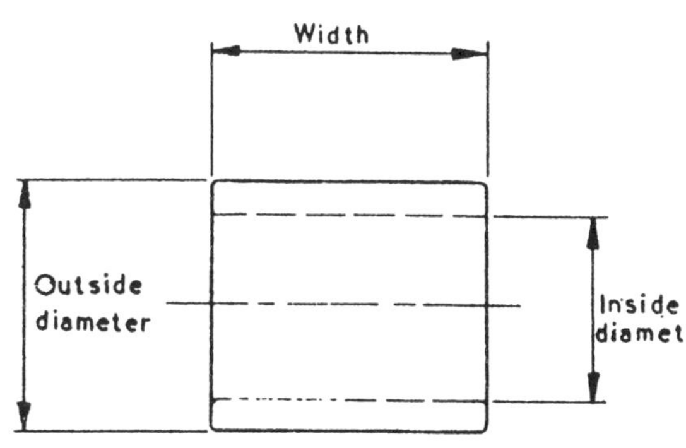

Width
Flange thickness
Outside diameter
Inside diameter
Flange diameter
Radius

DIMENSIONS OF MEDIUM INTERFERENCE BUSHES

Inside diameter			Outside diameters			
Nominal	Limits after fitting		Nominal			Widths
	upper deviation	lower deviation	D1	D	D3	
3	+0.07	+0.03		5	6	3-4
4				7	8	3- 4-6
5	+0.11	+0.04		8	9	4- 5-8
6				9	10	4- 6-10
7				10	11	5- 8-10
8				11	12	6- 8-12
9	+0.15	+0.05		12	14	6-10-14
10			13	14	16	8-10-16
12			15	16	18	8-12-20
14			17	18	20	10-14-20
15	+0.22	+0.08	18	19	21	10-15-25
16			19	20	22	12-16-25
18			21	22	24	12-18-30
20			24	25	26	15-20-25-30
22			26	27	28	15-20-25-30
25	+0.36	+0.13	29	30	32	20-25-30-35
28			32	33	36	20-25-30-40
30			34	35	38	20-25-30-40
32			36	38	40	20-25-30-40
35	+0.44	+0.16	39	41	45	25-35-45-50
38			42	44	48	25 35 45 55
40			45	46	50	30-40-50-60
42			47	48	52	30-40-50-60
45	+0.50	+0.19	50	51	55	35-45-55-65
48			53	55	58	35-50-60-70
50			55	58	60	35-50-70-75
55	+0.53	+0.22	60	63	65	35-50-70-75
60			65	68	72	40-55-70-80

DIMENSIONS OF FLANGED BUSHES

Nominal inside dia.	Nominal outside dia.	Nominal flange dia.	Flange thickness	Widths
3	6	9	1.5	4
4	8	12	2	6
5	9	13	2	8
6	10	14	2	10
7	11	15	2	8-10
8	12	16	2	8-12
9	14	19	2.5	10-12
10	16	22	3	10-16
12	18	24	3	12-20
14	20	26	3	10-14-20
15	21	27	3	10-15-25
16	22	28	3	12-16-25
18	24	30	3	12-18-30
20	26	32	3	15-20-25-30
22	28	34	3	15-20-25-30
25	32	39	3.5	20-25-30
28	36	44	4	20-25-30
30	38	46	4	20-25-30
32	40	48	4	20-25-30
35	45	55	5	25-35-40
38	48	58	5	25-35-45
40	50	60	5	30-40-50
42	52	62	5	30-40-50
45	55	65	5	35-45-55
48	58	68	5	35-50
50	60	70	5	35-50
55	65	75	5	35-50
60	72	84	6	50-60

ROLLING ELEMENT BEARINGS 5.2.1

Radial ball bearings: Construction, Selection and use

TYPICAL APPLICATIONS: Spindles for turning, milling, drilling and grinding machines, automotive transmissions, electric motors and dynamo spindles, pumps, fans and compressor shafts, aircraft control linkages, high speed processing and packaging machinery, conveyor belts, mechanical handling equipment, production machinery, heavy duty shakers and mixers, precision instruments.

DEFINITION:

A locality common to two members of a mechanism so designed that the members may move relatively to each other and transmit force from one to another by rolling motion. The locality is a separate item comprising several rolling ball elements which make point contact with the raceways of its inner and outer rings.

CONSTRUCTION:

Generally the rings and rolling elements are made from high grade, direct hardening, carbon chromium steels producing a surface hardness of between 59 and 65 HRC. The cages of small and medium size bearings are normally made from pressed steel or brass. Cages machined from solid material, usually brass, are used on larger sizes. Various plastics materials and, in some cases, special cast irons, are also specified depending on bearing size and duty.

NOTES ON SELECTION AND USE:

These bearings are generally used for light and medium load applications, and will take moderate axial loads in either direction alone or in combination with radial load. High speed running is common but there are limitations arising from permissible operating temperatures which may affect material hardness and lubrication and hence maximum load carrying capacity. There will be cases, e.g. high speed machinery, where selection is a compromise between bearings large enough to give the desired life before the onset of fatigue, and those with dimensions which will allow effective lubrication. Avoidance of axial loads through rolling elements is essential during assembly, and purpose made tools are advisable both for assembly and extraction. The maximum permissible temperature to be used when shrink fitting onto shafts is 120°C. Cleanliness is of major importance during handling, assembly, running and maintenance. Consideration should be given to the shielded or sealed types of bearing when operating environments are harsh and access for lubrication and maintenance is difficult. Other factors worthy of careful attention are: the method and type of lubrication, fitting clearances and allowable shaft misalignment. Manufacturers or suppliers advice must always be sought before final selection is made and it should be noted that while the radial ball bearing is the most popular type for general purposes, a range of variants is available which may be more suitable for specialist applications.

REFERENCES

BS 292 : Rolling bearings: ball bearings, cylindrical and spherical roller bearings.
Part 1 : 1982 : (1987) Specification for dimensions of ball bearings, cylindrical and spherical roller bearings (metric series)
BS 5512 : 1991 Method of calculating dynamic load ratings and rating life of rolling bearings
BS 5645 : 1987 Specification for static load ratings for rolling bearings
BS 5646 : Rolling bearings – accessories
BS 6107 : Rolling bearings – tolerances
ISO 15 = BS 6267 : 1982 Specification for rolling bearings : boundary dimensions for radial bearings

ROLLING ELEMENT BEARINGS 5.2.2

Single row, deep groove, radial ball bearings: Types, sizes and tolerances

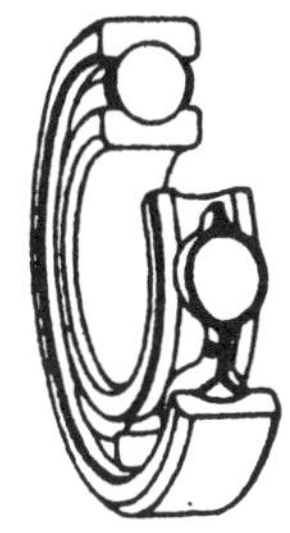

Single row radial ball bearing

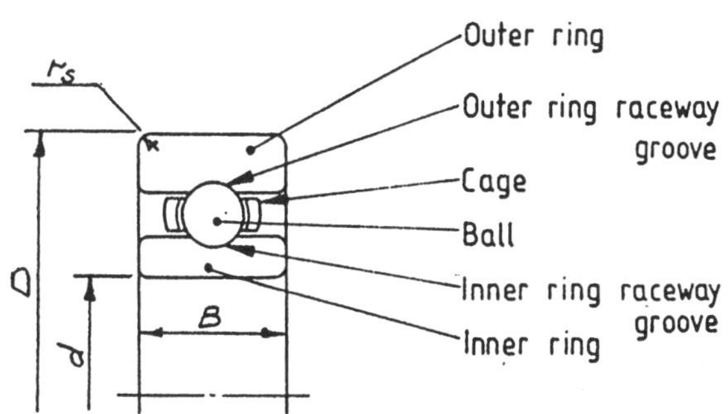

Variants

In addition to standard 'open' bearings, 'shielded' and 'sealed' types are also available as shown below. (Refer to BS 292 for preferred size ranges)

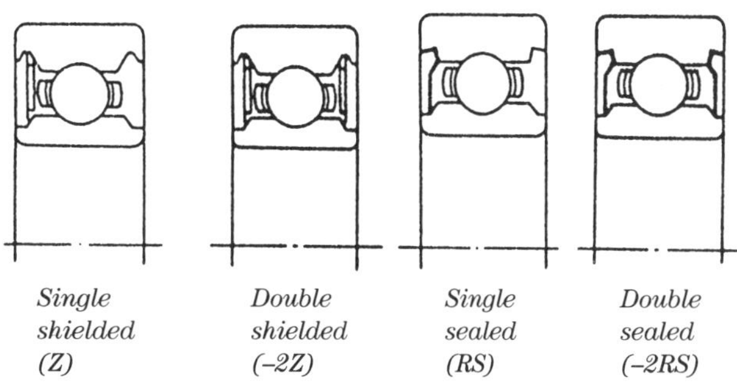

Single shielded (Z) — *Double shielded (-2Z)* — *Single sealed (RS)* — *Double sealed (-2RS)*

Note 1. *Metal shields, which are retained to the outer ring by various means, have a small running clearance about the inner ring and, consequently, this type of closure offers only limited protection against the ingress of foreign matter.*

Note 2. *Contact seals are of various designs but all have a flexible lip which makes rubbing contact with the inner ring, offering better protection than metal shields but absorbing more power. The most common type of seal is moulded in nitrile rubber and vulcanized to a metal insert. These seals are suitable for operational temperatures ranging from approximately –20°C to +100°C. Where higher or lower temperatures are involved, it is necessary to consult the bearing manufacturers.*

ISO DIMENSION SERIES 02

Designation (open bearing)	d (Dia)	D (Dia)	B	r_s min
6200	10	30	9	0.6
6201	12	32	10	0.6
6202	15	35	11	0.6
6203	17	40	12	0.6
6204	20	47	14	1
6205	25	52	15	1
6206	30	62	16	1
6207	35	72	17	1.1
6208	40	80	18	1.1
6209	45	85	19	1.1
6210	50	90	20	1.1
6211	55	100	21	1.5
6212	60	110	22	1.5
6213	65	120	23	1.5
6214	70	125	24	1.5
6215	75	130	25	1.5
6216	80	140	26	2
6217	85	150	28	2
6218	90	160	30	2
6219	95	170	32	2.1
6220	100	180	34	2.1
6221	105	190	36	2.1
6222	110	200	38	2.1
6224	120	215	40	2.1
6226	130	230	40	3
6228	140	250	42	3
6230	150	270	45	3
6232	160	290	48	3
6234	170	310	52	4
6236	180	320	52	4
6238	190	340	55	4
6240	200	360	58	4
6244	220	400	65	4

INNER RING TOLERANCES

d		Δ_{dmp}	V_{dp}	
over	incl.	high	low	max
2.5	10	0	–8	6
10	18	0	–8	6
18	30	0	–10	8
30	50	0	–12	9
50	80	0	–15	11
80	120	0	–20	15
120	180	0	–25	19
180	250	0	–30	23

Δ_{dmp} = single plane mean bore diameter deviation

V_{dp} = bore diameter variation in a single radial plane

OUTER RING TOLERANCES

d		Δ_{Dmp}	V_{Dp}	
over	incl.	high	low	max
6	18	0	–8	6
18	30	0	–9	7
30	50	0	–11	8
50	80	0	–13	10
80	120	0	–15	11
120	150	0	–18	14
150	180	0	–25	19
180	250	0	–30	23
250	315	0	–35	26
315	400	0	–40	30

Δ_{Dmp} = Single plane mean outside diameter deviation

V_{Dp} = outside diameter variation in a single radial plane

ROLLING ELEMENT BEARINGS 5.2.3

Roller bearings: Construction, selection and use

TYPICAL APPLICATIONS: Railway axle boxes, heavy electric motors, automotive transmissions, heavy fans, pumps and compressors, rolling mill shafts, heavy duty spindles on machine tools, gearbox pinion drives, rod and wire mill shafts, heavy duty pulleys, rotating dryers, large radar and telescope tracking systems, turbines, generators and compressors.

DEFINITION:

A locality common to two members of a mechanism so designed that the members may move relatively to each other and transmit force from one to another by rolling motion. The locality is a separate item comprising several rolling cylindrical elements which make line contact with the raceways of its inner and outer rings.

CONSTRUCTION:

Generally the rings and rolling elements are made from high grade, direct hardening, carbon chromium steels producing a surface hardness of between 59 and 65 HRC. The cages of small and medium size bearings are normally made from pressed steel or brass. Cages machined from solid material, usually brass, are used on larger sizes. Various plastics materials and, in some cases, special cast irons, are also specified depending on bearing size and duty.

NOTES ON SELECTION AND USE:

These bearings are generally used for medium and heavy load applications in the radial direction only. Although commonly used in the larger diameter range, their general resistance to dynamic radial loads makes them particularly attractive for all applications where shafts suffer continuous shock loading. Some shaft misalignment is tolerable and high speed running is common but there are limitations to permissible operating temperatures which may affect material hardness and lubrication and hence maximum load carrying capacity. There will be cases, e.g. high speed machinery, where selection is a compromise between bearings large enough to give the desired life before the onset of fatigue, and those with dimensions which will allow effective lubrication. Avoidance of axial loads through rolling elements is essential during assembly, and purpose made tools are advisable both for assembly and extraction. The maximum permissible temperature to be used when shrink fitting bearings of all metal construction onto shafts is around 120°C. Cleanliness is of major importance during handling, assembly, running and maintenance. Consideration should be given to separate shields or seals for these bearings when operating environments are harsh and access for lubrication and maintenance is difficult. Other factors worthy of careful attention are: method and type of lubrication, fitting clearances and allowable shaft misalignment. Manufacturers or suppliers advice must always be sought before final selection is made and although the cylindrical roller bearing is the most popular of its type, a range of variants is available which may be more suitable for specialist applications.

REFERENCES

BS 292 :	Rolling bearings: ball bearings, cylindrical and spherical roller bearings. Part 1 : 1982 : (1987) Specification for dimensions of ball bearings, cylindrical and spherical roller bearings (metric series)
BS 5512 : 1991	Method of calculating dynamic load ratings and rating life of rolling bearings
BS 5645 : 1987	Specification for static load ratings for rolling bearings
BS 5646 :	Rolling bearings – accessories
BS 6107 :	Rolling bearings – tolerances
ISO 15 = BS 6267 :	1982 Specification for rolling bearings: boundary dimensions for radial bearings

ROLLING ELEMENT BEARINGS 5.2.4

Single row, cylindrical roller bearings: Types, dimensions and tolerances

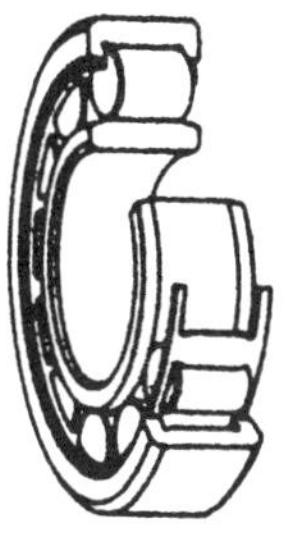
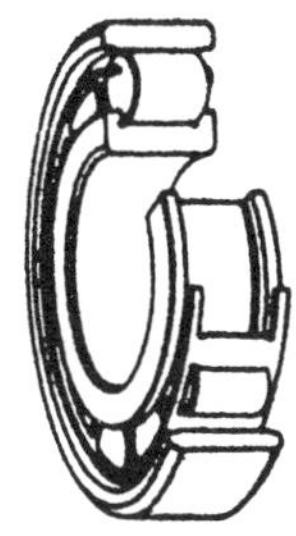

Cylindrical roller bearings

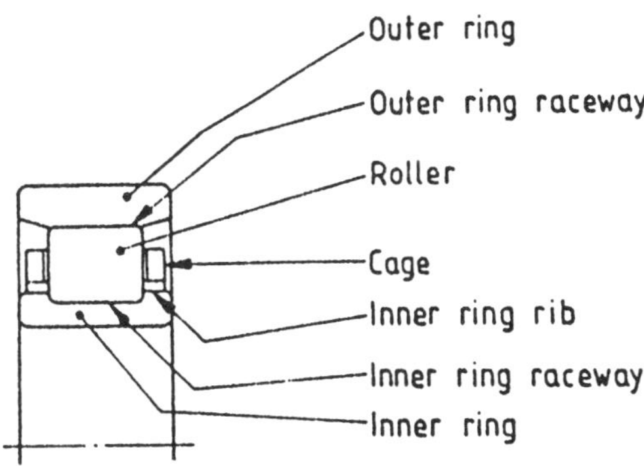

Variants

In addition to the most common types with non-locating outer or inner rings, two other variants are shown below for more specialist applications. Note that these bearings are not available with integral shields and seals.

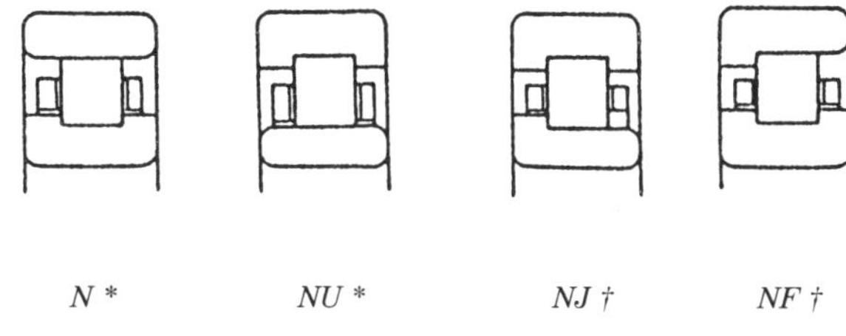

** Most commonly used types.*
† Suitable for axial location in one direction.

ISO DIMENSION SERIES 02				
Designation	**d**	**D**	**B**	**r_s min**
N or NU 200	10	30	9	0.6
N or NU 201	12	32	10	0.6
N or NU 202	15	35	11	0.6
N or NU 203	17	40	12	0.6
N or NU 204	20	47	14	1
N or NU 205	25	52	15	1
N or NU 206	30	62	16	1
N or NU 207	35	72	17	1.1
N or NU 208	40	80	18	1.1
N or NU 209	45	85	19	1.1
N or NU 210	50	90	20	1.1
N or NU 211	55	100	21	1.5
N or NU 212	60	110	22	1.5
N or NU 213	65	120	23	1.5
N or NU 214	70	125	24	1.5
N or NU 215	75	130	25	1.5
N or NU 216	80	140	26	2
N or NU 217	85	150	28	2
N or Nu 218	90	160	30	2
N or NU 219	95	170	32	2.1
N or NU 220	100	180	34	2.1
N or NU 221	105	190	36	2.1
N or NU 222	110	200	38	2.1
N or NU 224	120	215	40	2.1
N or NU 226	130	230	40	3
N or NU 228	140	250	42	3
N or NU 230	150	270	45	3
N or NU 232	160	290	48	3
N or NU 234	170	310	52	4
N or NU 236	180	320	52	4
N or NU 238	190	340	55	4
N or NU 240	200	360	58	4
N or NU 244	220	400	65	

INNER RING TOLERANCES				
d		**Δ_{dmp}**		**V_{dp}**
over	**incl.**	**high**	**low**	**max**
2.5	10	0	−8	6
10	18	0	−8	6
18	30	0	−10	8
30	50	0	−12	9
50	80	0	−15	11
80	120	0	−20	15
120	180	0	−25	19
180	250	0	−30	23

Δ_{dmp} = single plane mean bore diameter deviation

V_{dp} = bore diameter variation in a single radial plane

OUTER RING TOLERANCES				
d		**Δ_{Dmp}**		**V_{Dp}**
over	**incl.**	**high**	**low**	**max**
6	18	0	−8	6
18	30	0	−9	7
30	50	0	−11	8
50	80	0	−13	10
80	120	0	−15	11
120	150	0	−18	14
150	180	0	−25	19
180	250	0	−30	23
250	315	0	−35	26
315	400	0	−40	30

Δ_{Dmp} = Single plane mean outside diameter deviation

V_{Dp} = outside diameter variation in a single radial plane

BEARING SELECTION 5.3.1

Selection by load capacity

SELECTION BY LOAD CAPACITY OF BEARINGS WITH CONTINUOUS ROTATION

This figure gives guidance on the type of bearing which has the maximum load capacity at a given speed and shaft size. It is based on a life of 10,000 hrs for rubbing, rolling and porous metal bearings. Longer lives may be obtained at reduced loads and speeds. For the various plain bearings, the width is assumed to be equal to the diameter, and the lubricant is assumed to be a medium viscosity mineral oil.

In many cases the operating environment or various special performance requirements, other than load capacity, may be of overriding importance in the selection of an appropriate type of bearing. The tables give guidance for these cases.

RUBBING PLAIN BEARINGS in which the surfaces rub together. The bearing is usually non-metallic - - - - - - - - - -

PLAIN BEARINGS of porous metal impregnated with a lubricant. - · - · - · - · - ·

ROLLING BEARINGS. The materials are hard, and rolling elements separate the two moving components ————

FLUID FILM PLAIN BEARINGS. A hydrodynamic pressure is generated by the relative movement dragging a viscous fluid into a taper film. - · · - · · - · · -

These two facing pages reproduced from the 'Tribology Handbook' (Butterworths) with the permission of the author and editor M.J. Neale.

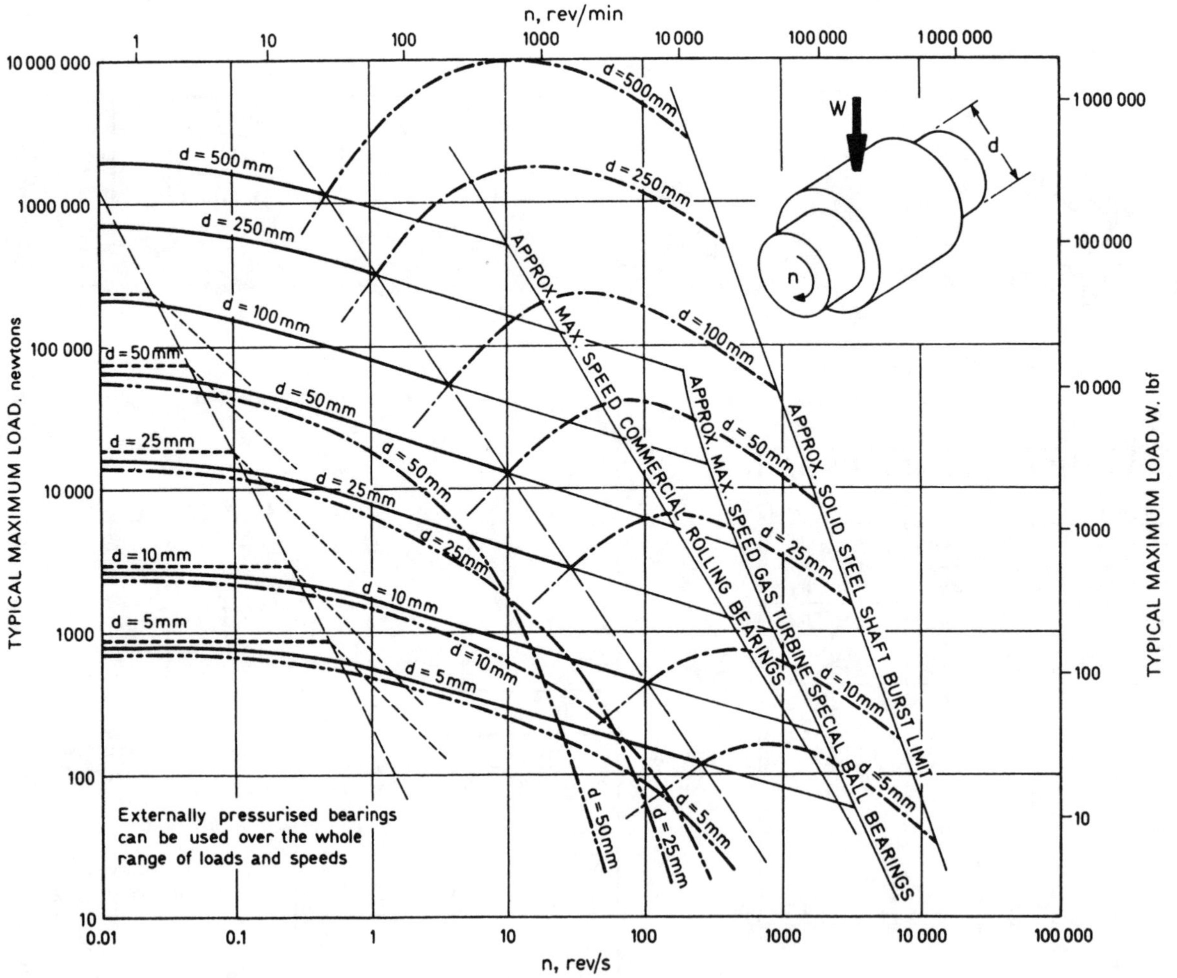

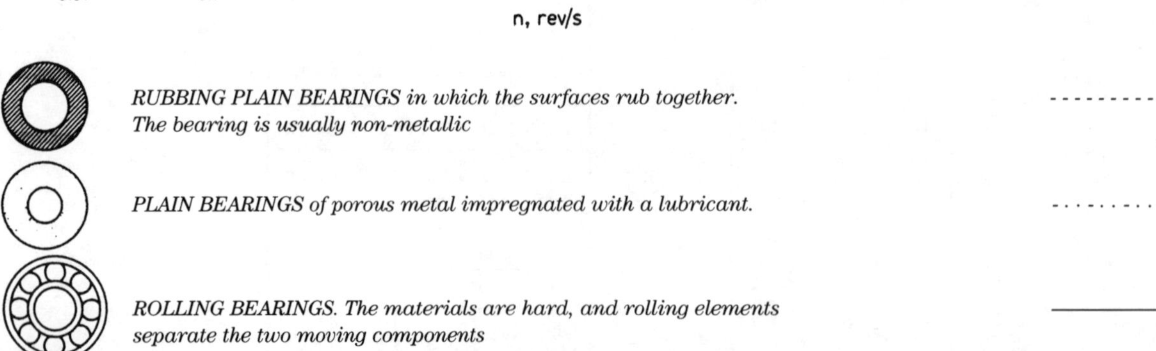

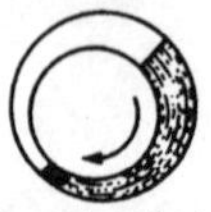

BEARING SELECTION 5.3.2

Selection for special environmental or performance conditions

SELECTION OF JOURNAL BEARINGS WITH CONTINUOUS ROTATION FOR SPECIAL ENVIRONMENTAL CONDITIONS

Type of bearing	High temp.	Low temp.	Vacuum	Wet & humid	Dirt & dust	External Vibration	Type of bearing
Rubbing plain bearings (non-metallic)	Good up to the temperature limit of material	Good	Excellent	Good but shaft must be incorrodible	Good but sealing helps	Good	
Porous metal plain bearings oil impregnated	Poor since lubricant oxidises	Fair; may have high starting torque	Possible with special lubricant	Good	Sealing essential	Good	
Rolling bearings	Consult makers above 150°C	Good	Fair with special lubricant	Good with seals	Sealing essential	Fair; consult makers	
Fluid film plain bearings	Good to temperature limit of lubricant	Good; may have high starting torque	Possible with special lubricant	Good	Good with seals and filtration	Good	
Externally pressurised plain bearings	Excellent with gas lubrication	Good	No; lubricant feed affects vacuum	Good	Good; excellent when gas lubricated	Excellent	
General comments	Watch effect of thermal expansion on fits			Watch corrosion		Watch fretting	

SELECTION OF JOURNAL BEARINGS WITH CONTINUOUS ROTATION FOR SPECIAL PERFORMANCE REQUIREMENTS

Type of bearing	Accurate radial location	Axial load capacity as well	Low starting torque	Silent running	Standard parts available	Simple lubrication	Type of bearing
Rubbing plain bearings (non-metallic)	Poor	Some in most cases	Poor	Fair	Some	Excellent	
Porous metal plain bearings oil impregnated	Good	Some	Good	Excellent	Yes	Excellent	
Rolling bearings	Good	Yes in most cases	Very good	Usually satisfactory	Yes	Good when grease lubricated	
Fluid film plain bearings	Fair	No; separate thrust bearing needed	Good	Excellent	Some	Usually requires a circulation system	
Externally pressurised plain bearings	Excellent	No; separate thrust bearing needed	Excellent	Excellent	No	Poor; special system needed	

SUPPLIERS

BEARINGS: Plain and Rolling Element Bearings

COMPANY	ADDRESS	TELEPHONE	FAX
PLAIN BEARINGS:			
Birkett & Sons Ltd	PO Box 16 Hightown Road CLECKHEATON W YORKS BD19 5JT	0274 873366	0274 862754
Coleherne Ltd	Lodge Street Newton HYDE Cheshire SK14 4LE	061 366 6603	061 367 8239
Glacier Metal Co Ltd	Winterhay Lane ILMINSTER Somerset TA19 9PH	0460 53221	0460 57832
Hall Rewinds Ltd	Unit 3 Aston Fields Road Whitehouse Industrial Estate RUNCORN Cheshire WA7 3DL	0928 717322	0928 712905
Manganese Bronze Ltd	PO Box 19 Elton Park Works Hadleigh Road IPSWICH IP2 0HX	0473 233300	0473 230424
Rose Bearings Ltd	Doddington Road LINCOLN LN6 3RA	0522 500933	0522 500975
ROLLING ELEMENT BEARINGS:			
Bridge Bearings Ltd	Stowvale Road Lye STOURBRIDGE W Midlands DY9 8PT	0384 424766	0384 424830
MC Hives Ltd	Primrose Avenue Fordhouses WOLVERHAMPTON W Midlands WV10 8AW	0902 782838	0902 781750
NSK Bearings Europe Ltd	South West Ind Estate PETERLEE Co Durham SR8 2JD	091 586 6111	091 578 1089
RHP Bearings RHP Industrial Bearings Div	PO Box 18 NEWARK NG24 2JF	0636 605123	0636 605000
SNFA Bearings Ltd	Wotton Road Charfield WOTTON-UNDER-EDGE Glos GL12 8SP	0453 843501	0453 842577

USEFUL ADDRESSES

BEARINGS

ADDRESS	TELEPHONE
Ball and Roller Bearing Manufacturers Association 136 Hagley Road BIRMINGHAM B16 9PN	021 454 4141
British Structural Bearings Manufacturers Association Rutland House 44 Masons Hill BROMLEY BR2 9EQ	081 464 0131
Institute of Tribology University of Leeds LEEDS LS2 9JT	0532 332155

Notes

SECTION 6 – POWER TRANSMISSION SYSTEMS

FRICTION DRIVES 6.1.1

Endless wedge and 'V' belt drives: Construction, selection and use

TYPICAL APPLICATIONS: Fan belts for vehicles, pump, motor and compressor drives, conveyor belts, mechanical handling drives, vehicle power transmissions, machine tool drives.

DEFINITIONS:

Wedge, V-belt or V-ribbed drive: A drive that consists of one or more or several integrally formed trapezoidal section belts mounted on grooved pulleys in such a way that the belts contact only the sides and not the base of the pulley grooves. Wedge belts have a relative height to pitch width ratio of around 0.95 whereas V-belts have a ratio of around 0.73.

CONSTRUCTION:

Belts: These are typically a continuous loop made from a combination of fabric, cord and elastomeric compounds bonded together into a uniform shape throughout.
Pulleys: These may be made from cast iron, steel, alloys or any material that can be shaped to the standardized dimensions and surface finish required, and can withstand without damage all normal conditions of service. Pulley hubs have, typically, taper bushes and keyways for shaft fitting.

NOTES ON SELECTION AND USE:

This type of transmission is suitable for operating at temperatures between −18°C and +60°C without any adverse effects on overall efficiency. Where multi-belt drives are used it is advisable to specify matched belts to avoid uneven distribution of load (interchangeability is guaranteed by some manufacturers) and under no circumstances should wedge and V -belts be mixed on the same drive. In the case of systems designed for wedge belts, replacements must be of the same type, but with V -belts either type may be re-ordered as long as due consideration is taken of minimum pulley diameters. Wedge belts are the most common type for use in continuous operation friction transmission drives, with the classical V -belt being now limited to uses in such areas as high duty drives, particularly in transportation where its heavy structure can be an advantage. Neither type of belt can accommodate flexure in more than one direction, therefore the use of guide or tension pulleys pressing on the top surface is prohibited. V-ribbed belts are an alternative to multiple single belts especially for permanent installations. Mounting must always be done without force, and the use of metal levers avoided. If anti-static or fire resistance properties are required, selection should be based on the strict guidelines given in the standards and in the supplier's literature.

Considerations to be taken into account during design of a transmission include: transmitted power, type of service, hours per day of operation, pulley diameters, belt speeds, locking pulley and pulley centre distances. (The latter factor is limited by a general rule that the arc of contact on the smallest pulley should not be less than 120 degrees.) Careful reference to standards and supplier's design is essential before a drive is finally specified.

REFERENCES

BS 3733 : 1974	Specification for endless V-belt drives for agricultural purposes
BS 3790 : 1981 (ISO 254)	Specification for endless wedge belt drives and endless V-belt drives
BS 4235 :	Specification for metric keys and keyways
BS AU 150b : 1984 (1990)	Specification for automotive V-belts and pulleys
BS 7620 : 1993	Specification for industrial belt drives. Dimensions of pulleys and V-ribbed belts of PH, PJ, PK*, PL and PM profiles
ISO 4183 (≈ BS 3790)	Grooved pulleys for classical and narrow V-belts
ISO 4184 (≈ BS 3790)	Classical and narrow V-belts – lengths

* Note: PK belts are for auto use – see ISO 9981

FRICTION DRIVES 6.1.2

Endless wedge and 'V' belt drives: Design method and table of service factors

DRIVE ASSEMBLY

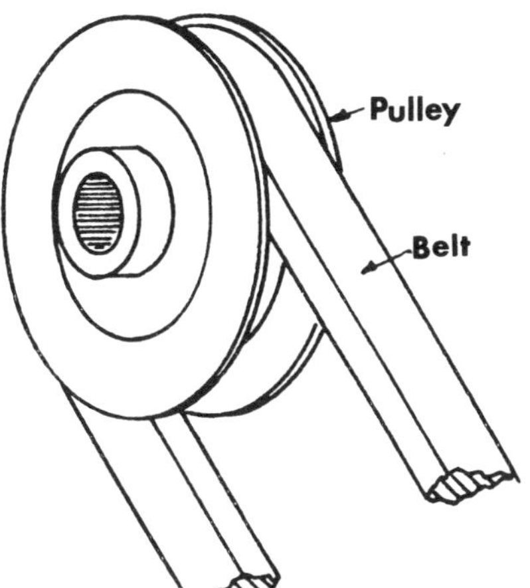

Belt cross-sections

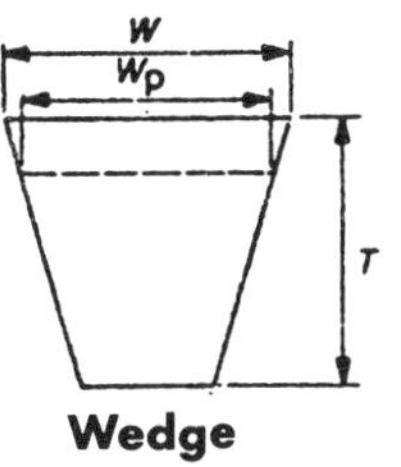

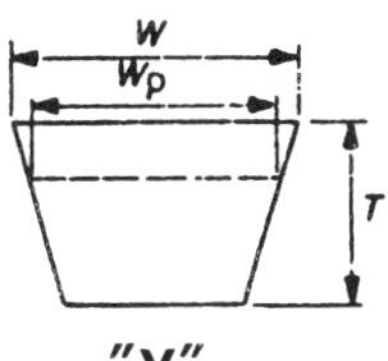

BELT CROSS SECTION DIMENSIONS mm			
Cross section * symbol	**Pitch width** W_p	**Nominal top width** W	**Nominal height** T
Wedge belts			
SPZ	8.5	10.0	8.0
SPA	11.0	13.0	10.0
SPB	14.0	17.0	14.0
V belts			
Z	8.5	10.0	6.0
A	11.0	13.0	8.0
B	14.0	17.0	11.0

* For full list see BS 3790

POWER TRANSMISSION DESIGN – FOR DRIVE BELTS AND PULLEYS

DESIGN POWER (Kw) : This is the prime mover power (Kw) multiplied by the service factor in *TABLE A* (below)

POWER RATINGS : The recommended power ratings of single belts at standard motor speeds are in *TABLE B* (6.1.3)

PITCH LENGTHS (L) * : $L = 2c + 1.57 (D + d) + \frac{(D - d)^2}{4c}$ where

c = Centre distance of drive
D = Large pulley pitch diameter
d = Small pulley pitch diameter
* L – See *TABLE C* for standard sizes (6.1.4)

CENTRE DISTANCE (c): If unknown consult BS 3790 Appendix A for formula

BELT CROSS SECTION : Consult *GRAPHS D* and *E* for the most favourable section (6.1.5)

PULLEY DIAMETERS : Consult *TABLE F* to obtain correct speed ratio (6.1.6)

NOTES – This is a guide only. BS 3790 and Suppliers must be consulted before selection.
See BS 7620 for V-ribbed belts

TABLE A

	Service factors for belt drives	**Service factor** (Refer to Table 8, BS 3790 for full list and special conditions)					
Class	**Examples of types of driven machine (where the application includes a 'speed increasing' drive see BS 3790, Table 8 for correction factors)**	**'Soft' starts** Hours of duty per day			**'Heavy' starts** Hours of duty per day		
		10 & under	**Over 10 to 16**	**Over 16**	**10 & under**	**Over 10 to 16**	**Over 16**
1 (Light)	Blowers / Agitators / Light Conveyors	1.0	1.1	1.2	1.1	1.2	1.3
2 (Medium)	Machine tools / Printing Machines	1.2	1.2	1.3	1.2	1.3	1.4
3 (Heavy)	Hoists / Heavy Conveyors / Hammer Mills	1.2	1.3	1.4	1.4	1.5	1.6
4 (Ex-Heavy)	Heavy Crushers / Ball, Rod, Tube Mills	1.3	1.4	1.5	1.5	1.6	1.8

TABLE B

BELT POWER – POWER RATINGS AT STANDARD ELECTRIC MOTOR SPEEDS – WEDGE AND 'V'-BELTS

POWER RATING FOR SPZ SECTION WEDGE BELTS, WITH 180° ARC OF CONTACT ON SMALLER PULLEY

Speed of Faster Shaft	Power rating for smaller pulley pitch diameter of											Additional power increment per belt, for speed ratio of									
	67.0 mm	71.0 mm	75.0 mm	80.0 mm	85.0 mm	90.0 mm	95.0 mm	100.0 mm	112.0 mm	125.0 mm	140.0 mm	1.00 to 1.01	1.02 to 1.05	1.05 to 1.11	1.12 to 1.18	1.18 to 1.26	1.27 to 1.38	1.39 to 1.57	1.58 to 1.94	1.95 to 3.38	3.39 and over
r/min	kw	kw	kw	kw	kw	kw	kw	kw	kw	kw	kw	kw	kw	kw	kw	kw	kw	kw	kw	kw	kw
720	0.61	0.70	0.79	0.90	1.01	1.12	1.23	1.34	1.60	1.88	2.20	0.00	0.01	0.03	0.05	0.06	0.08	0.09	0.10	0.11	0.12
960	0.77	0.88	1.00	1.15	1.29	1.44	1.58	1.72	2.06	2.42	2.84	0.00	0.01	0.04	0.06	0.08	0.10	0.12	0.13	0.15	0.15
1440	1.05	1.22	1.39	1.60	1.81	2.01	2.22	2.42	2.91	3.43	4.02	0.00	0.02	0.05	0.09	0.13	0.15	0.18	0.20	0.22	0.23
2880	1.73	2.04	2.35	2.73	3.11	3.49	3.86	4.22	5.08	5.97	6.97	0.00	0.04	0.11	0.18	0.25	0.30	0.36	0.40	0.44	0.46

POWER RATING FOR SPA SECTION WEDGE BELTS, WITH 180° ARC OF CONTACT ON SMALLER PULLEY

Speed of Faster Shaft	Power rating for smaller pulley pitch diameter of											Additional power increment per belt, for speed ratio of									
	100.0 mm	105.0 mm	112.0 mm	118.0 mm	125.0 mm	132.0 mm	140.0 mm	150.0 mm	160.0 mm	180.0 mm	200.0 mm	1.00 to 1.01	1.02 to 1.05	1.06 to 1.11	1.12 to 1.18	1.19 to 1.26	1.27 to 1.38	1.39 to 1.57	1.58 to 1.94	1.95 to 3.38	3.39 and over
r/min	kw	kw	kw	kw	kw	kw	kw	kw	kw	kw	kw	kw	kw	kw	kw	kw	kw	kw	kw	kw	kw
720 *	1.53	1.76	1.99	2.22	2.48	2.75	3.05	3.42	3.79	4.52	5.24	0.00	0.02	0.07	0.12	0.16	0.20	0.23	0.26	0.28	0.30
960 *	1.92	2.22	2.51	2.81	3.15	3.50	3.88	4.36	4.84	5.79	6.72	0.00	0.03	0.09	0.16	0.21	0.26	0.30	0.34	0.37	0.40
1440 *	2.61	3.04	3.46	3.89	4.38	4.87	5.42	6.10	6.78	8.10	9.40	0.00	0.05	0.14	0.24	0.32	0.39	0.46	0.51	0.56	0.59
2880 *	4.12	4.88	5.64	6.37	7.22	8.05	8.97	10.10	11.19	13.24	–	0.00	0.10	0.27	0.47	0.64	0.78	0.91	1.03	1.12	1.19

POWER RATING FOR SPB SECTION WEDGE BELTS, WITH 180° ARC OF CONTACT ON SMALLER PULLEY

Speed of Faster Shaft	Power rating for smaller pulley pitch diameter of											Additional power increment per belt, for speed ratio of									
	160.0 mm	170.0 mm	180.0 mm	190.0 mm	200.0 mm	212.0 mm	224.0 mm	236.0 mm	250.0 mm	280.0 mm	315.0 mm	1.00 to 1.01	1.02 to 1.05	1.06 to 1.11	1.12 to 1.18	1.19 to 1.26	1.27 to 1.38	1.39 to 1.57	1.58 to 1.94	1.95 to 3.38	3.39 and over
r/min	kw	kw	kw	kw	kw	kw	kw	kw	kw	kw	kw	kw	kw	kw	kw	kw	kw	kw	kw	kw	kw
720 *	4.54	5.11	5.68	6.25	6.81	7.49	8.15	8.82	9.58	11.21	13.07	0.00	0.05	0.14	0.25	0.33	0.40	0.47	0.53	0.58	0.62
960 *	5.73	6.47	7.21	7.94	8.66	9.52	10.38	11.23	12.20	14.26	16.61	0.00	0.07	0.19	0.33	0.45	0.54	0.63	0.71	0.78	0.82
1440 *	7.85	8.89	9.92	10.95	11.95	13.15	14.32	15.48	16.80	19.55	22.59	0.00	0.10	0.28	0.49	0.67	0.81	0.95	1.07	1.16	1.23
2880 *	12.04	13.68	15.25	16.76	–	–	–	–	–	–	–	0.00	0.21	0.56	0.98	1.34	1.62	1.90	2.14	2.33	2.46

POWER RATING FOR 'Z' SECTION V-BELTS, WITH 180° ARC OF CONTACT ON SMALLER PULLEY

Speed of Faster Shaft	Power rating for smaller pulley pitch diameter of						Additional power increment per belt, for speed ratio of									
	50 mm	56 mm	63 * mm	71 * mm	80 * mm	90 mm	1.00 to 1.02	1.03 to 1.04	1.05 to 1.08	1.09 to 1.12	1.13 to 1.18	1.19 to 1.24	1.25 to 1.34	1.35 to 1.50	1.51 to 1.99	2.0 & over
r/min	kw	kw	kw	kw	kw	kw	kw	kw	kw	kw	kw	kw	kw	kw	kw	kw
960 †	0.12	0.14	0.18	0.23	0.26	0.28	0.00	0.00	0.00	0.00	0.00	0.00	0.00	0.01	0.02	0.02
1440 †	0.16	0.19	0.25	0.30	0.35	0.36	0.00	0.00	0.01	0.01	0.01	0.02	0.02	0.02	0.02	0.03
2880 †	0.26	0.34	0.41	0.50	0.56	0.60	0.00	0.01	0.02	0.02	0.02	0.03	0.03	0.03	0.03	0.04

POWER RATING FOR 'A' SECTION V-BELTS, WITH 180° ARC OF CONTACT ON SMALLER PULLEY

Speed of Faster Shaft	Power rating for smaller pulley pitch diameter of									Additional power increment per belt, for speed ratio of									
	75 mm	80 mm	85 mm	90 * mm	100 * mm	106 * mm	112 * mm	118 * mm	125 * mm	1.00 to 1.01	1.02 to 1.04	1.05 to 1.08	1.09 to 1.12	1.13 to 1.18	1.19 to 1.24	1.25 to 1.34	1.35 to 1.41	1.52 to 1.99	2.00 and over
r/min	kw	kw	kw	kw	kw	kw	kw	kw	kw	kw	kw	kw	kw	kw	kw	kw	kw	kw	kw
720 †	0.53	0.60	0.68	0.75	0.90	0.99	1.07	1.16	1.26	0.00	0.01	0.02	0.03	0.04	0.05	0.06	0.07	0.08	0.09
960 †	0.66	0.76	0.86	0.95	1.14	1.25	1.37	1.49	1.61	0.00	0.01	0.03	0.04	0.05	0.06	0.08	0.09	0.10	0.12
1440 †	0.91	1.04	1.17	1.31	1.58	1.73	1.90	2.07	2.24	0.00	0.02	0.04	0.06	0.08	0.10	0.12	0.14	0.16	0.17
2880 †	1.42	1.67	1.91	2.14	2.59	2.76	3.11	3.36	3.63	0.00	0.04	0.08	0.12	0.16	0.20	0.23	0.27	0.31	0.35

POWER RATING FOR 'B' SECTION V-BELTS, WITH 180° ARC OF CONTACT ON SMALLER PULLEY

Speed of Faster Shaft	Power rating for smaller pulley pitch diameter of									Additional power increment per belt, for speed ratio of									
	125 mm	132 mm	140 * mm	150 * mm	160 * mm	170 * mm	180 * mm	190 * mm	200 * mm	1.00 to 1.01	1.02 to 1.04	1.05 to 1.08	1.09 to 1.12	1.13 to 1.18	1.19 to 1.24	1.25 to 1.34	1.35 to 1.51	1.52 to 1.99	2.00 and over
r/min	kw	kw	kw	kw	kw	kw	kw	kw	kw	kw	kw	kw	kw	kw	kw	kw	kw	kw	kw
720 †	1.61	1.79	1.99	2.24	2.48	2.73	2.97	3.21	3.45	0.00	0.03	0.05	0.08	0.10	0.13	0.15	0.18	0.20	0.23
960 †	2.02	2.24	2.50	2.82	3.13	3.44	3.75	4.05	4.35	0.00	0.03	0.07	0.10	0.14	0.17	0.20	0.24	0.27	0.30
1440 †	2.72	3.03	3.39	3.83	4.26	4.68	5.09	5.50	5.90	0.00	0.05	0.10	0.15	0.20	0.25	0.30	0.36	0.41	0.46
2880 †	3.96	4.44	4.95	5.55	6.11	6.62	7.08	7.48	–	0.00	0.10	0.20	0.30	0.41	0.50	0.61	0.71	0.81	0.91

* † These are standard motor shaft speeds.

FRICTION DRIVES 6.1.4

Wedge and 'V'-belts: Table of standard pitch lengths

TABLE C

STANDARD PITCH LENGTHS OF WEDGE BELTS AND V-BELTS AND PERMITTED TOLERANCES

PITCH LENGTH RANGE	STANDARD PITCH LENGTHS (L)						MAXIMUM PITCH LENGTH VARIATION		
	Wedge belts *			V-belts *			Non-matched sets	Matched sets	
	SPZ	SPA	SPB	Z	A	B		Allowable consecutive code numbers *	Maximum pitch length variation *
mm	mm	mm	mm	mm	mm	mm	mm		mm
200 to 399							+ 8 – 6	One length code number	2
400 to 529				405 475			+ 10 – 6		
530 to 709	630			530 625 700	630 700		+ 12 – 6		
710 to 899	710 800	800		780	790 890		+ 12 – 8		
900 to 1249	900 1000 1120	900 1000 1120		920 1080	990 1100	930 1000 1100 1210	+ 14 – 10		
1250 to 1599	1250 1400	1250 1400	1250 1400 1600		1250 1430 1550	1370 1560	+ 16 – 10		
1600 to 1899	1600 1800	1600 1800	1800		1750	1690 1760	+ 18 – 12		
1900 to 2249	2000	2000 2240	2000		1940 2050 2200	1950 2180	+ 30 – 16	Two length code numbers	4
2250 to 2799	2240 2500	2500	2240 2500		2300 2480 2570 2700	2300 2500 2700	+ 34 – 18		
2800 to 3149	2800	2800	2800		2910 3080	2870	+ 36 – 18		
3150 to 3699	3150 3550	3150 3550	3150 3550		3290 3540	3200 3600	+ 38 – 20	Three length code numbers	6
3700 to 4999			4000 4500	4000 4500		4060 4430 4820	+ 46 – 24		
5000 to 5999			5000 5600			5370	– 50 – 28	Four length code numbers	8
6000 to 6999			6300			6070	+ 56 – 32		
7000 to 8999			7100 8000				+ 66 – 38		
9000 to 9999							+ 66 – 38	Six length code numbers	12
10 000 to 12 499							+ 74 – 44		
12 500 to 16 000							+ 90 – 50	Seven length code numbers	14

* See BS 3790 and 7620 for full list of belt types.

FRICTION DRIVES 6.1.5

Wedge and 'V' belts: Selection of belt section

These graphs to be used in conjunction with the notes on **6.1.2** to determine the correct belt cross-section at given speed and power.

GRAPH D SELECTION OF WEDGE BELT CROSS-SECTION

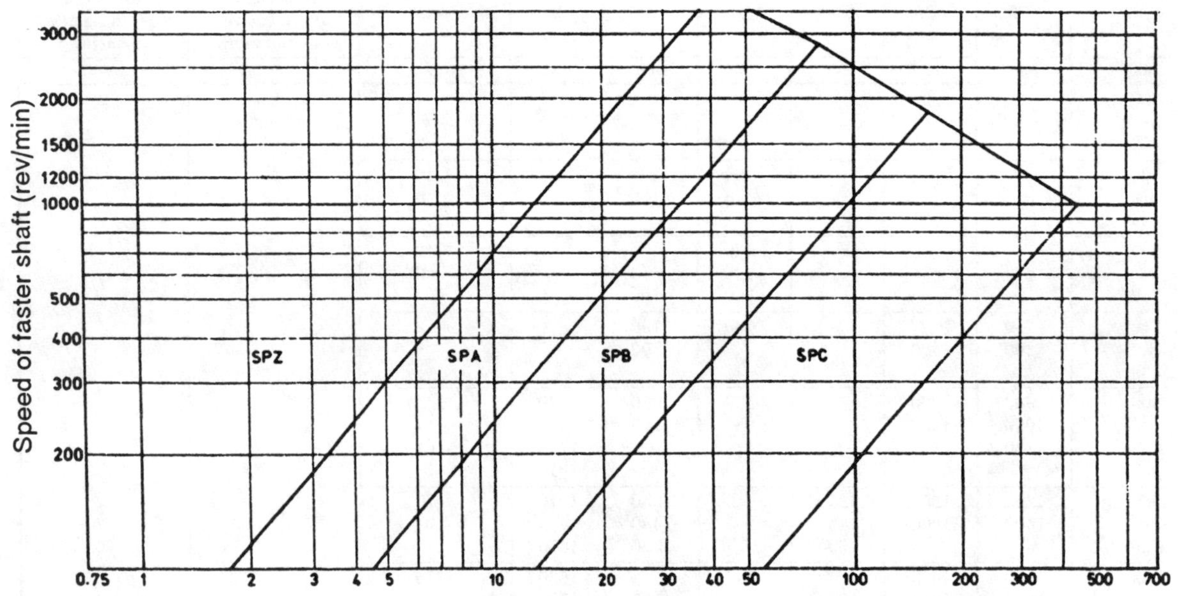

DESIGN POWER (KW)
(Cross-section dimensions of SPZ, SPA, SPB shown in 6.1.2)

GRAPH E SELECTION OF 'V' BELT CROSS-SECTION

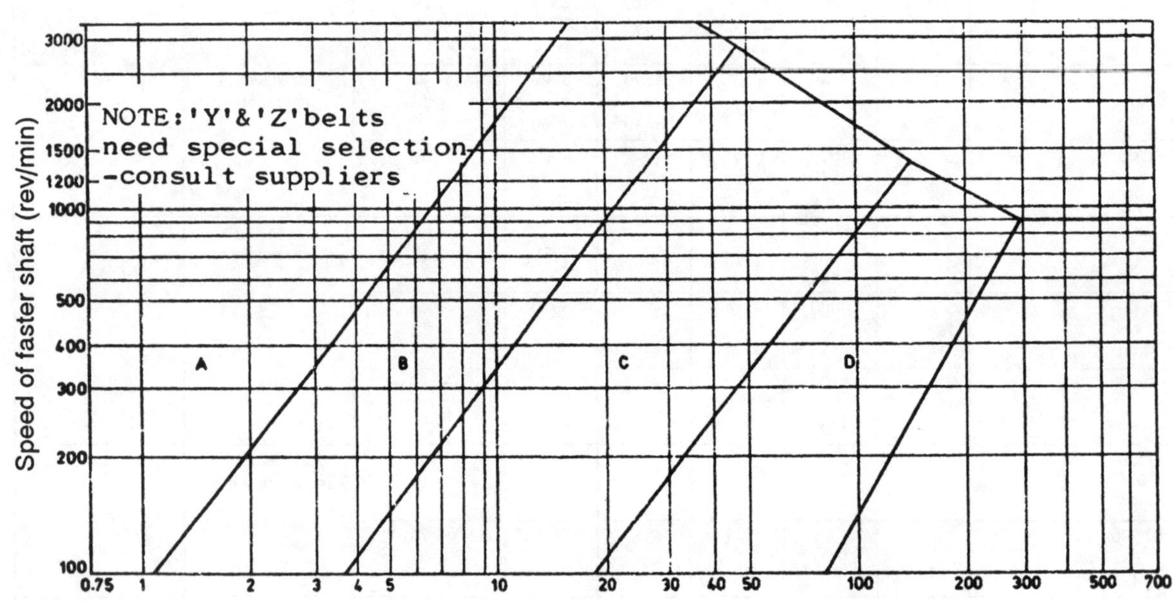

DESIGN POWER (KW)
(Cross-section dimensions of SPZ, SPA, SPB shown in 6.1.2)

FRICTION DRIVES 6.1.6

Wedge and 'V' belts: Table of pulley dimensions

TABLE F

PULLEY DIMENSIONS – SINGLE / MULTI GROOVED

d_p Pitch Diameter	PULLEY DIAMETERS (mm) – Outside diameter and number of grooves																			
	Z and SPZ	No. of grooves 1	2	3	4	A and SPA	No. of grooves 1	2	3	4	5	B and SPB	No. of grooves 2	3	4	5	6	8	Typical Shaft Dia.
67	71	+	+	+															28
71	75	+	+	+															28
75	79	+	+	+		80.5	+												32
80	84	+	+	+	+	85.5	+												32
85	89	+	+	+	+	90.5	+												42
90	94	+	+	+	+	95.5	+	+	+	+									42
95	99	+	+	+	+	100.5	+	+	+	+									42
100	104	+	+	+	+	105.5	+	+	+	+									42
106						111.5	+	+	+	+									42
112	116	+	+	+	+	117.5	+	+	+	+									42
118						123.5	+	+	+	+									42
125	129	+	+	+	+	130.5	+	+	+	+	+								42
132						137.5	+	+	+	+									42
140	144	+	+	+	+	145.5	+	+	+	+	+	147	+	+	+				42
150	154	+	+	+	+	155.5	+	+	+	+		157	+	+	+				50
160	164	+	+	+	+	165.5	+	+	+	+	+	167	+	+	+				50
170												177	+	+	+				50
180	184	+	+	+	+	185.5	+	+	+	+	+	187	+	+	+				50
190												197	+	+	+				50
200	204	+	+	+	+	205.5	+	+	+	+	+	207	+	+	+				50
212												219	+	+	+				50
224												231	+	+	+				50
236												243	+	+	+				50
250	254	+	+	+	+	255.5	+	+	+	+	+	257	+	+	+	+			50
265																			
280												287	+	+	+	+	+		50
315	319	+	+	+	+	320.5	+	+	+	+	+	322	+	+	+	+	+		50
355												362	+	+	+	+	+	+	60
375																			
400	404	+	+	+	+	405.5		+	+	+	+	407	+	+	+	+	+	+	60

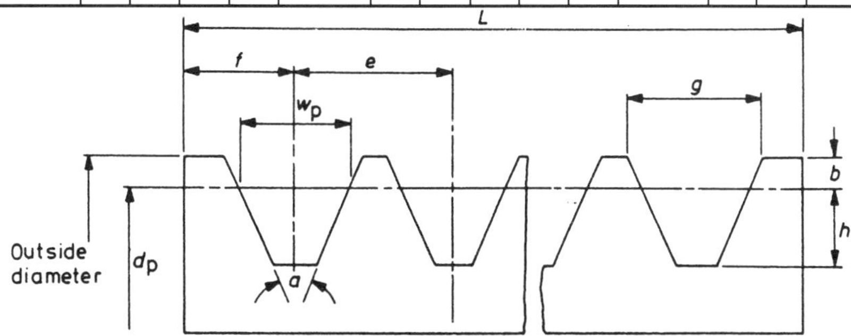

** MULTI-GROOVE PULLEY CROSS-SECTION*

Facewidth (L) = e + 2f (X-1) where X is the number of grooves

Dimensions of Standard V-grooved Pulleys (mm)

Type	W_p	b	h	e	f	d_p	a	g
Z, SPZ	8.5	2.0	9.0	12 ± 0.3	8.0 ± 1.0	Up to 80 Over 80	34 ± 0.5 38 ± 0.5	9.7 9.9
A, SPA	11.0	2.75	11.0	15 ± 0.3	10.0 + 2.0 – 1.0	Up to 118 Over 118	34 ± 0.5 38 ± 0.5	12.7 12.9
B, SPB	14.0	3.5	14.0	19 ± 0.4	12.5 + 2.0 – 1.0	Up to 190 Over 190	34 ± 0.5 38 ± 0.5	16.1 16.4

NOTE: Belts SPZ, SPA, SPB, Z, A, B only shown here – full list in BS 3790.
* BS 7620 and ISO 9981 deals with multiple 'V'-ribbed belts and pulleys.

SUPPLIERS

FRICTION DRIVES: Endless wedge and 'V' belt drives

COMPANY	ADDRESS	TELEPHONE	FAX
Arntz Belting Co Ltd	Pennyburn Pass LONDONDERRY Northern Ireland BT48 0AE	0504 261221	0504 263386
BTL Ltd	Hudson Road LEEDS W Yorks LS9 7DF	0532 493486	0532 489656
Gandy Belting Ltd	Centurion Way Farington LEYLAND Lancs PR5 2RE	0772 456100	0772 436610
Polyurethane Products Ltd	Alfred Road Sparkhill BIRMINGHAM B11 4PB	021 772 8669	021 766 6722
Reliance Electric (UK) Ltd Telford Division	Halesfield 19 TELFORD Shropshire TF7 4PT	0952 580888	0952 684367
Transmission Developments Co (GB) Ltd	Dawkins Road Hamworthy POOLE Dorset BH15 4HF	0202 675555	0202 677466
Wellman Bibby Co Ltd	Cannon Way Mill Street DEWSBURY W Yorks WF13 1EH	0924 460801	0924 457668
Wraxall Engineering Products Ltd	2 Dunchurch Trading Est London Rd Dunchurch RUGBY Warwicks CV23 9LL	0788 817522	0788 817852

Notes

TOOTHED DRIVES 6.2.1

Synchronous belt drives: Construction, selection and use

TYPICAL APPLICATIONS: Timing belts for motor vehicles, stepper motor drives, drives for robotic devices, positioning mechanisms, belts for indexing and metering equipment, copying and photographic equipment drives.

DEFINITIONS:

A drive that consists of one or more continuous belts with equi-spaced teeth on their inside and/or outside surfaces engaging with pulleys having matching teeth around their circumference which are cut parallel to the pulley bore. (Often referred to as 'timing' or 'gear belt' drives.)

CONSTRUCTION:

Belts: These are typically a continuous loop made from combinations of polymeric and/or elastomeric materials with fabric, cord or steel wire reinforcement. The teeth are an integral part of the belt material and may be moulded on inside and/or outside surfaces.
Pulleys: These may be made from various metals, plastics, aluminum alloys, steel, cast iron and cast steel, or any material that has the strength and can be shaped to the dimensions and surface finish required. They must withstand without damage all normal conditions of service and in particular not suffer from contact with oil and water.

NOTES ON SELECTION AND USE:

Synchronous belt drives are intended for mechanical power transmission where positive indexing or synchronous speeds are required. They can operate at temperatures between –26°C and +85°C without adverse effects on overall efficiency. The accuracy of tooth spacing is such that they can be used for precision mechanisms as well as power drives. Most belts are lightweight, maintenance-free, suffer little or no post-elongation and require very low initial tension therefore imposing minimum loads on bearings. Their high flexibility makes them suitable for both multiple shaft and dihedral drives although the latter reduces the overall drive power. Idler pulleys may be used to pre-tension a belt, increase the belt contact on a small pulley, or to provide a power take-off. These should preferably be toothed but flat, uncrowned pulleys can be used on the smooth side of the belt. As a guide, idler pulleys should only be used on the slack side of belts and their diameter should not be smaller than the smallest pulley in the system. Two side discs or flanges must be fitted to at least one pulley on each single belt drive. When the distance between pulley centres exceeds eight times minimum pulley diameter or when the drive is on a vertical shaft, both pulleys must be flanged. During installation avoid forcing or kinking the belts and ensure that shafts and their pulleys are parallel and aligned. Always set belt pre-tensions below the load capacities of bearings and shafts in the system. Number of teeth in mesh (TIM), speed, power, thrust, oscillation, load reversal, heavy shock and high inertia are all factors to be taken into account during design and selection by full reference to the supplier's data. Special belts with dogs or cams can be supplied for transportation and conveying, and directional changes by means of angular twisting can be done if the drive is carefully designed.

REFERENCES

BS 4235 :	Specification for metric keys and keyways
BS 4548 : 1987	Specification for synchronous belt drives
BS 6889 : 1987	Specification for generating racks for synchronous belt drive pulleys
BS AU218.1987	Specification for automotive synchronous belt drives

TOOTHED DRIVES 6.2.2

Synchronous belt drives: Dimensions

DRIVE ASSEMBLY

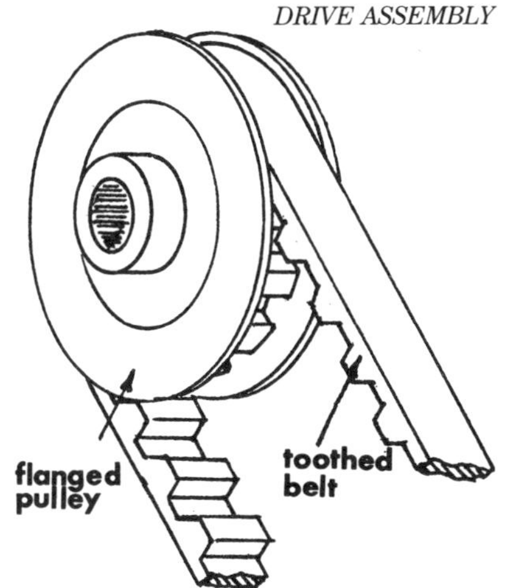

BELT AND PULLEY IN MESH (ONLY ONE END SHOWN)

BELT PITCHES	
Code *	**Pitch** (mm)
XL	5.080
X	9.525
H	12.700
XH	22.225
XXH	31.750

* Letters refer to grades from 'Extra Light' to 'Double Extra Heavy' – for full range see BS 4548

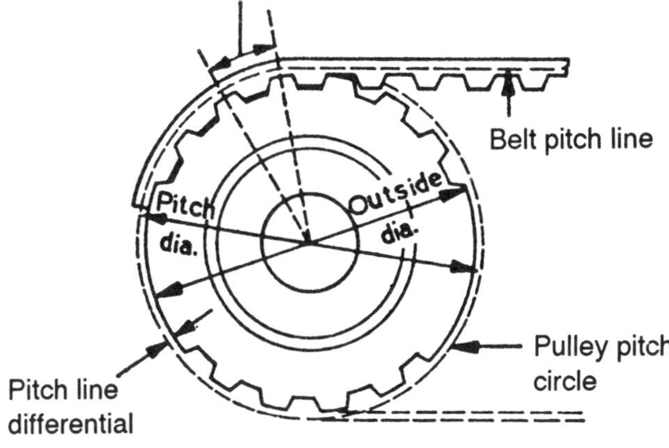

NOMENCLATURE

BELT TENSIONING
'D' to be 1/64 of value 'S'

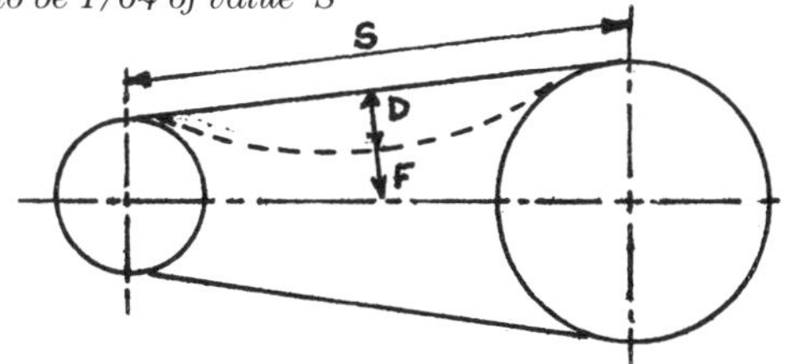

(Tension force 'F' may be calculated from BS 4548 App. C)

BELT WIDTHS

Belt width		Width code		
in	**mm**	**Pitch code XL**	**Pitch code L**	**Pitch code H**
¼	6.4	025	–	–
5/16	7.9	031	–	–
⅜	9.6	037		
½	12.7		050	–
¾	19.1	–	075	075
1	25.4	–	100	100
1½	38.1	–	–	150
2	50.8	–	–	200
3	76.2	–	–	300

BELT PITCH LENGTHS

Belt length designation	Belt pitch length (L)		Number of teeth		
			Pitch code XL	**Pitch code L**	**Pitch code H**
	in	mm			
60	6.000	152.40	30	–	–
70	7.000	177.80	35	–	–
80	8.000	203.20	40	–	–
90	9.000	228.60	45	–	–
100	10.000	254.00	50	–	–
110	11.000	279.40	55	–	–
120	12.000	304.80	60	–	–
124	12.375	314.33	–	33	–
130	13.000	330.20	65	–	–
140	14.000	355.60	70	–	–
150	15.000	381.00	75	40	–
160	16.000	406.40	80	–	–
170	17.000	431.80	85	–	–
180	18.000	457.20	90	–	–
187	18.750	476.25	–	50	–
190	19.000	482.60	95	–	–
200	20.000	508.00	100	–	–
210	21.000	533.40	105	56	–
220	22.000	558.80	110	–	–
225	22.500	571.50	–	60	–
230	23.000	584.20	115	–	–
240	24.000	609.60	120	64	48
250	25.000	635.00	125	–	–
255	25.500	647.70	–	68	–
260	26.000	660.40	130	–	–
270	27.000	685.80	–	72	54
285	28.500	723.90	–	76	–
300	30.000	762.00	–	80	60
322	32.250	819.15	–	86	–
330	33.000	838.20	–	–	66
345	34.500	876.30	–	92	–
360	36.000	914.40	–	–	72
367	36.750	933.45	–	98	–
390	39.000	990.60	–	104	78
420	42.000	1 066.80	–	112	84
450	45.000	1 143.00	–	120	90
480	48.000	1 219.20	–	128	96
507	50.750	1 289.05	–	–	–
510	51.000	1 295.40	–	136	102
540	54.000	1 371.60	–	144	108
560	56.000	1 422.40	–	–	–
570	57.000	1 447.80	–	–	114
600	60.000	1 524.00	–	160	120
630	63.000	1 600.20	–	–	126
660	66.000	1 676.40	–	–	132
700	70.000	1 778.00	–	–	140
750	75.000	1 905.00	–	–	150
770	77.000	1 955.80	–	–	–
800	80.000	2 032.00	–	–	160
840	84.000	2 133.60	–	–	–
850	85.000	2 159.00	–	–	170
900	90.000	2 286.00	–	–	180
980	98.000	2 489.00	–	–	–
1 000	100.000	2 540.00	–	–	200
1 100	110.000	2 794.00	–	–	220
1 120	112.000	2 844.80	–	–	–
1 200	120.000	3 048.00	–	–	–
1 250	125.000	3 175.00	–	–	250
1 260	126.000	3 200.40	–	–	–
1 400	140.000	3 556.00	–	–	280

TOOTHED DRIVES 6.2.3

Synchronous belt drives: Power Transmission Design

POWER TRANSMISSION DESIGN – FOR DRIVE BELTS AND PULLEYS

NOTE: The term 'HORSEPOWER' is still in wide use and is therefore included in all tables. The ISO recommended unit of power is the KILOWATT (kW).
1 hp = 746 W

DESIGN HORSEPOWER

Multiply the hp required to be transmitted by the appropriate service factor in Table A according to application, power source and length of daily operating period.

BELT HORSEPOWER RATINGS

To find the correct belt consult **Tables B**, **C** or **D** (noting the belt widths available shown in 6.2.2) and correct, if necessary, by the width factors in **Table E.**

TEETH IN MESH FACTOR

Correct, if necessary, belt hp ratings from **Tables B**, **C** or **D** by the relevant TIM factor in **Table F**. This will give the *Corrected Horsepower.*

BELT WIDTH FACTOR = $\dfrac{\text{Design Horsepower}}{\text{Corrected Horsepower}}$

Using this factor consult **Table G** to obtain the appropriate pitch code. Select the belt width with a factor equal to or greater than that calculated.

SPEEDS

The hp and pulley tables are based on speeds of standard electric motors.

NOTE: This is a guide only – BS 4548 and drive suppliers must be consulted before final selection.

TABLE A

SERVICE FACTORS FOR SYNCHRONOUS BELT DRIVES

TYPES OF DRIVEN MACHINES – CLASSIFICATION GUIDE			Operational Hours per Day		
If drive conditions are unknown, the following guide * will help the designer select an appropriate factor. Contact drive suppliers if in doubt. See also note below.		**Momentary peak load as percent of rated load**	**10 and under**	**Over 10 to 16 inclusive**	**Over 16 + continuing service**
			Factor	Factor	Factor
Electric typewriters / Audio visual equipment	Class 1	No load above nominal	1.00	1.39	1.49
Light conveyors / Woodworking machines	Class 2	Nominal to 149	1.45	1.59	1.72
Medium conveyors / Generators /Presses	Class 3	150 to 249	1.59	1.72	1.85
Heavy conveyors / Paper machines / Pulverizers	Class 4	250 to 400	1.72	1.85	1.96
Hoists / Mills /Compressors / Crushers	Class 5	Frequent peak loads 250 +	1.85	1.96	2.04

TABLE B

HORSEPOWER RATINGS FOR PITCH CODE XL BELTS

Rated h.p.** for 25.4 mm (1 in) wide belt on small pulley
For pulley sizes shown by: 10, 11, 12, etc. = No. of grooves & Pitch diameter = (in) and [mm]

Rev/min of faster shaft	10 (0.637) [16.170]	11 (0.700) [17.787]	12 (0.764) [19.404]	14 (0.891) [22.638]	15 (0.955) [24.255]	16 (1.019) [25.872]	18 (1.146) [29.106]	20 (1.273) [32.340]	22 (1.401) [35.574]	24 (1.528) [38.808]	26 (1.655) [42.042]	28 (1.783) [45.276]	30 (1.910) [48.042]
960	0.19	0.21	0.23	0.28	0.29	0.32	0.35	0.39	0.43	0.47	0.51	0.54	0.59
1440	–	0.32	0.35	0.41	0.44	0.47	0.53	0.59	0.65	0.71	0.77	0.83	0.89
2880	–	–	0.73	0.85	0.91	0.97	1.09	1.21	1.32	1.44	1.56	1.69	1.80

* Additional service factors can cause wide variations in these values, consult BS 4548 Table 14 for a more detailed guide.
**1 hp = 746 W.

TABLE C

HORSEPOWER RATINGS FOR PITCH CODE L BELTS

Rated h.p.* for 25.4 mm (1 in) wide belt on small pulley
Pulley sizes: 12, 13, 14, etc. = No. of grooves & Pitch diameter = (in) **and** [mm]

Rev/min of faster shaft	12 (1.432) [36.382]	13 (1.552) [39.415]	14 (1.671) [42.445]	15 (1.790) [45.478]	16 (1.910) [45.510]	17 (2.029) [51.542]	18 (2.149) [54.574]	19 (2.268) [57.606]	20 (2.387) [60.638]	21 (2.507) [63.670]	22 (2.626) [66.702]
720	0.45	0.48	0.52	0.56	0.60	0.64	0.68	0.71	0.75	0.79	0.82
960	0.60	0.65	0.70	0.75	0.80	0.85	0.90	0.95	1.00	1.05	1.10
1440	–	–	1.05	1.12	1.19	1.27	1.34	1.42	1.49	1.56	1.63
2880	–	–	–	–	2.41	2.56	2.70	2.83	2.97	3.11	3.25

TABLE C *(continued)*

Rated h.p.* for 25.4 mm (1 in) wide belt on small pulley
Pulley sizes: 23, 24, 25, etc. = No. of grooves & Pitch diameter = (in) **and** [mm]

Rev/min of faster shaft	23 (2.745) [69.734]	24 (2.865) [72.766]	25 (2.964) [75.797]	26 (3.104) [78.829]	27 (3.223) [81.861]	28 (3.342) [84.893]	30 (3.581) [90.957]	32 (3.820) [97.021]	36 (4.297) [109.142]	40 (4.775) [121.276]	48 (5.730) [145.531]
720	0.86	0.90	0.94	0.98	1.01	1.03	1.12	1.19	1.34	1.49	1.78
960	1.14	1.19	1.24	1.29	1.33	1.39	1.49	1.59	1.78	1.97	2.35
1440	1.71	1.78	1.85	1.92	2.00	2.07	2.21	2.35	2.63	2.90	3.42
2880	3.38	3.51	3.64	3.77	3.89	4.01	4.25	4.49	4.92	5.30	5.90

TABLE D

HORSEPOWER RATINGS FOR PITCH CODE H BELTS

Rated h.p.* for 25.4 mm (1 in) wide belt on small pulley
Pulley sizes: 16, 17, etc. = No. of grooves & Pitch diameter = (in) **and** [mm]

Rev/min of faster shaft	16 (2.546) [64.681]	17 (2.706) [68.723]	18 (2.865) [72.766]	19 (3.024) [76.808]	20 (3.183) [80.851]	21 (3.342) [84.893]	22 (3.501) [88.963]	23 (3.661) [92.978]	24 (3.820) [97.021]	25 (3.979) [101.063]
720	1.78	2.16	2.29	2.42	2.54	2.66	2.80	2.92	3.04	3.18
960	2.37	2.88	3.05	3.21	3.38	3.55	3.72	3.89	4.05	4.22
1440	–	–	4.55	4.80	5.05	5.29	5.54	5.79	6.03	6.28
2880	–	–	–	–	10.10	10.57	11.04	11.49	11.93	12.38

TABLE D *(continued)*

Rated h.p.* for 25.4 mm (1 in) wide belt on small pulley
Pulley sizes: 26, 27, etc. = No. of grooves & Pitch diameter = (in) **and** [mm]

Rev/min of faster shaft	26 (4.138) [105.106]	27 (4.297) [109.148]	28 (4.456) [113.191]	30 (4.775) [121.276]	32 (5.093) [129.361]	36 (5.730) [145.531]	40 (6.366) [161.701]	48 (7.639) [194.042]
720	3.30	3.42	3.55	3.80	4.05	4.55	5.05	6.04
960	4.39	4.55	4.72	5.05	5.38	6.04	6.69	7.98
1440	6.53	6.77	7.02	7.50	7.98	8.93	9.86	11.65
2880	12.83	13.26	13.69	14.50	15.29	16.79	18.10	20.23

TABLE E

WIDTH FACTORS

To calculate h.p.* for belt sizes *other than 25.4 mm*, multiply values obtained in Tables B, C, D by the relevant WIDTH FACTOR (below)

Belt width												
	in	½	⅝	¾	⅞	1	1¼	1½	1¾	2	2½	3
	mm	12.7	15.9	19.1	22.2	25.4	31.7	38.1	44.4	50.8	63.5	76.2
WF (Width factor)		0.42	0.57	0.71	0.86	1.00	1.29	1.56	1.84	2.14	2.72	3.36

TABLE F

TEETH IN MESH FACTOR

Teeth in mesh	Factor F
6 or more	1.00
5	0.80
4	0.60
3	0.40
2	0.20

Note: Pulley dimensions are given in 6.2.6
* 1 hp = 746 W

TOOTHED DRIVES 6.2.5

Synchronous belt drives: Pulley selection

PULLEY TYPES AND BELT WIDTH FACTORS

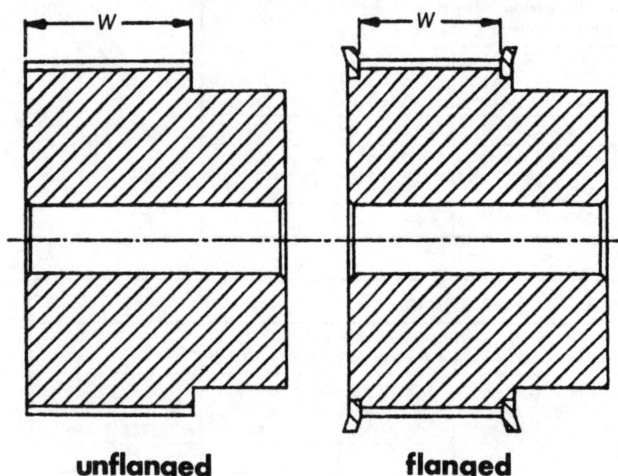

Notes: Flanges may be on one side of pulley only, and conditions may demand special arrangements, see BS 4548 App. B

Pulleys may be fixed to shafts by tapers, keyways, threaded ends etc. All pulleys should be statically balanced.

TABLE G BELT WIDTH FACTORS

		STANDARD BELT WIDTHS								
PIT CODE	FACTOR	6.4 mm (¼ inch)	7.9 mm (5/16 inch)	9.5 mm (⅜ inch)	12.7 mm (½ inch)	19.1 mm (¾ inch)	25.4 mm (1 inch)	38.1 mm (1½ inch)	50.8 mm (2 inch)	76.2 mm (3 inch)
XL	N lbf	3.82 0.85	5.39 1.2	7.55 1.7	12.06 2.7	20.88 4.7	29.81 6.7			
L	N lbf			37.85 8.5	44.03 9.9	75.71 17	106.79 24	164.75 37	226.93 51	226.75 78
H	N lbf				75.71 17	142.49 32	204.77 46	316.07 71	422.97 95	676.68 152

PULLEY SELECTION TABLES:

When the belt width has been calculated, pulley sizes can be worked out using **Tables H, J, K** (see below). Note that number of grooves cross-refers to **Tables B, C, D** (6.2.4).

TABLE H STANDARD PULLEY WIDTHS

Pitch code	Standard nominal pulley width		Standard pulley width designation	Minimum pulley width *W*	
	in	mm		in	mm
XL	0.25	6.35	25	0.28	7.11
	0.31	7.87	31	0.34	8.64
	0.37	9.40	37	0.40	10.16
L	0.50	12.7	50	0.55	13.97
	0.75	19.1	75	0.80	20.32
	1.00	25.4	100	1.05	26.67
H	0.75	19.1	75	0.80	20.32
	1.00	25.4	100	1.05	26.67
	1.50	38.1	150	1.55	39.37
	2.00	50.8	200	2.07	52.58
	3.00	76.2	300	3.11	79.00

TABLE J MINIMUM NUMBER OF GROOVES

Rev/min of fastest shaft	Pitch code		
	XL	L	H
2880	12	16	20
1440	11	14	18
960	10	12	16

TABLE K RECOMMENDED PULLEY DIAMETERS

Number of grooves	XL Pitch dia. in	XL Pitch dia. mm	XL Outside dia. in	XL Outside dia. mm	L Pitch dia. in	L Pitch dia. mm	L Outside dia. in	L Outside dia. mm	H Pitch dia. in	H Pitch dia. mm	H Outside dia. in	H Outside dia. mm
10	0.637	16.170	0.617	15.662					Note: 12 & 13 grooves available in 12.7 & 19 mm widths only			
11	0.700	17.787	0.680	17.179								
12	0.764	19.404	0.744	18.896	1.432	36.382	1.402	35.620				
13	0.828	21.021	0.808	20.513	1.552	39.415	1.522	38.653				
14	0.891	22.638	0.871	22.130	1.671	42.446	1.641	41.684				
15	0.955	24.255	0.935	23.747	1.790	45.478	1.760	44.716				
16	1.019	25.872	0.999	25.364	1.910	48.510	1.880	47.748	2.546	64.681	2.492	63.309
17	1.082	27.489	1.062	26.981	2.029	51.542	1.999	50.780	2.706	68.723	2.652	67.351
18	1.146	29.106	1.126	28.598	2.149	54.574	2.119	53.812	2.865	72.766	2.811	71.394
19	1.210	30.723	1.190	30.215	2.268	57.606	2.238	54.844	3.024	76.808	2.970	75.436
20	1.273	32.340	1.253	31.832	2.387	60.638	2.357	59.876	3.183	80.851	3.129	79.479
21	1.337	33.957	1.317	33.449	2.507	63.670	2.477	62.908	3.342	84.893	3.288	83.521
22	1.401	35.574	1.381	35.066	2.626	66.702	2.596	65.940	3.501	88.936	3.447	87.564
23	1.464	37.191	1.444	36.683	2.745	69.734	2.715	68.972	3.661	92.978	3.607	91.606
24	1.528	38.808	1.508	38.300	2.865	72.766	2.835	72.004	3.820	97.021	3.766	94.649
25	1.592	40.425	1.572	39.917	2.984	75.797	2.954	75.035	3.979	101.063	3.925	99.69
26	1.655	42.042	1.635	41.534	3.104	78.829	3.074	78.067	4.138	105.106	4.084	103.734
27	1.719	43.659	1.699	43.151	3.223	81.861	3.193	81.099	4.297	109.148	4.243	107.176
28	1.783	45.276	1.763	44.768	3.342	84.893	3.312	84.131	4.456	113.191	4.402	111.319
30	1.910	48.510	1.890	48.002	3.581	90.957	3.551	90.195	4.775	121.276	4.721	119.904
	Note: normally flanged up to and including 30 grooves											
32	2.037	51.744	2.017	51.236	3.820	97.021	3.790	96.259	5.093	129.361	5.039	127.989
36	2.292	58.213	2.272	57.705	4.297	109.148	4.267	108.386	5.730	145.531	5.676	144.159
40	2.546	64.681	2.526	64.173	4.775	121.276	4.745	120.514	6.366	161.701	6.312	160.329
48	3.056	77.617	3.036	77.109	5.730	145.531	5.700	144.769	7.639	194.042	7.585	192.670
60	3.820	97.021	3.800	96.513	7.162	181.914	7.132	181.152	9.549	242.552	9.495	241.180
	Note: normally flanged up to and including 48 grooves											
72	4.584	116.425	4.564	115.917	8.594	218.297	8.564	217.535	11.459	291.063	11.405	289.691
84					10.027	254.680	9.997	253.918	13.369	339.573	13.315	338.201
96					11.459	291.063	11.429	290.301	15.279	388.084	15.225	386.712
120					14.324	363.828	14.294	363.066	19.099	485.104	19.045	483.732
156									24.828	630.636	24.774	629.264

POWER TRANSMISSION SYSTEMS

SUPPLIERS

TRANSMISSIONS: Synchronous belt drives

COMPANY	ADDRESS	TELEPHONE	FAX
Davall Moulded Gears Ltd	Welham Green HATFIELD Herts AL9 7JB	0707 265432	0707 274054
Hinchliffe Precision Components Ltd	Storforth Lane Trad Est Storforth Lane CHESTERFIELD Derbys S41 0QZ	0246 209683	0246 205795
Pentag Manufacturing Co Ltd	PO Box 24 Edmund Road SHEFFIELD S Yorks S2 4EF	0742 738651	0742 724386
Pirellin Transmissions (UK) Ltd	Arthur Drive Hoo Farm Ind Est Worcester Road KIDDERMINSTER Worcs DY11 7RA	0562 820464	0562 755124
Reliance Gear Co Ltd	St Helens Gate Almondbury HUDDERSFIELD W Yorks HD4 6SF	0484 539441	0484 513335
William Kenyon & Sons (Power Transmissions) Ltd	Shepley Works Dukinfield Road PO Box 45 Hyde CHESHIRE SK14 4RP	061 368 4131	061 367 8723

USEFUL ADDRESSES

TRANSMISSIONS

ADDRESS	TELEPHONE
British Gear Association St James House Frederick Road Edgbaston BIRMINGHAM B15 1JJ	021 456 3445
Mechanical Handling Engineers Association 8th Floor 121 Smallbrook Queensway BIRMINGHAM B5 4JP	021 643 3377

GEAR DRIVES 6.3.1

Spur gears: Construction, selection and use

TYPICAL APPLICATIONS: Manual and automatic motor vehicle gearboxes, machine tool drives, conveyor systems, electric motor gearboxes, timing mechanisms, hoists and cranes, mechanical gauges and instruments, mechanical handling devices, domestic appliance mechanisms and power tool drives.

DEFINITIONS:

Gear: Any toothed member designed to transmit or receive motion with another by means of successively engaging teeth. The 'wheel' is referred to as the larger and the 'pinion' the smaller gear.
Spur gear: A cylindrical gear whose tooth traces are straight line generators of the reference cylinder.

CONSTRUCTION:

Gears may be cast, moulded, stamped or cut from solid from iron, steel, brass, bronze, ceramics and plastics. Cast irons and wrought and case hardening steels comprise the great majority of materials for general engineering gears. Frequently used combinations for wheel and pinion respectively are: cast iron/cast iron; cast iron/carbon steel; carbon steel/alloy steel; alloy steel/case hardened steel; case hardened steel/case hardened steel. Material for gears is often supplied in the form of standard blanks for finish machining. Complete, self-contained gearboxes are common and are often part of a standard motor drive.

NOTES ON SELECTION AND USE:

Spur gears are the cheapest of all types for parallel shaft applications and their straight cut teeth allow running engagement/disengagement using sliding shafts and clutch mechanisms. All gear trains demand continuous lubrication which must be pressure-fed for high speed gears to counteract centrifugal force effects on the oil. In certain cases plastics materials may be used which do not require lubrication (e.g. nylon), but these are limited in their applications owing to the low strength and low thermal conductivity of plastics. However, the use of plastic gears in a train can contribute considerably to noise and cost reduction and therefore are being increasingly used in motor vehicles and domestic appliances. Quiet and vibration-free operation is often an important feature of gear box design and therefore careful attention must be paid to: gear tooth finish, clearance, backlash, correct alignment, drive shaft length, bearing selection and housing stiffness. Service failures normally arise from tooth fracture and surface damage effects and therefore careful selection must be made by considering speeds, loads and materials used. Loading levels can significantly increase under conditions of shock, mis-alignment, manufacturing inaccuracies and vibration. Surface damage can be caused by excessive abrasion, corrosion, pitting and scoring.. The provision of one more tooth than is needed to give the required ratio in a pair of mating gears is called a 'hunting tooth' and serves to distribute wear evenly amongst all teeth on the pair. As the pinion does more work per tooth than the wheel, wear can be further equalized by making it harder than the wheel. Steel gears are often supplied in an unhardened form to allow for grub screws, keyways, splines, etc. to be cut before final hardening and finishing is done. Condition monitoring (e.g. by continuous checking of temperature and noise) is common practice for critical gearbox installations. Standards and manufacturers data should be referred to at all times when designing geared systems.

REFERENCES:

BS 436 :	Spur and helical gears
BS 970 :	Specification for wrought steels for mechanical & allied engineering purposes
BS 1452 : 1990	Specification for flake graphite cast iron
BS 2519 :	Glossary for gears
BS 3696 :	Specification for master gears Part 1 : 1977 (1990)
BS 4500 :	ISO limits and fits
PD 6457: 1970 (1990)	Guide to the application of addendum modification to involute spur and helical gears
BS 978 :	Fine pitch gears
BS 4582 :	Fine pitch gears – metric units
PD 3376 :	Double circular arc-type gears
BS 6168 : 1987	Non-metallic spur gears
BS 4517 : 1969 (1990)	Spur and helical geared motor units

GEAR DRIVES 6.3.2

Spur gears: Sizes and tolerances

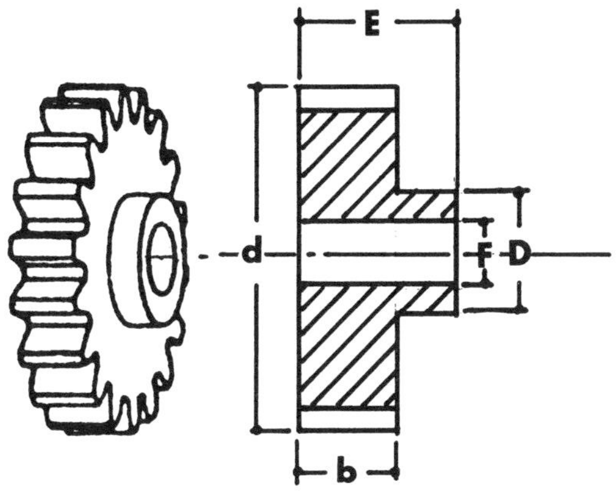
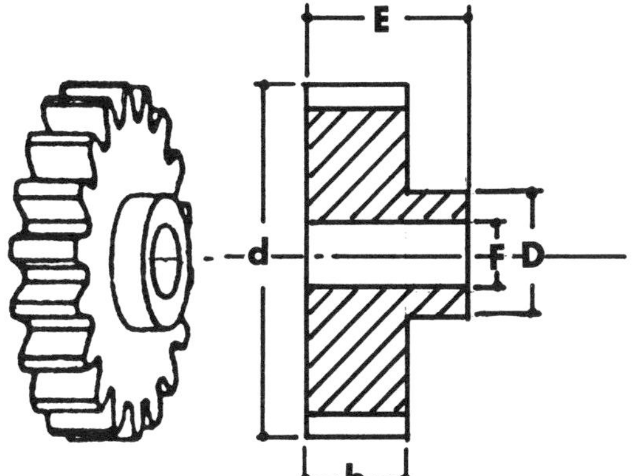

Spur Gear

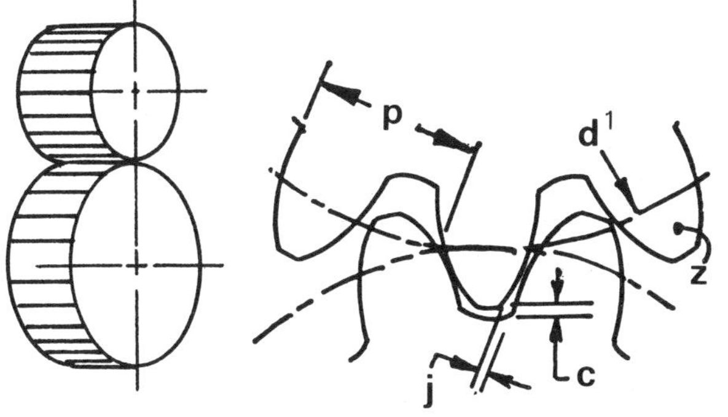

Gear Pair

SYMBOL DEFINITIONS

d = outside diameter	*d^1 = pitch diameter*
b = face width	*p = pitch*
m = module	*j = backlash*
z = no. of teeth	*D = boss diameter*
F = bore diameter	*E = width*

BASIC FORMULA

module (m) $= \frac{d^1}{z}$ *pitch (p)* $= m\,\pi$

outside dia. (d) $= m\,(z + 2)$

clearance (c) is from 0.25 x m to 0.40 x m

TOLERANCES FOR GEAR MOUNTING								
Gear grade	**3, 4**	**5**	**6**	**7**	**8**	**9**	**10**	**11, 12**
Bore tol.	all	IT5	IT6	IT7	IT7	IT8	IT8	all
Shaft tol.	IT4	IT5	IT5	IT6	IT6	IT7	IT7	IT8

NOTE: 'IT' Nos. refer to BS 4500

BS normal modules mn (mm): 1*, 1.25, 1.5*, 2*, 2.5*, 3, 4, 5, 6, 8, 10, 12, 16, 20, 25, 32, 40, 50

TABLE OF GEAR SIZE DATA FOR COMMONLY USED NORMAL MODULES

No. of Teeth	* m 1.0 module					* m 1.5 module					* m 2.0 module					*m 2.5 module				
(z)	d	b	E	D	F	d	b	E	D	F	d	b	E	D	F	d	b	E	D	F
12	14	15	25	9	6	21	18	30	13.5	8	28	20	35	18	10	35	25	41	23	16
15	17	15	25	12	6	25.5	18	30	18	8	34	20	35	24	15	42.5	25	41	30	19
16	18	15	25	13	6	27	18	30	20	12	36	20	35	25	15	45	25	41	33	19
18	20	15	25	14	8	30	18	30	20	12	40	20	35	30	20	50	25	41	38	19
20	22	15	25	16	8	33	18	30	26	17	44	20	35	30	20	55	25	41	43	19
24	26	15	25	25	10	39	18	30	26	17	52	20	35	37	20	65	25	41	44	19
30	32	15	25	25	10	48	18	30	38	17	64	20	35	45	20	80	25	47	44	19
32	34	15	25	25	10	51	18	30	38	17	68	20	42	45	20	85	25	47	44	19
36	38	15	25	25	10	57	18	33	38	17	76	20	42	45	20	95	25	47	54	19
40	42	15	25	25	10	63	18	33	38	17	84	20	42	45	20	105	25	47	54	22
45	47	15	25	35	10	70.5	18	33	38	17	94	20	42	50	25	117.5	25	47	54	22
48	50	15	25	35	10	75	18	33	38	17	100	20	42	50	25	125	25	47	54	22
50	52	15	25	35	12	78	18	33	38	17	104	20	42	50	25	130	25	47	54	22
54	56	15	25	35	12	84	18	33	38	17	112	20	42	50	25	142	25	47	54	22
56	58	15	25	35	12	87	18	33	38	17	116	20	42	50	25	145	25	47	54	22
60	62	15	25	35	12	93	18	33	38	17	124	20	42	50	25	155	25	47	70	22
64	66	15	25	35	12	99	18	36	45	20	132	20	42	50	25	165	25	47	70	22
70	72	15	25	35	12	108	18	36	45	20	144	20	42	50	25	180	25	47	70	22
72	74	15	25	35	12	111	18	36	45	20	148	20	42	50	25	185	25	47	70	22
75	77	15	25	35	12	115.5	18	36	45	20	154	20	42	50	25	192.5	25	47	70	22

GEAR DRIVES 6.3.3

Helical, worm and bevel gears: Construction selection and use

TYPICAL APPLICATIONS: Helical: heavy-duty power transmissions, turbine drives, locomotive gearboxes and drives, machine tool drives. **Worm:** Steering gear, remote control of valves, engine and motor drive control, ships gear operation, manual and clockwork instrument drives. **Bevel:** motor transmission final drives, valve control, right angle electric motor drives, mechanical instruments.

DEFINITIONS:

Gear: Any toothed member designed to transmit or receive motion with another by means of successively engaging teeth. The 'wheel' is referred to as the larger and the 'pinion' the smaller gear. **Helical gear:** a cylindrical gear whose tooth traces are helices. **Bevel gear:** a gear whose reference surface is a cone. **Worm gear:** a cylindrical helical gear with one or more threads. **Wormwheel:** a cylindrical gear with flanks in such a way as to ensure contact with the flanks of a wormgear.

CONSTRUCTION:

Gears may be cast, moulded or cut from solid from iron, steel, brass, bronze, ceramics and plastics. Cast irons and wrought and case hardening steels comprise the great majority of materials for general engineering gears. Frequently used combinations for wheel and pinion respectively are: cast iron/cast iron; cast iron/carbon steel; carbon steel/alloy steel; alloy steel/case hardened steel; case hardened steel/case hardened steel. Material for gears is often supplied in the form of standard blanks for finish machining.

NOTES ON SELECTION AND USE:

Helical gears: these are more expensive than spur gears and are generally used for high sped (pinion rpm > 3600), high load applications. Noise levels are lower because, unlike spur gears, teeth in mesh make point rather than line contact. Lubrication demands are high and bearings used must withstand the thrust component arising from helical meshing. Common helix angles are between 15° and 30° and gears have left or right handed helixes. Double helical or herringbone gears, which consist of LH and RH facewidths, have tooth geometry which eliminates the need for thrust bearings. Although most common in parallel shaft drives, single helical gears can be used for non-intersecting, non-parallel applications as long as they have the same pitch and pressure angle. These are known as crossed helical gears and can only carry comparatively low loads.
Worm gears: worm gear sets are capable of high speed reduction and high load applications where non-parallel, non-intersecting shafts are used and therefore have an advantage over crossed helical gears. The 90° shaft configuration is the commonist with the worm as driver and the set being irreversible and self-locking. The frictional heat generated during operation is large compared with other types of gear and therefore continuous lubrication and heat dissipating casings are essentials. Reversibility is possible with worm lead angles in excess of 10° and load capacity can be increased by the use of a double enveloping gear pair.
Bevel gears: these have teeth cut on conical blanks and hence a gear pair can connect non-parallel intersecting shafts. The most common types are straight cut and usually mounted on shafts at 90° to each other and are used for fairly low speed applications where smoothness and noise are not a problem. Spiral bevel gears have curved teeth and can be used for higher loads and speeds and have quieter operation. For high speed reductions and low noise (e.g. automotive drives), hypoid bevel gears are used.

REFERENCES:

BS 436 : Spur and helical gears
BS 545 : 1982 (1987) Specification for bevel gears (machine cut) (≈ ISO 677 & 678 Straight bevel gears)
BS 2519 : Glossary for gears

GEAR DRIVES 6.3.4

Helical, worm and bevel gears: Types and modules

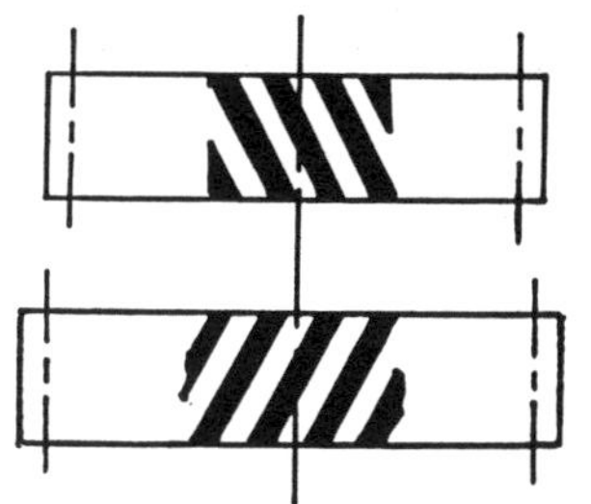

Helical gear (or gear pair)

Double helical gear (or gear pair)

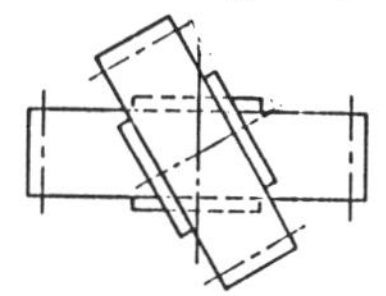

Gear pair with non-parallel, non-intersecting axes

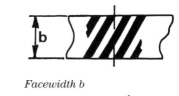

Facewidth b

Lead angle γ

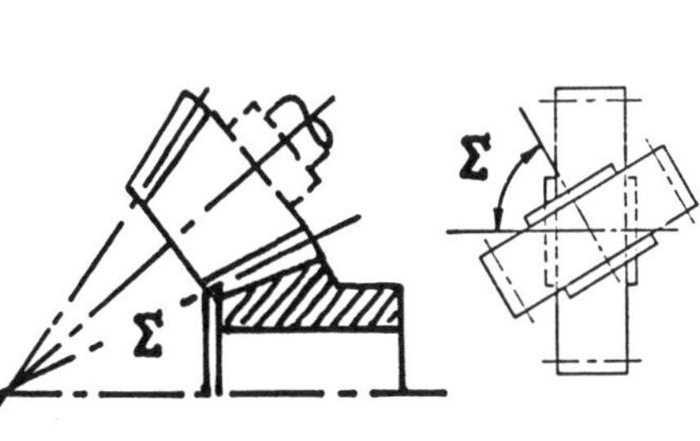

Shaft angle Σ

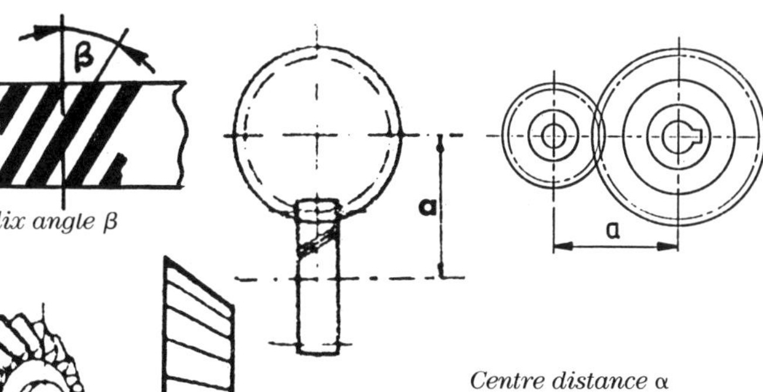

Helix angle β

Centre distance α

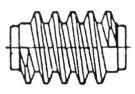

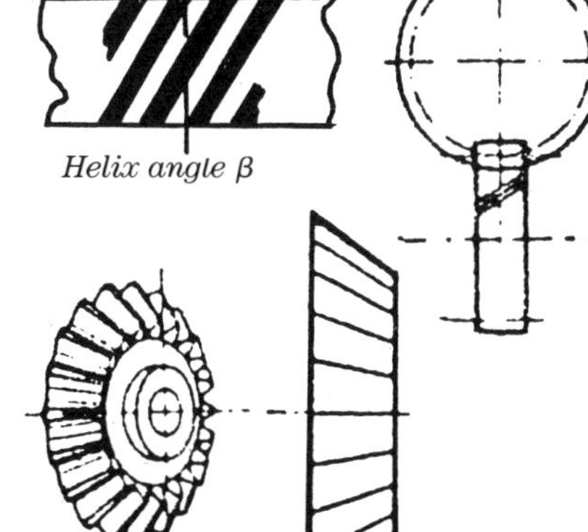

Straight bevel gear

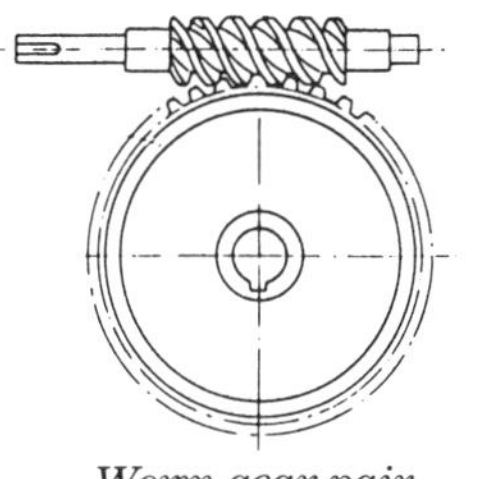

Worm gear pair

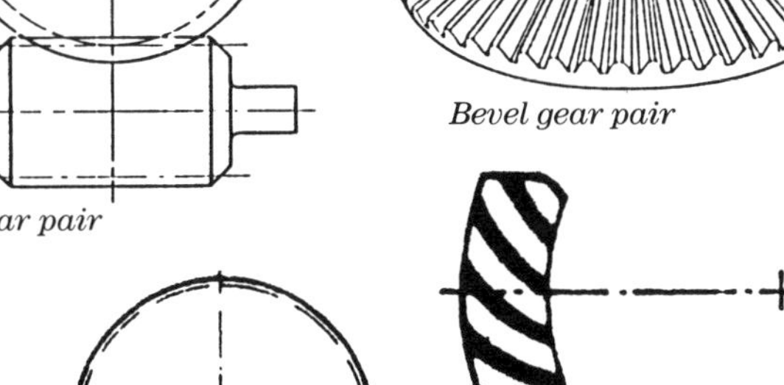

(Cylindrical) worm gear pair

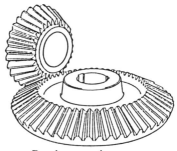

Bevel gear pair

Spiral gear (or gear pair)

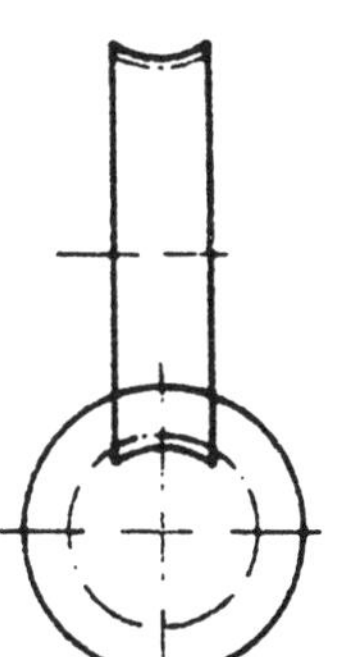

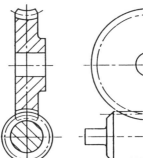

Double enveloping worm gear pair

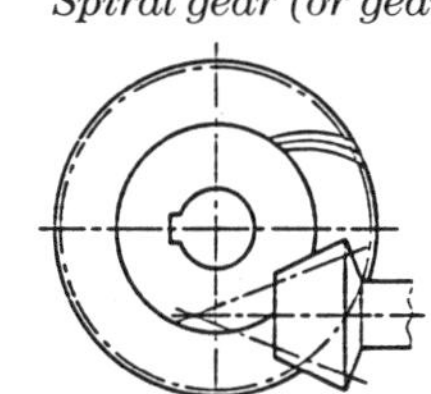

Hypoid gear pair

STANDARD NORMAL MODULES FOR HELICAL AND BEVEL GEARS
1st choice Normal modules m_n
mm
1
1.25
1.5
2
2.5
3
4
5
6
8
10
12
16
20
25
32
40
50

SUPPLIERS

TRANSMISSIONS: Gears

COMPANY	ADDRESS	TELEPHONE	FAX
Brown Gear Industries Ltd	Park Gear Works HUDDERSFIELD W Yorks HD4 5DD	0484 22180	0484 514732
Davall Moulded Gears Ltd	Welham Green HATFIELD Herts AL9 7JB	0707 265432	0707 274054
David Brown Radicom Ltd	Pallion Gear Works SUNDERLAND Tyne & Wear SR4 6RF	091 510 9999	091 565 5081
Highfield Gears Ltd	Nile Street HUDDERSFIELD W Yorks HD1 3LP	0484 424466	0484 512433
Muffet Ltd	14 Woodbury Park Road TUNBRIDGE WELLS Kent TN4 8AB	0892 42111	0892 42117
Newmont Engineering Co Ltd	Nodis Works Julien Road Ealing LONDON W5 4XE	081 567 3924	081 569 3630
Power Plant Gears	PO Box 35 Newtown Works Cradley Road DUDLEY W Midlands DY2 0DX	0384 410510	0384 368280
Staffs Silent Gear Co Ltd	Gear Works Salem Street Etruria STOKE ON TRENT Staffs ST1 5PR	0782 280136	0782 269913
Westley Smith & Co Ltd	Blackhorse Road LETCHWORTH Herts SG6 1HL	0462 480988	0462 480988

USEFUL ADDRESSES

TRANSMISSIONS

ADDRESS	TELEPHONE
British Gear Association St James House Frederick Road Edgbaston BIRMINGHAM B15 1JJ	021 456 3445

Notes

SECTION 7 – ELECTRICAL MACHINES

ELECTRIC MOTORS 7.1.1

a.c. and d.c. motors: Construction, selection and use

TYPICAL APPLICATIONS: Industrial and domestic appliances, machine tools, heating, ventilating and refrigeration equipment, auxiliary power on vehicles and aircraft, electric and diesel electric trains, flow control systems, remotely operated valves and instruments.

DEFINITIONS:

A machine which directly converts electrical energy into rotary mechanical motion.

CONSTRUCTION:

The rotor is typically copper wire wound on an iron core with a central steel shaft running in plain or rolling element bearings. The stator is a cast iron, pressed steel or aluminium shell also wound internally with copper wire on iron. Cooling is by a fan on the rotor and ribbing with ventilators on the stator. The stator frame is constructed with feet, flanges or pads for mounting purposes and may incorporate an enclosure to provide degrees of protection normally ranging from drip-proof up to flame-proof, depending on the operating conditions. Rotors may or may not be fitted with commutators and brushes depending on type and application of the motor, and on some motors a starting device may be integral with the stator construction. One end of the rotor shaft is usually keyed for direct power take-off although some smaller motors are supplied with integral gearboxes.

NOTES ON SELECTION AND USE:

Electric motors are classified according to operating principle, enclosure construction, ventilation and output characteristics. The three broad groupings are Induction, Synchronous and Universal. The induction motor is the most commonly used for general purposes, because of its high start up torque and general reliability. The synchronous motor has constant speed characteristics, but to achieve this it requires relatively complex control and starting devices. It is a fairly costly machine but does serve for applications such as some pumps and generators. The universal motor will run on a.c. or d.c. supplies, is self starting and is at its most efficient when used in small portable tools and domestic appliances. 'Shunt' wound a.c. induction machines are most widely used because speed is virtually independent of load. The 'squirrel cage' type is the cheapest and most efficient of these but takes high starting currents when switched directly on line. Cage motors may be wound for two or more specific speeds but variable speed control is expensive and is easier to do with 'slip ring' motors by wiring in resistances, but these cause speed variations with load change. d.c. motors are most suitable for economic speed variation but suffer the disadvantage of needing special voltage supplies. Motor enclosures should be matched to working conditions especially in hazardous environments and a number of degrees of protection are available for this purpose. Excessive temperature rises can also seriously affect motor performance and several methods of cooling are available to meet most demands. Note that height above sea level of an installation can cause an increase in working temperature. Where motors are running close to people, then special noise reducing enclosures are available. Motor bearings are normally capable of running continuously for two years before additional lubrication is needed.

REFERENCES:

BS 2048:	Specification for dimensions of fractional horse-power motors Part 1: 1961 (1989)
BS EN 60947	Specification for low-voltage switchgear and controlgear
BS 4941:	Spec. for motor starters for voltages up to & including 1000V a.c. & 1200V d.c. Parts 1–4
BS 4999:	General requirements for rotating electrical machines Index, Parts 101–109, 111, 112, 115, 116, 140–145, 147
BS 5000:	Specification for rotating electrical machines of particular types or for particular applications Index, Parts 2, 3, 10, 11, 15–17, 25, 40, 50, 60, 99
BS 5501:	Electrical apparatus for potentially explosive atmospheres Parts 2–9
BS 6467:	Electrical apparatus with protection by enclosure for use in the presence of combustible dusts Parts 1, 2
BS AU 234 1989	Road vehicle starter motors
BS 4683	Specification for electrical apparatus for explosive atmospheres

ELECTRIC MOTORS 7.1.2

a.c. and d.c. motors: Sectional details and types available

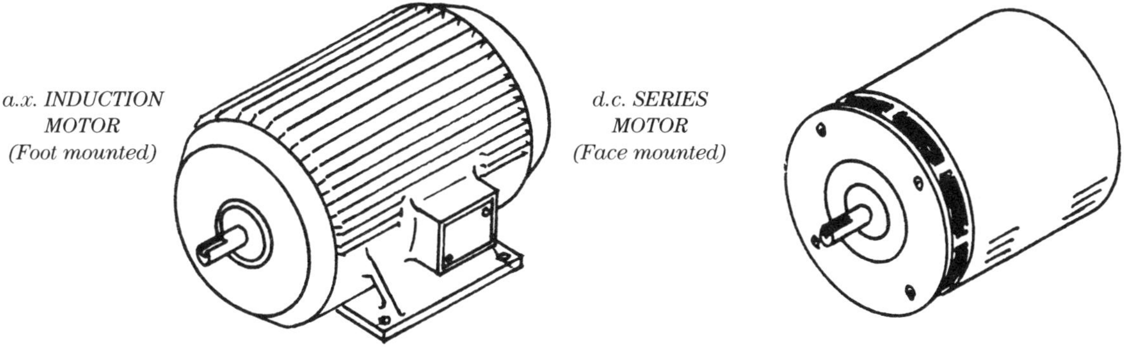

GENERAL APPEARANCE OF TWO TYPES OF MOTOR

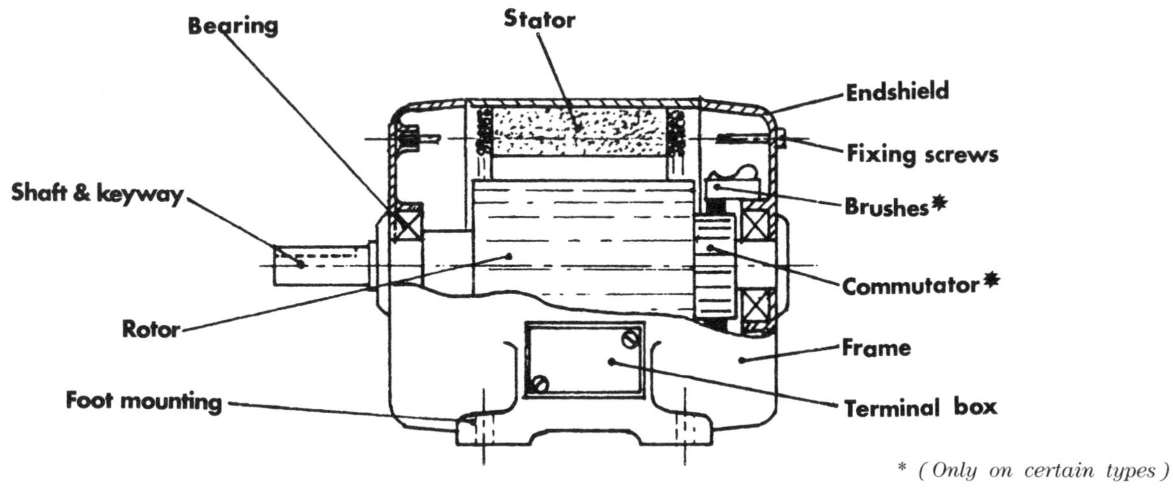

PART SECTIONED VIEW OF TYPICAL ELECTRIC MOTOR

TYPES OF MACHINE COMMONLY AVAILABLE

Single Phase a.c. machines	Polyphase a.c. machines
split - phase	cage induction
capacitor start, induction run	d.c. machines
capacitor start, capacitor run (two value capacitor)	compound
capacitor start and run (single value capacitor permanently in circuit)	shunt
shaded pole	series
series commutator	separately excited
	a.c./ d.c. machines
	universal series commutator

TYPES OF MOUNTING ARRANGEMENT COMMONLY AVAILABLE *

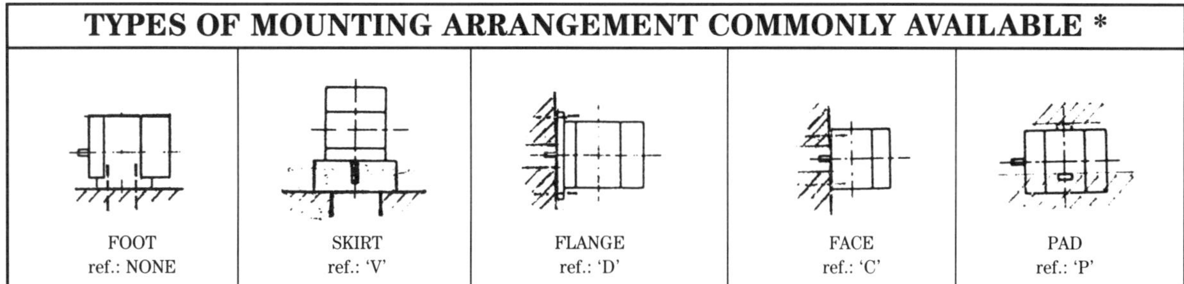

FOOT ref.: NONE	SKIRT ref.: 'V'	FLANGE ref.: 'D'	FACE ref.: 'C'	PAD ref.: 'P'

* Note: For full details of varieties of mounting methods see BS 4999 Part 107

ELECTRIC MOTORS 7.1.3

a.c. and d.c. motors: Applications

Single phase a.c. machines

Type	*Notes*
Split phase	Started by reactance or resistance in series and are therefore suitable for light loads with low inertia requiring infrequent starting.
Capacitor start, induction run	These can be used for drives with light to moderate loads with more frequent starting but do need internal switching.
Capacitor start, capacitor run	Similar characteristics to above but are more efficient and quieter running. This type does need internal (eg centrifugal) switching.
Capacitor start and run	Very quiet smooth running motor for applications where a low locked rotor torque is acceptable.
Shaded pole	These have the advantage of being self-starting but will only tolerate low locked rotor torques. Overall efficiency is low for these machines.
Series commutator	An older type often used when permanent connection to the load was guaranteed (ie traction) but does suffer the disadvantage of brush gear.

Polyphase a.c. machines

Type	*Notes*
Three phase cage induction	By far the best general purpose machines being self-starting and capable of sustaining high starting torques and working loads virtually independent of speed. Starting current is, however, high and switchgear must be rated accordingly. Easily reversible.

d.c. machines

Type	*Notes*
Compound	These need a series winding for starting and although give constant speed, suffer reducing torque with load and cannot be overloaded without damage.
Shunt	Speed is generally constant at low loads and torque will increase in proportion to armature current. Relatively easy to provide variable speed control.
Series	Speed falls (parabolic) with load and torque will increase proportional to armature current. Will ‘runaway’ if unloaded.
Separately excited	This is a term relating to speed control rather than the motor. By separately energising field and armature circuits a closely controlled variable speed system can be created.

a.c. / d.c. machines

Type	*Notes*
Universal series commutator	These have the advantages of operating on a.c. or d.c. supplies and being self-starting. They are most economic when used for low power portable tools and domestic appliances. Brush gear and commutators suffer long term wear.

ELECTRIC MOTORS 7.1.4

Motor selection

SELECTION OF MOTORS

The tables and data on this and the following pages contain the basic information needed for motor selection.
The parts of BS 4999 listed below are a guide to the general requirements to consider when drafting a specification.

Motors shall comply with the requirements of the following Parts of BS 4999, except where such Parts are modified or extended in BS 5000:

Part 101	Specification for rating and performance. The class of rating assigned shall be maximum continuous rating (MCR). In the absence of any special agreement the insulation of the windings may be class E, class B or class F at the discretion of the manufacturer
Part 102	Methods for determining losses and efficiency from tests (excluding machines for traction vehicles).
Part 103	Specification for symbols.
Part 105	Classification of degrees of protection provided by enclosures for rotating machinery. The enclosure shall be either of the totally enclosed type or of the ventilated type having degree of protection IP44 or IP22 respectively.
Part 106	Classification of methods of cooling. Motors with IP44 enclosure shall have cooling class IC41 or IC48 and motors with IP22 enclosure shall have cooling class IC01.
Part 112	Specification for starting performance of single-speed three-phase cage induction motors.
Part 141	Specification for standard dimensions.
Part 142	Specification for mechanical performance : vibration.
Part 143	Specification for tests.

A useful checklist for designers is as follows:

Standard dimensions.
Tolerances.
Operating conditions.
Limits of temperature rise.
General performance characteristics.
Duty and rating.
Rating plate markings.
Types of enclosure.
Methods of cooling.
Mechanical vibration.
Tests.

System of frame nomenclature

For frame sizes up to and including 400 which are primarily intended for low voltage induction type motors, the nomenclature is set out below:
Firstly a *letter* indicating enclosure: **C** for enclosed ventilated, **D** for totally enclosed (other than flameproof)
Secondly a *number* of two or three digits, which is the *height* in millimetres of the shaft centre above the feet (dimension H) on the foot-mounted frame.
Thirdly a *letter* **S**, **M** or **L**, which characterizes the *longitudinal* dimensions (short, medium or long) where more than length is used.
Fourthly, for other than foot-mounted frames, a letter that indicates the type of mounting:

- **D** for flange mounting
- **V** for skirt mounting
- **C** for face-flange mounting
- **P** for pad mounting

***Note**: For example, a totally enclosed fan-ventilated motor of frame size 160M, suitable for flange mounting, is designated D160MD.*
A similar foot mounted motor is D160M.

TYPES OF ENCLOSURE AND METHODS OF COOLING

PROTECTION BY ENCLOSURE BS 4999 Pt. 105		METHODS OF COOLING BS 4999 Pt. 106	
Type	**Code**	**Type**	**Code**
open or non-protected	IP00	free convection	IC00
protected	IP20	self ventilated	IC01
drip proof	IP22	totally enclosed free convection	IC041
totally enclsoed	IP44 or 54	totally enclosed fan ventilated	IC0141
hose proof	IP45	drip proof, air over motor	IC08
weather proof	IPW44 or 54	totally enclosed, air over motor	IC0841
submersible	IP58		
flameproof	BS 4683		

ELECTRIC MOTORS 7.1.5

Motor characteristics: Torque/speed

OUTPUT CHARACTERISTICS

The following curves represent the general performance of some of the more common electric motors. They are approximate graphs only but should give a guide for selection.

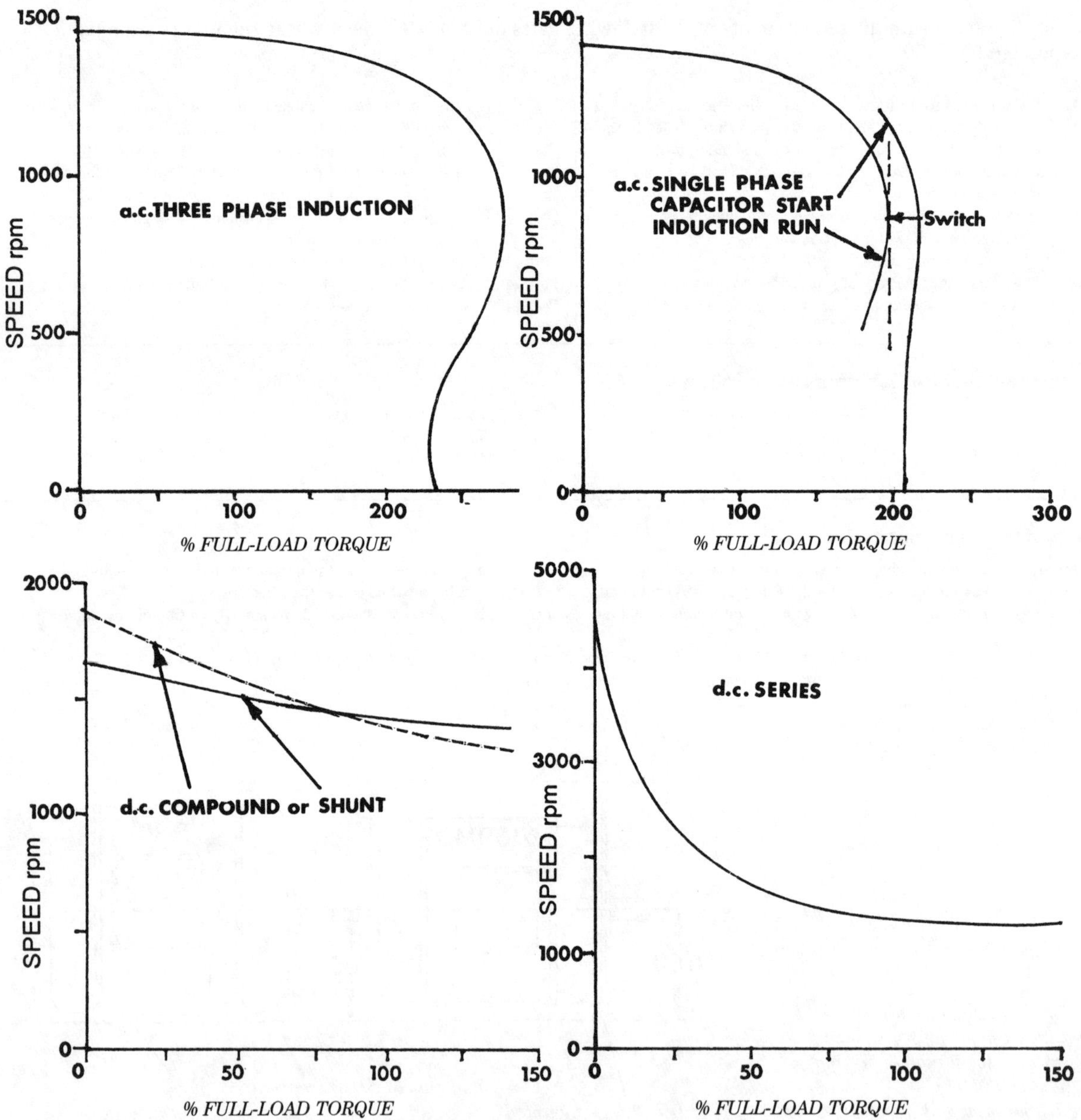

MOTOR SPEEDS		
PREFERRED APPROXIMATE SPEEDS IN rev / min FOR ALL MOTORS (EXCLUDING SERIES COMMUTATOR, SERIES d.c. AND UNIVERSAL MACHINES)		
950	1425	2850

Note: Full load speed for general purpose a.c./ d.c. motors should preferably be not less than 6000 rev / min.

POWER OUTPUTS																			
PREFERRED OUTPUTS IN WATTS (W) * FOR ALL MOTORS (Note: 746W = 1hp)																			
2.5	4	6	10	16	25	40	60	80	90	100	120	180	250	370	550	750	1100	1500	2200

*Note: Large outputs follow the same number series but in kW

ELECTRIC MOTORS 7.1.6

Outputs and shaft numbers for fan-ventilated or airstream rated cage induction motors

This table covers various types of induction motors only and is derived from BS 5000 Part 10 which should be referred to for full data, if required.

OUTPUTS AND SHAFT NUMBERS FOR TOTALLY ENCLOSED FAN-VENTILATED (TEFV) OR AIRSTREAM RATED CAGE INDUCTION MOTORS.

Single speed, maximum continuous rated, class E, class G or class F insulation, enclosure IP44, cooling class IC41 or IC48 *.

Suitable for 3-phase, 50Hz, 415 V† supply.

FRAME NUMBER	OUTPUT IN KW at Synchronous speed (r / min)				SHAFT NUMBER at Synchronous speed (r / min)	
	3000	1500	1000	750	3000	1500 or less
D 56	0.09 and 0.12	0.06 and 0.09	–	–	9	9
D 63	0.18 and 0.25	0.12 and 0.18	–	–	11	11
D 71	0.37 and 0.55	0.25 and 0.37	–	–	14	14
D 80	1.1	0.75	0.55	–	19	19
D 90 S	1.5	1.1	0.75	0.37	24	24
D 90 L	2.2	1.5	1.1	0.55	24	24
D 100 L	3.0	2.2 and 3.0	1.5	0.75 and 1.1	28	28
D 112 M	4.0	4.0	2.2	1.5	28	28
D 132 S	5.5 and 7.5	5.5	3.0	2.2	38	38
D 132 M	–	7.5	4.0 and 5.5	3.0	38	38
D 160 M	11 and 15	11	7.5	4.0 and 5.5	42	42
D 160 L	18.5	15	11	7.5	42	42
D 180 M	22	18.5	–	–	48	48
D 180 L	–	22	15	11	48	48
D 200 L	30 and 37	30	18.5 and 22	15	55	55
D 225 S	–	37	–	18.5	55	60
D 225 M	45	45	30	22	55	60
D 250 M	55	55	37	30	60	65
D 280 S	75	75	45	37	65	75
D 280 M	90	90	55	45	65	75
D 315 S	110	110	75	55	65	80
D 315 M	132	132	90	75	65	80

* In the case of airstream rated motors these output allocations are applicable only to foot-mounted or flange-mounted machines up to and including frame D250M. For pad-mounted or rod-mounted outputs refer to table 5, BS 5000 Part 10.

† By agreement motors may be wound for the standard outputs at other voltages not exceeding 660V.

IMPORTANT NOTE

Symbols used on tables and sketches on pages 110–116 are selected from those given in BS 4999: Part 103 and affect interchangeability.

ELECTRIC MOTORS 7.1.6

Outputs and shaft numbers for fan-ventilated or airstream rated cage induction motors *(contd.)*

This table covers various types of induction motors only and is derived from BS 5000 Part 10 which should be referred to for full data, if required.

OUTPUTS AND SHAFT NUMBERS FOR ENCLOSED VENTILATED CAGE INDUCTION MOTORS

Single speed, maximum continuous rated, class E, class B or class F insulation, enclosure IP22, cooling class ICO1.

Suitable for 3-phase, 50Hz, 415V * supply.

FRAME NUMBER	OUTPUT IN KW at Synchronous speed (r / min)				SHAFT NUMBER at Synchronous speed (r / min)	
	3000	1500	1000	750	3000	1500 or less
C 160 M	11 and 15	11	7.5	5.5	48	48
C 160 L	18.5 and 22	15 and 18.5	11	7.5	48	48
C 180 M	30	22	15	11	55	55
C 180 L	37	30	18.5	15	55	55
C 200 M	45	37	22	18.5	60	60
C 200 L	55	45	30	22	60	60
C 225 M	75	55	37	30	60	65
C 250 S	90	75	45	37	65	75
C 250 M	110	90	55	45	65	75
C 280 S	–	110	75	55	65	80
C 280 M	132	132	90	75	65	80
C 315 S	160	160	110	90	70	90
C 315 M	200	200	132	110	70	90

* By agreement motors may be wound for the standard outputs at other voltages not exceeding 660V.

OUTPUTS AND SHAFT NUMBERS FOR TOTALLY ENCLOSED AIRSTREAM RATED PAD-MOUNTED OR ROD-MOUNTED CAGE INDUCTION MOTORS

Single speed, maximum continuous rated, class E, class B or class F insulation, enclosure IP44, cooling class IC48.

Suitable for 3-phase, 50Hz, 415 V ** supply.

FRAME NUMBER	OUTPUT IN KW at Synchronous speed (r / min)				SHAFT NUMBER at Synchronous speed (r / min)	
	3000	1500	1000	750	3000	1500 or less
D 80	1.1	0.75	0.55	–	19	19
D 90 L	1.5 and 2.2	1.1 and 1.5	0.75 and 1.1	0.37 and 0.55	24	24
D 100 L	3.0	2.2 and 3.0	1.5	0.75 and 1.1	28	28
D 112 M	4.0	4.0	2.2	1.5	28	28
D 132 M	5.5 and 7.5	5.5 and 7.5	3.0, 4.0 and 5.5	2.2 and 3.0	38	38
D 160 L	11, 15 and 18.5	11 and 15	7.5 and 11	4.0, 5.5 and 7.5	42	42
D 180 L	22	18.5 and 22	15	11	48	48
D 200 L	30 and 37	30	18.5 and 22	15	55	55
D 225 M	45	37 and 45	30	18.5 and 22	55	60
D 250 M	55	55	37	30	60	65

** By agreement motors may be wound for the standard outputs at other voltages not exceeding 660V.

ELECTRIC MOTORS 7.1.7

Outputs and shaft numbers for slip ring induction motors

These tables cover various types of induction motors only and are derived from BS 5000 Part 10 which should be referred to for full data, if required.

OUTPUTS AND SHAFT NUMBERS FOR TOTALLY ENCLOSED FAN-VENTILATED WOUND ROTOR (SLIP RING) INDUCTION MOTORS

Maximum continuous rated, class E, class B or class F insulation, enclosure IP44, cooling class IC41.

Suitable for 3-phase, 50Hz, 415 V * supply.

FRAME NUMBER	OUTPUT IN KW at Synchronous speed (r / min)			SHAFT NUMBER
	1500	1000	750	
D 160 M	7.5	5.5	–	42
D 160 L	11	7.5	5.5	42
D 180 L	15	11	7.5	48
D 200 L	18.5 and 22	15	11	55
D 225 M	30	18.5 and 22	15 and 18.5	60
D 250 M	37 and 45	30	22	65
D 280 S	55	37	30	75
D 280 M	75	45	37	75
D 315 S	90	55	45	80
D 315 M	110	75	55	80

* By agreement motors may be wound for the standard outputs at other voltages not exceeding 660V.

OUTPUTS AND SHAFT NUMBERS FOR ENCLOSED VENTILATED WOUND ROTOR (SLIP RING) INDUCTION MOTORS

Maximum continuous rated, class E, class B or class F insulation, enclosure IP22, cooling class IC01.

Suitable for 3-phase, 50Hz, 415 V ** supply.

FRAME NUMBER	OUTPUT IN KW at Synchronous speed (r / min)			SHAFT NUMBER
	1500	1000	750	
C 160 M	7.5	5.5	4.0	48
C 160 L	11 and 15	7.5	5.5	48
C 180 M	18.5	11	7.5	55
C 180 L	22	15	11	55
C 200 M	30	18.5	15	60
C 200 L	37	22	18.5	60
C 225 M	45 and 55	30 and 37	22 and 30	65
C 250 S	75	45	37	75
C 250 M	90	55	45	75
C 280 S	110	75	55	80
C 280 M	132	90	75	80
C 315 S	160	110	90	90
C 315M	200	132	110	90

** By agreement motors may be wound for the standard outputs at other voltages not exceeding 660V.

ELECTRIC MOTORS 7.1.8

Motors: Flange mounted frames

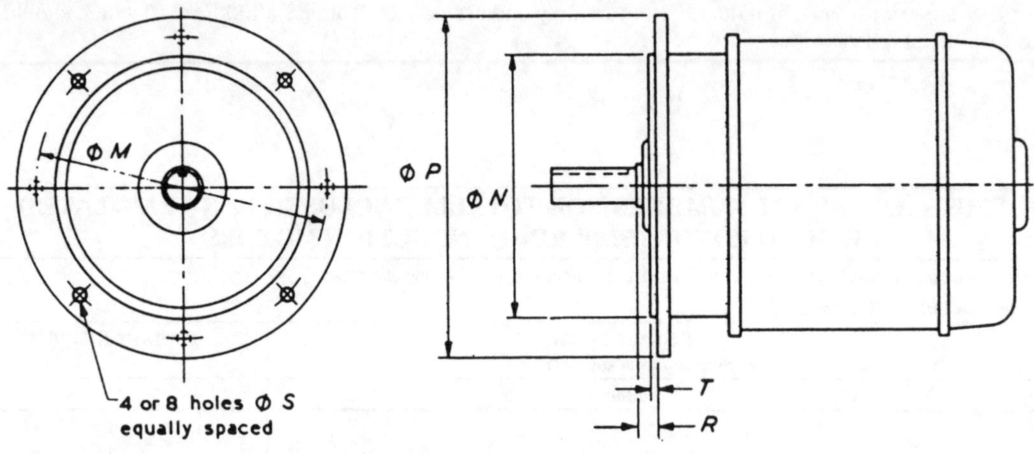

FIXING DIMENSIONS OF FLANGE-MOUNTED FRAMES, ENCLOSURE D (see BS 4999 Pt 103)

Frame number	*M*	*N*			*P*	Flange holes		Thread †	*T* max.	*R*	Limit of spigot run-out and flange face squareness ‡
		Nominal	Tolerance			Number	*S* *				
56	100	80	h8	+ 0 − 0.046	120	4	7	M6	–	0	0.080
63	115	95	h8	+ 0 − 0.054	140	4	10	M8	–	0	0.080
71	130	110	h8	+ 0 − 0.054	160	4	10	M8	3.5	0	0.100
80 90 S and 90 L	165	130	h8	+ 0 − 0.063	200	4	12	M10	3.5	0	0.100
100 S and 100 L 112 S and 112 M	215	180	h8	+ 0 − 0.063	250	4	15	M12	4	0	0.100
132 S and 132 M	265	230	h8	+ 0 − 0.072	300	4	15	M12	4	0	0.100
160 M and 160 L 180 M and 180 L	300	250	h8	+ 0 − 0.072	350	4	19	M16	5	0	0.125
200 M and 200 L	350	300	h8	+ 0 − 0.081	400	4	19	M16	5	0	0.125
225 S and 225 M	400	350	h8	+ 0 − 0.089	450	8	19	M16	5	0	0.125
250 S and 250 M 280 S and 280 M	500	450	h8	+ 0 − 0.097	550	8	19	M16	5	0	0.125
315 S, 315 M and 315 L	600	550	h8	+ 0 − 0.110	660	8	24	M20	6	0	0.160
355 S and 355 L	740	680	h8	+ 0 − 0.125	800	8	24	M20	6	0	0.160
400 S and 400 L	940	880	h8	+ 0 − 0.140	1000	8	28	M24	6	0	0.200

* S dimensions are selected from the coarse series in BS EN 20273.
† Recommended threads for screws used in flange holes S.
‡ These limits are by full indicator measurement.
All dimensions in mm. For full data see BS 4999 : Part 141

ELECTRIC MOTORS 7.1.9

Motors: Foot mounted frames

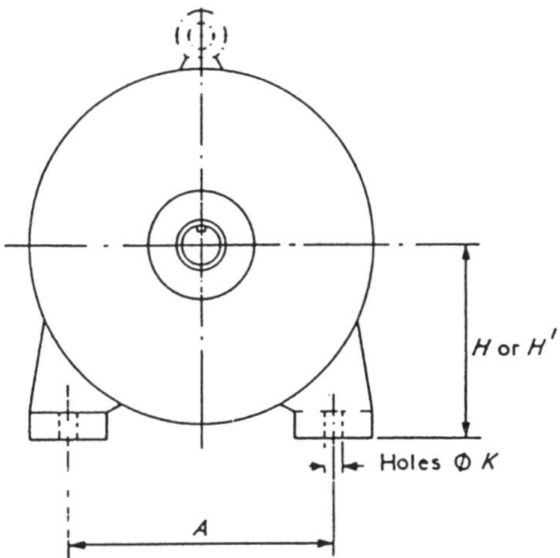

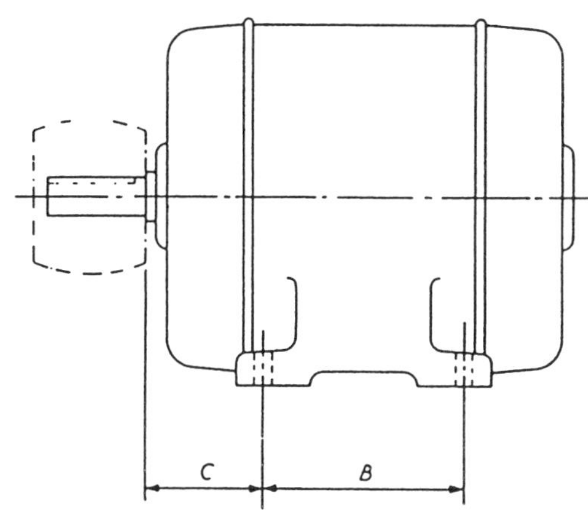

FIXING DIMENSIONS OF FOOT- MOUNTED FRAMES, ALL ENCLOSURES

Frame number	H Nominal	H Negative tolerance *	A	B	C †	K ‡	Fixing bolt or screw
56	56	0.5	90	71	36	5.8	M5
63	63	0.5	100	80	40	7	M6
71	71	0.5	112	90	45	7	M6
80	80	0.5	125	100	50	10	M8
90 S	90	0.5	140	100	56	10	M8
90 L	90	0.5	140	125	56	10	M8
100 S	100	0.5	160	112	63	12	M10
100 L	100	0.5	160	140	63	12	M10
112 S	112	0.5	190	114	70	12	M10
112 M	112	0.5	190	140	70	12	M10
132 S	132	0.5	216	140	89	12	M10
132 M	132	0.5	216	178	89	12	M10
160 M	160	0.5	254	210	108	15	M12
160 L	160	0.5	254	254	108	15	M12
180 M	180	0.5	279	241	121	15	M12
180 L	180	0.5	279	279	121	15	M12
200 M	200	0.5	318	267	133	19	M16
200 L	200	0.5	318	305	133	19	M16
225 S	225	0.5	356	286	149	19	M16
225 M	225	0.5	356	311	149	19	M16
250 S	250	0.5	406	311	168	24	M20
250 M	250	0.5	406	349	168	24	M20
280 S	280	1.0	457	368	190	24	M20
280 M	280	1.0	457	419	190	24	M20
315 S	315	1.0	508	406	216	28	M24
315 M	315	1.0	508	457	216	28	M24
315 L	315	1.0	508	508	216	28	M24
355 S	355	1.0	610	500	254 ‡	28	M24
355 L	355	1.0	610	630	254 ‡	28	M24
400 S	400	1.0	686	560	280 ‡	35	M30
400 L	400	1.0	686	710	280 ‡	35	M30

FIXING DIMENSIONS OF FOOT- MOUNTED FRAMES, VENTILATED ENCLOSURE, FOR D.D.; MACHINES

Frame number	H Nominal	H Negative tolerance*	A	B	C †	K ‡
132	132	0.5	216	No values assigned (see note below)	89	12
160	160	0.5	254		108	15
180	180	0.5	279		121	15
200	200	0.5	318		133	19
225	225	0.5	356		149	19
250	250	0.5	406		168	24
280	280	1.0	457		190	24
315	315	1.0	508		216	28
355	355	1.0	610		254	28
400	400	1.0	686		280	35
450	450	1.0	750		315	–
500	500	1.0	850		335	–

* There are no positive tolerances.
† Dimension C assumes ball and roller bearings.
‡ The K dimensions are selected from the coarse series in BS EN 20273.

Note: Select figures for B (associated with a particular H) from adjacent table, or from the R20 series listed in BS 2045.

All dimensions in mm

For full data see BS 4999 : Part 141

ELECTRIC MOTORS 7.1.10

Motors: Face mounted frames

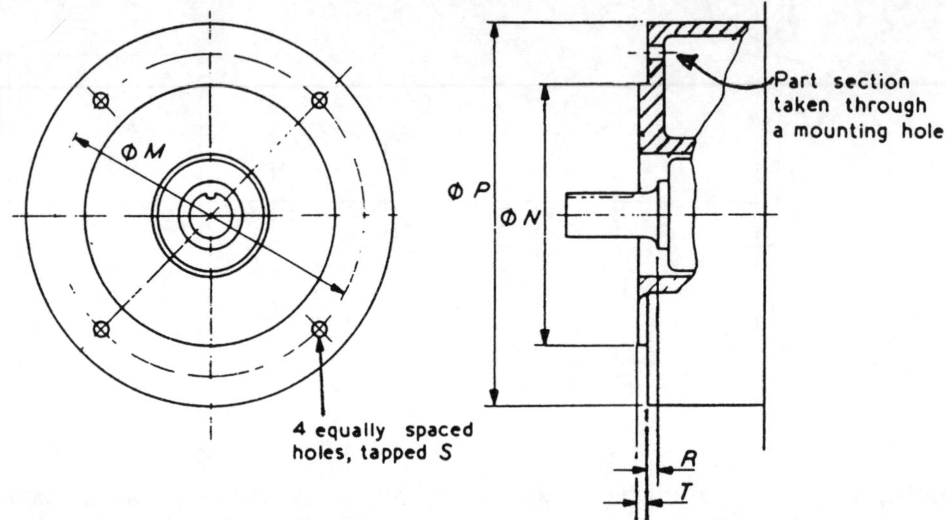

FIXING DIMENSIONS OF FACE-FLANGE FRAMES, ENCLOSURES C AND D (SEE BS 4999 PT 103)

Frame number	*M*	*N*			*P*	Flange holes		*T* max.	*R*	Limit of spigot run-out and flange face squareness ‡
		Nominal	Tolerance			Number	*S*			
56	65	50	h8	+ 0 − 0.039	80	4	M5	2.5	0	0.080
63	75	60	h8	+ 0 − 0.046	90	4	M5	2.5	0	0.080
71	85	70	h8	+ 0 − 0.046	105	4	M6	2.5	0	0.080
80	100	80	h8	+ 0 − 0.046	120	4	M6	3	0	0.080
90 S and 90 L	115	95	h8	+ 0 − 0.054	140	4	M8	3	0	0.080
100 S and 100 L 112 S and 112 M	130	110	h8	+ 0 − 0.054	160	4	M8	3.5	0	0.100
132 S and 132 M	165	130	h8	+ 0 − 0.063	200	4	M10	3.5	0	0.100
160 M and 160 L	215	180	h8	+ 0 − 0.063	250	4	M12	4	0	0.100

* These limits are by full indicator measurement.
All dimensions in mm.
For full data see BS 4999 : Part 141

ELECTRIC MOTORS 7.1.11

Motors: Skirt and pad mounted frames

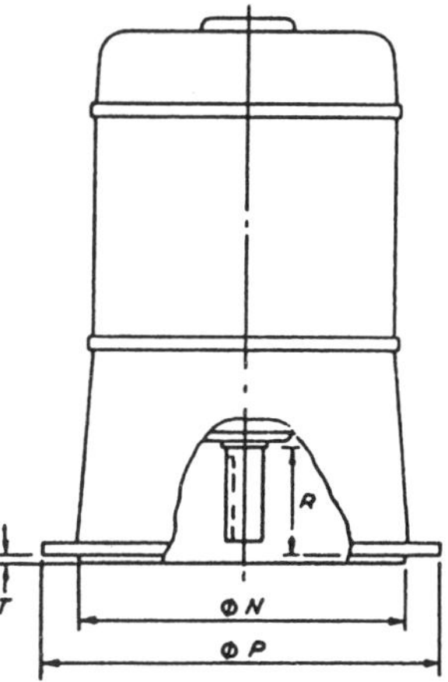

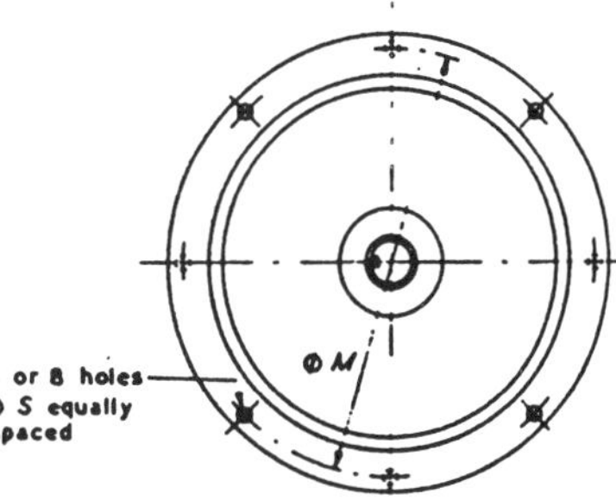

FIXING DIMENSIONS OF SKIRT-MOUNTED FRAMES, ENCLOSURE D

Frame number	*M*	*N* Nominal	*N* Tolerance		*P*	Flange holes Number	*S**	*T* max.	*R*	Limit of spigot run-out and flange face squareness ‡
80 90 S and 90 L	165	130	h8	+ 0 − 0.063	200	4	12	3.5	53	0.100
100 S and 100 L 112 S and 112 M	215	180	h8	+ 0 − 0.063	250	4	15	4	63	0.100
132 S and 132 M	265	230	h8	+ 0 − 0.072	300	4	15	4	83	0.100
160 M and 160 L 180 M and 180 L	300	250	h8	+ 0 − 0.072	350	4	19	5	113	0.125
200 M and 200 L	350	300	h8	+ 0 − 0.081	400	4	19	5	113	0.125
225 S and 225 M	400	350	h8	+ 0 − 0.089	450	8	19	5	143	0.125
250 S and 250 M 280 S and 280 M	500	450	h8	+ 0 − 0.097	550	8	19	5	173	0.125
315 S, 315 M and 315 L	600	550	h8	+ 0 − 0.110	660	8	24	6	173	0.160
355 S and 355 L	740	680	h8	+ 0 − 0.125	800	8	24	6	213	0.160
400 S and 400 L	940	880	h8	+ 0 − 0.140	1000	8	28	6	213	0.200

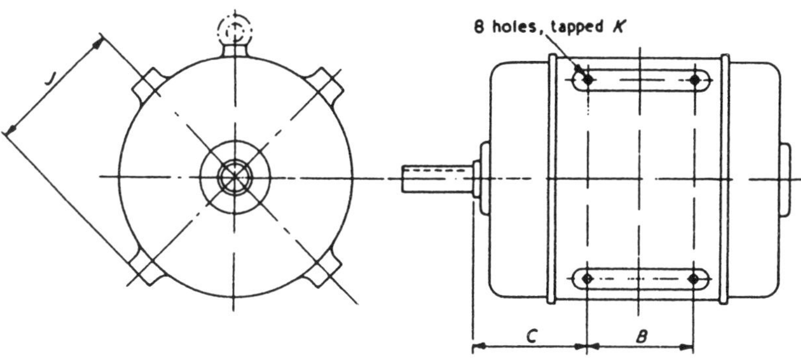

NOTES:
** S dimensions are selected from the coarse series in BS EN 20273.*

† These limits are by full indicator measurement.

All dimensions in mm

For full data see BS 4999 : Part 141

FIXING DIMENSIONS OF PAD-MOUNTED OR ROD-MOUNTED FRAMES, ENCLOSURE D

Frame numbers	J *	B	C †	K ‡
80	95	90	55	M 12
90 L	105	90	73.5	M 12
100 L	117	100	83	M 12
112 M	130	100	90	M 12
132 M	155	140	108	M 16
160 L	185	200	135	M 20
180 L	205	200	160.5	M 20
200 L	229	224	173.5	M 24
225 M	255	224	192.5	M 24
250 M	285	224	230.5	M 24

NOTES
* These are maximum dimensions
† The dimension C assumes ball and/or roller bearings.
‡ The dimensions for K are selected from BS 3643 : Part 2.

Motors: Shaft dimensions

(This table to be used with output data for induction motors)

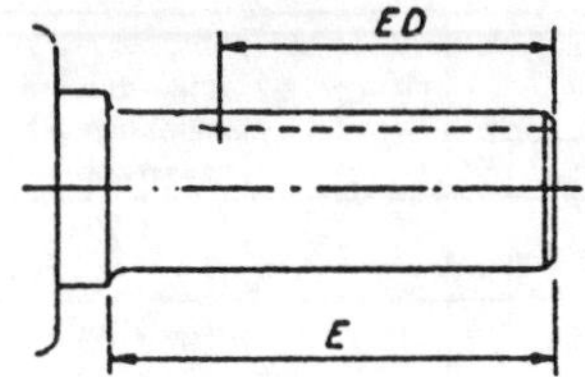

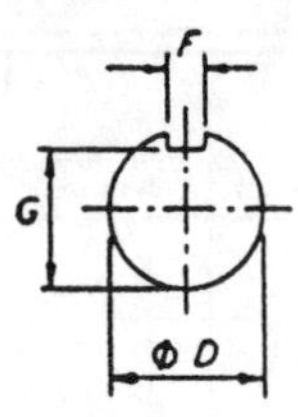

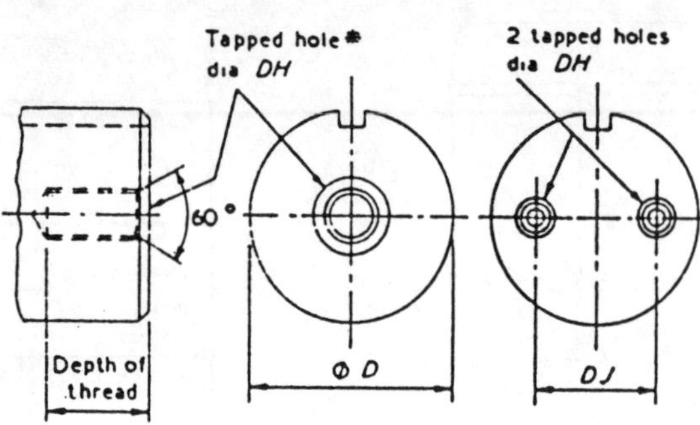

SHAFT ENDS AND KEYWAYS

* *(For detail of tapped hole or holes in shaft extension see BS 4999 : Part 141)*

DIMENSIONS OF SHAFT ENDS AND KEYWAYS (see BS 4999 : Part 141)

Shaft number	Diameter *D*			Length *E*	Limit of shaft extension run-out (note 1)	Width of keyway *F*			*G*		*ED* (min.)
	Nominal	Tolerance				Nominal	Tolerance		Nominal	Tolerance	
9	9	j6	+ 0.007 − 0.002	20	0.03	3	N9	− 0.004 − 0.029	7.2	+ 0 − 0.1	8
11	11	j6	+ 0.008 − 0.003	23	0.035	4	N9	+ 0 − 0.030	8.5	+ 0 − 0.1	10
14	14	j6	+ 0.008 − 0.003	30	0.035	5	N9	+ 0 − 0.030	11	+ 0 − 0.1	14
19	19	j6	+ 0.009 − 0.004	40	0.04	6	N9	+ 0 − 0.030	15.5	+ 0 − 0.2	25
22	22	j6	+ 0.009 − 0.004	50	0.04	6	N9	+ 0 − 0.030	18.5	+ 0 − 0.2	32
24	24	j6	+ 0.009 − 0.004	50	0.04	8	N9	+ 0 − 0.036	20.0	+ 0 − 0.2	32
28	28	j6	+ 0.009 − 0.004	60	0.04	8	N9	+ 0 − 0.036	24.0	+ 0 − 0.2	40
32	32	k6	+ 0.018 − 0.002	80	0.05	10	N9	+ 0 − 0.036	27.0	+ 0 − 0.2	56
38	38	k6	+ 0.018 − 0.002	80	0.05	10	N9	+ 0 − 0.036	33.0	+ 0 − 0.2	56
42	42	k6	+ 0.018 − 0.002	110	0.05	12	N9	+ 0 − 0.043	37.0	+ 0 − 0.2	80
48	48	k6	+ 0.018 − 0.002	110	0.05	14	N9	+ 0 − 0.043	42.5	+ 0 − 0.2	80
55	55	m6	+ 0.030 − 0.011	110	0.06	16	N9	+ 0 − 0.043	49.0	+ 0 − 0.2	80
60	60	m6	+ 0.030 − 0.011	140	0.06	18	N9	+ 0 − 0.043	53.0	+ 0 − 0.2	110
65	65	m6	+ 0.030 − 0.011	140	0.06	18	N9	+ 0 − 0.043	58.0	+ 0 − 0.2	110
70	70	m6	+ 0.030 − 0.011	140	0.06	20	N9	+ 0 − 0.052	62.5	+ 0 − 0.2	110
75	75	m6	+ 0.030 − 0.011	140	0.06	20	N9	+ 0 − 0.052	67.5	+ 0 − 0.2	110
80	80	m6	+ 0.030 − 0.011	170	0.06	22	N9	+ 0 − 0.052	71.0	+ 0 − 0.2	140
85	85	m6	+ 0.035 − 0.013	170	0.07	22	N9	+ 0 − 0.052	76.0	+ 0 − 0.2	140
90	90	m6	+ 0.035 − 0.013	170	0.07	25	N9	+ 0 − 0.052	81.0	+ 0 − 0.2	140

ELECTRIC MOTORS 7.1.13

Electric motors: detailed definitions

SOME USEFUL DEFINITIONS:

Important Note: See BS 4999 : Part 101 for comprehensive definitions and further details of duties and ratings to be used in technical specifications.

Rating The whole of the numerical values of the electrical and mechanical quantities with their duration and sequence assigned to the machine by the manufacturer and stated on the rating plate, the machine complying with the specified conditions.

Classes of Rating

1. *Maximum continuous rating* The statement of the load and conditions, assigned to the machine by the manufacturer at which the machine may be operated for an unlimited period while complying with the requirements of BS 4999.
2. *Short-time rating* The statement of the load, time and conditions assigned to the machine by the manufacturer, at which the machine may be operated for a limited period, starting at the ambient temperature, while complying with the requirements of BS 4999.
3. *Equivalent continuous rating* The statement of the load and conditions, assigned to the machine for test purposes, by the manufacturer, at which the machine may be operated until thermal equilibrium is reached, and which is considered to be equivalent to one of the periodic duty types while complying with the requirements of BS 4999.
4. *Periodic duty type rating* The statement of the loads and conditions, assigned to the machine by the manufacturer, at which the machine may be operated on duty cycles while complying with the requirements of BS 4999.
   This class of rating if applied shall correspond to one of the periodic duty types defined in BS 4999 : Part 101 Sub-clauses 4.3 to 4.8.
   The time for a duty cycle shall be 10 min and the cyclic duration factor shall be one of the following values: 15 % , 25 % , 40 % , 60 % .
5. *Non-periodic duty type rating* The statement of the varying loads over varying speeds and conditions, including overloads, assigned to the machine by the manufacturer, at which the machine may be operated non-periodically while complying with the requirements of BS 4999.
   This class of rating if applied shall correspond to the non-periodic duty with non-periodic load and speed variations, as defined in BS 4999 : Part 101 Sub-clause 4.9.

Rated value The numerical value of a quantity included in the rating.

Rated output The numerical value of the output included in the rating.

Load All the numerical values of the electrical and mechanical quantities that signify the demand to be made on a rotating machine by an electrical circuit or mechanism at a given instant.

No-load (operation) The state of a machine rotating with zero output power (but under otherwise normal operating conditions).

Full load The highest value of load specified for a machine operating at rated output.

Full load power The highest value of power specified for a machine operating at rated output.
Note – This concept also applies to torque, current, speed, etc.

Rest and de-energized The complete absence of all movement and of all electrical supply or mechanical drive.

Duty The statement of the load(s) to which the machine is subjected, including, if applicable, starting, electric braking, no-load and rest and de-energized periods, and including their durations and sequence in time.

Duty-type A continuous, short time or periodic duty, comprising one or more loads remaining constant for the duration specified, or a non-periodic duty in which generally load and speed vary within the permissible operating range.

Thermal equilibrium The state reached when the temperature rises of the several parts of the machine do not vary by more than 2 K over a period of 1 h.

Cyclic duration factor The ratio between the period of loading, including starting and electric braking, and the duration of the duty cycle, expressed as a percentage.

Locked rotor torque The minimum measured torque which the motor develops with the rotor locked and rated voltage applied at rated frequency.

Locked rotor current The measured steady-state root-mean-square current taken from the line with the rotor locked with rated voltage and frequency applied.

Pull-up torque (of an a.c. motor) The smallest torque which the motor develops between zero speed and the speed which corresponds to the breakdown torque when the motor is supplied at the rated voltage, and frequency.

This definition does not apply to those asynchronous motors of which the torque continually decreases with increase in speed.
Note – This value applies to the usual mean torque characteristic which excludes transient effects.

Breakdown torque (of an a.c. motor) The maximum torque which the motor develops with rated voltage and frequency applied at operating temperature without an abrupt drop in speed.

This definition does not apply to those asynchronous motors of which the torque continually decreases with increase in speed.
Note – This value applies to the usual mean torque characteristic which excludes transient effects.

Pull-out torque (of a synchronous motor) The maximum torque which the synchronous motor develops at operating temperature and at synchrounous speed with rated voltage, frequency and field current.

SUPPLIERS

PRIME MOVERS: a.c. and d.c. motors

COMPANY	ADDRESS	TELEPHONE	FAX
FRACTIONAL HORSEPOWER MOTORS BELOW 1HP (746 W) OUTPUT:			
Brook Crompton Parkinson Motors	Fractional Motor Division Wheatly DONCASTER S Yorks DN2 4NB	0302 322155	0302 364738
Electrodrives Ltd	Cakemore Rd Rowley Regis WARLEY W Midlands B65 0QT	021-559 1500	021-561 3068
MCP Electronics Ltd	City Gate House 399–425 Eastern Ave Gants Hill ILFORD Essex IG2 6LR	081 518 2000	081 518 3222
MSI-Blantyre Ltd	53/56 South Ave Blantyre Ind Est Blantyre GLASGOW G72 0UZ	0698 829535	0698 820169
Park Products Ltd	Ordance Street BLACKBURN Lancs BB1 3BN	0254 671121	0254 698324
Parvalux Electric Motors Ltd	Wallisdown Road BOURNEMOUTH Dorset BH11 8PU	0202 512575	0202 530885
SEW-Eurodrive Ltd	PO Box 1 Beckbridge Ind Est NORMANTON W Yorks WF6 1QR	0924 893855	0924 893702
MOTORS ABOVE 1HP (746W):			
Brook Motors Ltd	Small Industrial Motors Honley HUDDERSFIELD W Yorks HD1 3LJ	0484 422150	
Brush Electrical Machines Ltd	PO Box 18 LOUGHBOROUGH Leics LE11 1HJ	0509 611511	0509 610440
Crompton Parkinson Motors Ltd	Large Industrial Motors Netherfield Road Guiseley LEEDS LS20 9NZ	0943 73211	0943 870028
Electrodrives Ltd	Cakemore Rd Rowley Regis WARLEY W Midlands B65 0QT	021-559 1500	021-561 3068
Mellor Electrics Ltd	Sett End Road Shadworth Ind Park BLACKBURN Lancs BB1 2NW	0254 53854	0254 678625

SUPPLIERS

PRIME MOVERS: a.c. and d.c. motors *(contd)*

COMPANY	ADDRESS	TELEPHONE	FAX
MOTORS ABOVE 1HP (746 W) *(contd)*:			
Park Products Ltd	Ordance Street BLACKBURN Lancs BB1 3BN	0254 671121	0254 698324
Reliance Electric (UK) Ltd Telford Division	Halesfield 19 TELFORD Shropshire TF7 4PT	0952 580888	0952 684367
SEW-Eurodrive Ltd	PO Box 1 Beckbridge Ind Est NORMANTON W Yorks WF6 1QR	0924 893855	0924 893702

USEFUL ADDRESSES

ELECTRIC MOTORS

ADDRESS	TELEPHONE
BEAMA Ltd Federation of British Electrotechnical and Allied Manufacturers Associations 8 Leicester Street LONDON WC2H 7BN	071 437 0678
Electrical Power Engineers Association Station House Fox Lane North CHERTSEY Surrey KT16 9HW	0932 564131
Institution of Electrical Engineers Savoy Place LONDON WC2R 0BL	

Notes

SECTION 8 – FLUID EQUIPMENT

8.1 VALVES

8.2 HYDRAULIC CYLINDERS

SECTION 8 – FLUID EQUIPMENT *(contd.)*

8.3 PIPES

8.3.1 Rigid, semi-rigid and flexible hydraulic tubing: Construction, selection and use

8.3.2 Semi-rigid and flexible tubing: Sectional details and types available

8.3.3 Wire reinforced flexible hose: Sizes

8.3.4 Cold finished and welded tube: Materials, sizes and pressure ratings

8.3.5 Tubing for compression fittings: Weights and measures

8.3.6 Tube / hose assemblies: Installation notes

8.3.7 Ductile iron pipes and fittings

8.3.8 Ductile iron pipes and fittings: Methods of joining pipes

Suppliers: Hydraulic tubing and hose

8.4 PIPE FITTINGS

8.4.1 Couplings for hydraulic tube and components: Construction, selection and use

8.4.2 Hydraulic couplings: Sectional details, types available and pressure ratings

8.4.3 Equal elbow, equal cross and equal tee compression fittings: Sizes

8.4.4 Stud, stud elbow and straight coupling compression fittings: Sizes

8.4.5 Male stud tees (branch and run) compression fittings: Sizes

8.4.6 Couplings for flexible tubing: Interface details

8.4.7 Straight and tubular elbow couplings for flexible tubing

8.4.8 Block elbow couplings and adaptors for flexible tubing

8.4.9 Port and stud coupling with 'O'-ring seals: Sizes and details

8.4.10 Threaded studs for couplings: Sizes and details

8.4.11 Flanges: Construction, selection and use

8.4.12 Selecting a flange

Suppliers: Couplings for hydraulic tube and components

VALVES 8.1.1

Manually operated valves: General construction, selection and use

TYPICAL APPLICATIONS: Industrial and domestic water and gas systems, food and petrochemical plant, fluid engineering systems, process plant, land irrigation and drainage, ship and boiler engineering, heat exchangers and cooling systems.

DEFINITION:

A mechanical device applied to a pipe or aperture to control the passage of liquids, solids or gases.

CONSTRUCTION:

Most valve bodies are mouldings or castings because of the intricate shapes often required for passageways and seatings. Main materials are usually copper alloys, cast irons and steels with a growth in recent years in the use of high performance plastics. Plastics and rubbers are also increasingly used for seals, seats, gaskets and flexible membranes of valves. A primary concern during valve design and construction is the avoidance of corrosion, either from dissimilar materials setting up an electrolytic action, or from the effects of contact with the fluid being transported. Ease of maintenance is also of major importance, with most modern valves being designed so that all internal moving parts can be removed in situ for repair or replacement.

NOTES ON SELECTION AND USE:

Manually operated valves fall broadly into four categories which describe their principles of operation: obturating (the action of 'stopping up'), rotating (an internal passage is rotated to control flow), sliding (a slide or gate cuts across the flow) and squeezing (the flow is controlled by a 'pinching' action). Four common valves in use in these categories are globe, ball, gate and diaphragm, respectively. As a general guide to use: the globe and ball are suitable for frequent use, the diaphragm regular use, and the gate valve infrequent use. Selection is made on the basis of: size, temperature, pressure, capacity and stress, although not necessarily in that order. A crucial factor in selection is the resistance of disks, seals and body material to high pressures, wide ranges of temperature and chemical attack. Demand for improvements in energy saving also influences valve choice and it should be noted that, for instance, the flow resistance of a traditional globe valve can be forty times greater than a ball valve of the same nominal size. Standardization of the two main features of a valve: dimensions and pressure rating, is by no means complete, with 'imperial' and 'metric' types freely available over a wide range of sizes. Currently, imperial sizes are referred to under 'CLASS' pressure ratings and metric sizes under 'PN' (Nominal Pressure) ratings with, for example, flanges on valves conforming to ANSI (American National Standards Institution), or BSI (ISO) standards. Care must therefore be taken when selecting, especially if existing jointing systems (flanges, threads, welds etc.) must be matched up.

REFERENCES:

References for specific valve types are to be found under the separate sections.

BS 6683 : 1985 (1991) Guide to installation and use of valves
BS 2080 : 1989 Specification for basic dimensions for flanged end butt-weld valves
For fluid control valves see BS 5793, 1655, 7296, 6494, 7389
BS EN 19 : 1992 Marking of general purpose industrial valves

VALVES 8.1.2

Globe, ball, gate, diaphragm valves: Types, selection and end fittings

VALVE TYPE	ADVANTAGES	DISADVANTAGES
Globe valve (Frequent use) Flow	Best shut-off and regulating characteristics. Ease of in-situ repair	High head loss.
Ball valve (Frequent use) Flow	Fast acting. Low head loss. Through flow. Easy operation. Compact.	Temperature limited by seating material.
Gate valve (Infrequent use) Flow	Simplicity. Low head loss. Through flow.	Slow acting. Bulky. In-situ seat repair cumbersome
Diaphragm valve (Regular use) Flow	Glandless Positive shut-off on all fluids. Easy maintenance.	Pressure and temperature limited by diaphragm material.

VALVE SELECTION

Detailed information for each of the valve types shown is given on accompanying pages and is based on the following standard data:

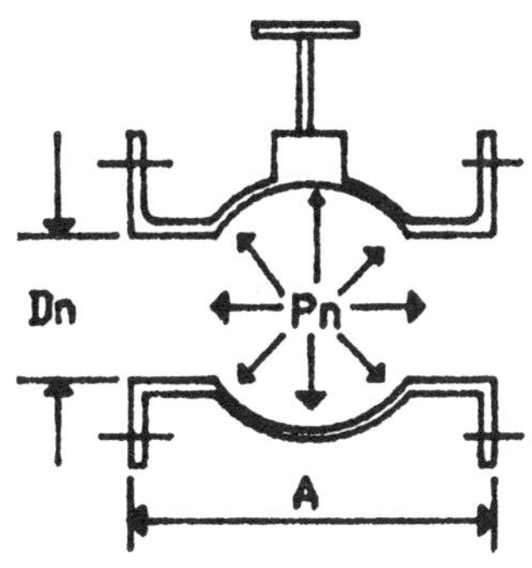

DN = Nominal size (bore diameter)
PN = Nominal pressure rating
A = Face to face dimension

The pressure ratings of end fixings are a limiting factor and the tables below cross-reference relevant standards.

Materials of construction and changes in pressure ratings with increases in temperature are given in the detail data for each type of valve.

REFERENCE TABLE OF EQUIVALENT SIZES FOR DIFFERENT TYPES OF VALVE ENDS

Flange, thread or weld ends		Capillary or compression ends		
PN *Rated* (Excluding threaded ends)	*CLASS* *Rated* (Including threaded ends)	Dimensions & performance as in British Standard: BS 864 Part 2	BS 864 Part 3	BS 2051 Part 1
DN	inch	mm	inch	mm
–	¼	8	–	–
10	⅜	10 & 12	⅜	10 & 12
15	½	15 & 18	½	15, 16 & 18
20	¾	22	¾	20 & 22
25	1	28	1	26 & 28
32	1 ¼	35	1 ¼	30 & 35
40	1 ½	42	1 ½	38 & 42
50	2	54	2	–
65	2 ½	67	–	–
80	3	–	–	–
100	4	–	–	–
125	5	–	–	–
150	6	–	–	–
200	8	–	–	–
250	10	–	–	–
300	12	–	–	–
350	14	–	–	–

REFERENCE TABLE for BRITISH STANDARDS relating to METRIC DIMENSIONS and PERFORMANCE OF INTEGRAL FLANGES FOR VALVES *

Nominal Operating Pressure (PN)	*FLANGE MATERIAL* *Cast Iron* BS 4504 Pt 3.2	*Steel* BS 4504 Pt 3.1	*Copper Alloy* BS 4504 Pt 3.3
bar	Table No.	Table No.	Table No.
10	10 / 11	–	10 / 21
16	16 / 11	16 / 1	16 / 21
25	25 / 11	25 / 1	25 / 21
40	–	40 / 1	40 / 21

REFERENCE TABLE for AMERICAN STANDARDS (ANSI) relating to IMPERIAL DIMENSIONS and PERFORMANCE OF FLANGES FOR VALVES *

Nominal Operating Pressure (CLASS)	*FLANGE MATERIAL* *Cast Iron*	*Steel*	*Copper Alloy*
125 to 2500	ANSI B 16.1	ANSI B 16.5 see also BS 1560 Pt.3	ANSI B 16.24

* ISO Standard: ISO 7005 combines some European and USA flange sizes.

VALVES 8.1.3

Straight globe valves: Construction, selection and use

TYPICAL APPLICATIONS: Domestic and industrial hot and cold water control, regulation of petrochemical fluids, needle valves for hydraulic systems, general regulating where head loss is not important.

DEFINITION:

A screw down stop valve in which the axis of the stem is at right angles to the body seat face and in which the sealing disc is attached only to the stem.

CONSTRUCTION:

Main materials of body construction are: copper alloys, cast iron, steel and plastics with variations of these materials for the main internal and external components. Of particular importance is the need to minimise wear and corrosion on the screw and the seat but at the same time to avoid electrolytic action between materials. Discs and sometimes body seats may be made in plastic, rubbers or composite materials. Almost universally, globe valve bodies are castings or mouldings with the other components such as stems being turned parts typically. Pipe connections are by screw thread, bolted or welded flange or compression joints.

NOTES ON SELECTION AND USE:

Globe valves are very widely used in applications where low to medium pressure fluids are transported. Cast iron bodies are cheapest and are used for low pressures, copper alloys and some plastics for medium pressures where corrosion is to be avoided, eg. industrial/domestic water supplies. Steel bodies are commonly used in applications involving petroleum and petrochemicals. The wide range of sizes available indicates the universal application of this type of valve although bores in excess of 200mm create limitations on maximum pressures that the valve body can sustain. Small bore needs, for instance in hydraulic systems, are often met with a needle rather than a disc seating globe valve. A major advantage of the globe valve over other types is that the bonnet assembly with handwheel, stem and disc can be removed and serviced with the valve body in situ exposing the valve seat for easy renewal or repair. The physical separation of the disc from the seat where the valve is opened minimises wear and also permits a 'spindle rotation' feature to be included where valve seat descaling is needed during use. For larger valves or where corrosion caused by the flow of fluid is a serious problem, the screw thread on the stem is arranged to be outside the sealed valve body. The 'under and over' design of the globe valve causes a higher resistance to flow than in other types and the handwheel and stem are vulnerable to accidental damage, particularly in transit. Obturating valves are generally best suited for *frequent* use.

REFERENCES:

BS 21 : 1985	Specification for pipe threads for tubes and fittings where pressure-tight joints are made on the threads (metric dimensions) ≈ ISO 7/1, ISO 7/2
BS 970 :	Specification for wrought steels for mechanical and allied engineering purposes Part 4 : 1970 (1987) Valve steels
BS 1873 : 1975 (1991)	Specification for steel globe and globe stop and check valves (flanged and butt-welding ends) for the petroleum, petro-chemical and allied industries
BS 4504 :	Circular flanges for pipes, valves and fittings: (PN designated)
BS 5152 : 1974 (1991)	Specification for cast iron globe and globe stop and check valves for general purposes
BS 5154 : 1991	Specification for copper alloy globe, globe stop and check, check and gate valves
BS 5160 : 1989	Specification for steel globe valves, glove stop and check valves and lift type check valves
BS 5352 : 1981 (1991)	Specification for steel wedge gate, globe and check valves 50mm and smaller for the petroleum, petro-chemical and allied industries
BS 7350 : 1990	Specification for double regulating globe valves (etc) for heating and chilled water systems
ISO 5752 : 1982	Metal valves for use in flanged pipe systems
BS 5041 : 1987 : Pt 1	Specification for landing valves for wet risers

VALVES 8.1.4

Globe valves: Sectional details, sizes and pressure ratings

GLOBE VALVE WITH OUTSIDE SCREW AND CONVENTIONAL DISK

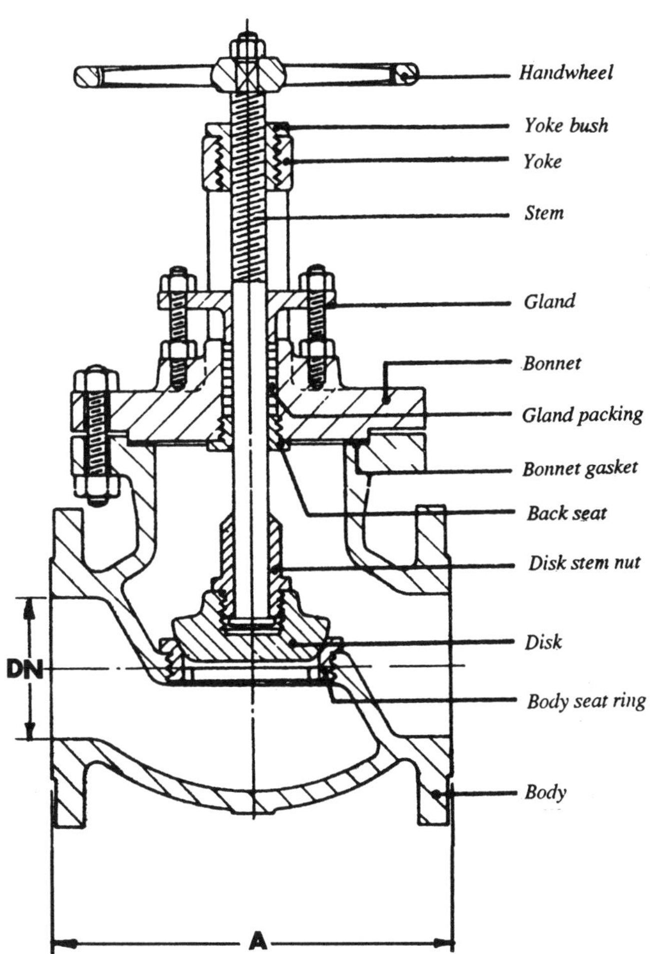

Face to face dimension (A)
Nominal size (DN)

ALTERNATIVE DISK ARRANGEMENTS

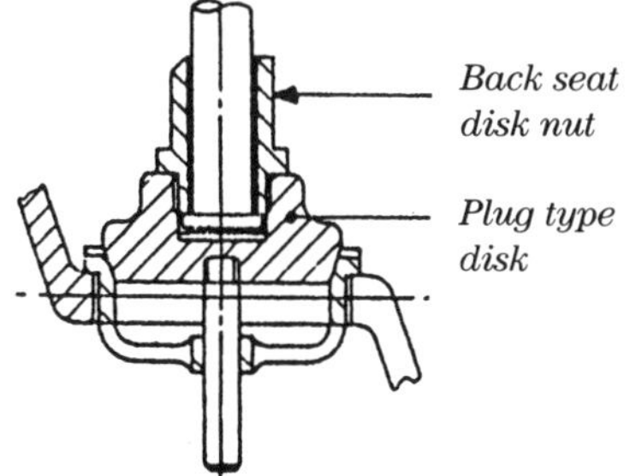

PLUG TYPE DISK – GUIDED

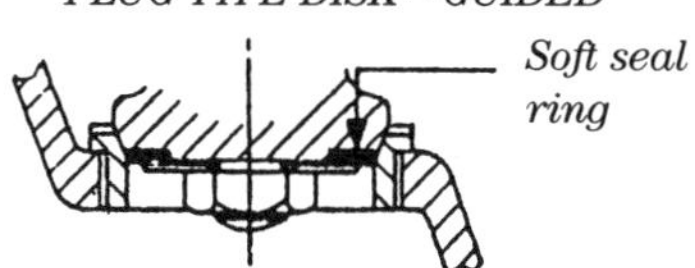

SOFT SEAL IN PLUG TYPE DISK

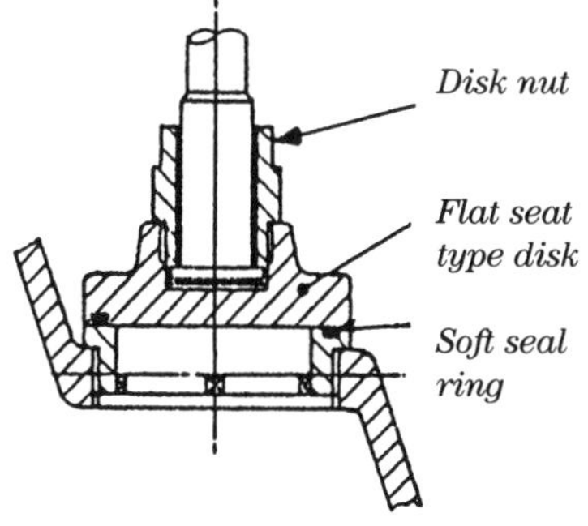

FLAT SEAT TYPE DISK SHOWING SOFT SEAL RING IN DISK OR IN SEAT RING

NOTE: Flat seat type disk can be metal-to-metal without soft seal

DIMENSIONS OF FLANGED GLOBE VALVES FOR NOMINAL PRESSURES

Bore Diameter Nominal size (DN)	Dimensions (A) of short & long series valves at the given nom. pressures (PN) at an operating temp of 20°C*					
	PN 10 / 16 bar		PN 25 / 40 bar			
	(Imperial Class 125 / 150)		(Imperial Class 250 / 300)		(Imperial Class 600)	
	A short	A long	A short	A long	A short	A long
mm	mm	mm	mm	mm	mm	mm
10	–	130	–	130	–	210
15	108	130	152	130	165	210
20	117	150	178	150	190	230
25	127	160	216	160	216	230
32	140	180	229	180	229	260
40	165	200	241	200	241	260
50	203	230	267	230	292	300
65	216	290	292	290	330	340
80	241	310	318	310	356	380
100	292	350	356	350	432	430
125	330	400	400	400	508	500
150	356	480	444	480	559	550
200	495	600	533	600	660	650
250	622	730	622	730	787	775
300	698	850	711	850	838	900
350	787	980	838	980	889	1 025

* See overleaf for pressure / temperature tables and basic materials.

VALVES 8.1.5

Copper alloy globe valves: Pressure / temperature ratings and materials

PRESSURE / TEMPERATURE RATINGS FOR COPPER ALLOY GLOBE VALVES WITH FLANGED OR THREADED ENDS											
***Series A Valves*: Upper working limit of 260°C with metallic disk / seat.** ***Series B*: Working limits as shown in the table below.**											
Service temperature °C	Maximum permissible gauge working pressure (bar) [note: 1 bar = 10^5 N/m^2 = 10^2 kPa]										
	PN 16 (bar)		PN 20 (bar)			PN 25 (bar)		PN 32 (bar)		PN 40 (bar)	PN 50
	Flanged or threaded		Flanged	Flanged	Threaded	Flanged or threaded		Threaded		Flanged or threaded	Flanged
	Series A	Series B	Series A	Series B	Series B	Series A	Series B	Series A	Series B	Series A	Series A
– 10 to 66	16.0	16.0	15.5	15.5	20.0	25.0	25.0	32.0	32.0	40.0	34.5
100	16.0	16.0	14.5	14.3	20.0	25.0	25.0	32.0	32.0	40.0	32.3
120	16.0	13.5	13.9	13.5	17.2	25.0	21.8	32.0	28.3	40.0	31.1
150	16.0	9.5	13.2	12.4	13.0	25.0	16.5	31.4	22.8	38.5	29.2
170	16.0	7.0	12.6	11.7	10.3	25.0	12.8	29.3	19.2	35.5	28.0
180	16.0	–	12.4	11.3	9.0	25.0	11.3	27.5	17.4	34.0	27.4
186	15.3	–	12.2	11.1	–	24.1	10.5	26.7	16.2	32.8	27.0
198	13.7	–	11.9	–	–	21.7	–	24.0	14.0	30.4	26.2
200	13.5	–	11.8	–	–	21.2	–	23.0	–	30.0	26.1
220	11.3	–	11.3	–	–	17.5	–	19.6	–	25.5	24.9
250	8.0	–	10.6	–	–	12.2	–	15.5	–	19.5	23.0
260	7.0	–	10.3	–	–	10.5	–	14.0	–	17.5	22.4

MATERIALS FOR *SERIES A VALVES*

Component	Material	BS reference	Grade or designation
Body Bonnet Cover	Gunmetal	1400	LG2 LG4
Disk Wedge Piston Ball Body seat and disk facing ring, where renewable	Gunmetal	1400	LG2 LG4
	Nickel copper alloy		32 % Ni minimum
		3071 3076	NA1 NA2 NA3 NA13
	Stainless steel	Martensitic stainless steel complying with BS 970 or austenitic stainless steel complying with BS 1503 or BS 1504	
Stem Hinge Hinge-pin Disk stem nut Stem bush Belt ring Stuffing box Gland Union nut Disk nut	Brass	2872 2874	CZ 112 CZ 114 CZ 116
	Aluminium bronze	2872 2874 1400	DGS 8453 DGS 1044 CA103 CA104 AB2
	Stainless steel	Martensitic stainless steel complying with BS 970 or austenitic stainless steel complying with BS 1503 or BS 1504	
	Gunmetal * *	1400	LG2 LG4
Internal fasteners (where applicable)	Brass	2870 2873	CZ106, CZ107 CZ108
	Phosphor bronze	2870 2873 2874 2875 1400	PB102 PB1
Handwheel	Grey cast iron	1452	Grade 180
	Steel		Any grade
	Aluminium alloy	1490	LM6
	Zinc alloy	1004	Grade A
	Malleable iron	310	B290/6
	Ductile iron	2789	500/7, 420/12, 370/17
Bolting (See BS 4882)	Carbon steel except free cutting	1506	111

MATERIALS FOR *SERIES B VALVES*

Component	Matl.	BS ref.	Grade
Body Bonnet Cover Stuffing box Gland Union nut Disk	Brass	1400 2872 2874	DCB 1 DCB 3 PCB 1 CZ 121 * CZ 122 * CZ 132 *
Wedge Piston Ball Body seat where renewable			A metal †
Stem Hinge Hinge pin Stem bush Belt ring Stem nut	Brass	2872 2874	CZ 121 CZ 122 CZ 132 A metal †

* Limited to size DN 50 or smaller.

* * Gunmetal: This is continuously cast when used for stems.

† See BS 5154 for specification.

VALVES 8.1.6

Cast iron globe valves: Pressure / temperature ratings and materials

PRESSURE / TEMPERATURE RATINGS FOR CAST IRON VALVES WITH FLANGED ENDS

Nominal pressure PN (bar)	For flanged end valves only: BS 4504 table number	Maximum permissible gauge working pressures at temperatures (° C) of:				
		– 10 to 120	150	180	200	220
		bar	bar	bar	bar	bar
10	10/11	10	9.2	8.5	8	8
16	16/11	16	14.8	13.9	13	13
25	25/11	25	23	21.2	20	19

MATERIALS OF CONSTRUCTION FOR CAST IRON GLOBE VALVES

Component		Copper alloy faced			Nickel alloy faced or stainless steel faced			Resilient seated	All iron
		Material	BS	Grade or designation	Material	BS	Grade or designation	Material	Material
Body, bonnet		Cast Iron	1452	220, 180 *	Cast Iron	1452	220, 180 *	Cast Iron to BS 1452 grade 220, 180 *	Cast Iron to BS 1452 grade 220, 180 *
Disks	With integral faces	Gunmetal	1400	G1 LG 2 LG 4	Nickel alloy or stainless steel	Manufacturer's option		Same as copper alloy faced or all iron	Cast iron not inferior to body material
	With separate facing rings	Cast iron not inferior to body material			Cast iron not inferior to body material				
Disk facing rings Body seat rings		Gunmetal	1400	G1 LG 2 LG 4	Nickel alloy or stainless steel	Manufacturer's option		Resilient material	If separate not inferior to body or disk material
		Aluminium bronze	1400	AB2					
Stem Disk stem nut Back seat bushing Gland *		Brass	2872 & 2874	CZ 114 CZ 116	Stainless steel or same as copper alloy faced	Manufacturer's option		Same as copper alloy faced or all iron	Carbon steel to BS 970 Part 1 grade 220M07
		Stainless steel	970 Pt. 4	410S21 302S25 431S29					
		Aluminium bronze	2872 & 2874	CA 103 CA 104 CA 106	Aluminium bronze	2872 & 2874	CA 103 CA 104 CA 106		Stainless steel
		Gunmetal	1400	LG 2 *	Gunmetal	1400	LG 2 *		
Bolting		Carbon steel; tensile strength 390 N/mm^2 (= MPa) *			Carbon steel; tensile strength 390 N/mm^2 (= MPa) *			Carbon steel; tensile strength 390 N/mm^2 (= MPa) *	Carbon steel; tensile strength 390 N/mm^2 (= MPa) *
Hand wheel		Cast Iron	1452	180	Cast Iron	1452	180	Cast Iron to BS 1452 grade 180	Cast Iron to BS 1452 grade 180
Seals & gaskets when fitted		Manufacturer's standard; suitable for duty			Manufacturer's standard; suitable for duty			Manufacturer's standard; suitable for duty	Manufacturer's standard; suitable for duty

* Refer to BS 5152, Table 5 for special details.

VALVES 8.1.7

Ball valves: Construction, selection and use

TYPICAL APPLICATIONS: On/off control of a wide range of gases and fluids, particularly important for hazardous materials. Uses where the minimum flow resistance is important. Quick operation for fast shut-off.

DEFINITION:

A valve where the moving element is a ball with a central through hole which, in the open condition, is axial to the direction of flow and can be turned through 90° to fully restrict the flow.

CONSTRUCTION:

Main materials of construction are cast irons, carbon and stainless steels and special alloys with an increasing growth in the use of all-plastic bodies and/or ball inserts. Seals may be metal, plastic, or elastomeric or composite with general trend toward all purpose, high performance moulded plastics. Bodies are universally made as castings or mouldings with pipe connections being by screwed, bolted, welded or compression joint.

NOTES ON SELECTION AND USE:

The ball valve (not to be confused with the 'ball float' or 'ball check' non-return valves) is an adaption of the simple plug valve and when in the fully open position offers the lowest flow resistance of any type of valve. It has only one moving part and does not rely on screwthreads for the application of sealing forces. A quarter turn (90°) of the operating lever gives full shut off and although commonly used as an 'on' or 'off' valve, current developments are producing types which can be used effectively in flow control applications. Compared with other valves it is very compact and robust, presenting little exposure to external corrosive or accidental damage and allowing installation in restricted areas. It can also operate in a wide range of temperature conditions and its internal simplicity permits reliable operation with many dangerous acids and solvents, limited only by the material of the seating. Because of high flow efficiencies it is often economic to select ball valves with a reduced bore in the ball insert which still gives very good flow characteristics. Full bore must, however, be specified if intended use is with powders or if remote pipeline cleaning or 'pigging' is required.

Pressure capabilities are high with the right materials of construction because of uniform distribution of forces on the spherical seating which also contributes to the low operating torque. Due to the rotating action, abrasive particles can scour the ball and embed in the seals causing a rise in the operating torque. These types of rotating valves are generally best suited for *intermittent* use.

REFERENCES:

BS 21: 1985	Specification for pipe threads for tubes and fittings where pressure-tight joints are made on the threads (metric dimensions)
BS 970:	Specification for wrought steels for mechanical and allied engineering purposes Part 4: 1970 (1987) Valve steels ≠ ISO 683/13, 15, 17
BS 4504:	Circular flanges for pipes, valves and fittings: (PN Designated)
BS 5159: 1974 (1991)	Specification for cast iron and carbon steel ball valves for general purposes
BS 5351: 1986 (1991)	Specification for steel ball valves for the petroleum, petro-chemical and allied industries
BS 5353: 1989	Specification for steel plug valves
ISO 5752: 1982	Metal valves for use in flanged pipe systems – face to face and centre to face dimensions
BS 3N 28233 : 1992	Thermoplastic valves. Torque. Test method

VALVES 8.1.8

Ball valves: Sectional details, sizes and pressure / temperature ratings

BALL VALVE WITH THREE PIECE SANDWICH BODY

Wrench assembly
Indicator stop
Stem location ring
Stem thrust seal
Stem and pin
Ball
Nominal size (DN)
Gland nut
Gland
Gland packing
Stem location ring
Connector bolt
Connector nut
Body
Body connector seal
Seat ring
Seat ring housing
Face to face dimension (A)

TYPICAL CONSTRUCTION VARIANTS

One piece bodies *Split bodies*

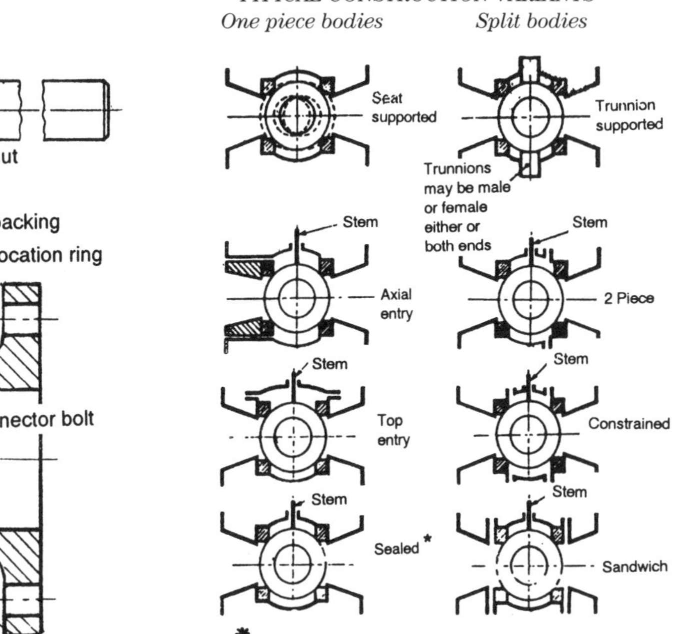

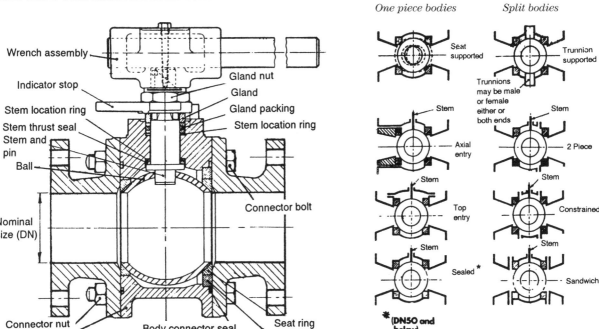

Bore Diameter	FACE TO FACE DIMENSIONS for BALL VALVES at the following NOMINAL PRESSURES (PN) at an OPERATING TEMPERATURE OF 20° C					
Nominal size (DN)	PN 10 / 16 bar (Imperial Class 125 / 150)			PN 25 / 40 bar (Imperial Class 250 / 300)		(Imperial Class 600)
mm	short *	medium	long	short	long	
10	102	130	130	–	130	–
15	108	130	130	140	130	165
20	117	130	150	152	150	190
25	127	140	160	165	160	216
32	140	165	180	178	180	229
40	165	165	200	190	200	241
50	178	203	230	216	230	292
65	190	222	290	241	290	330
80	203	241	310	283	310	356
100	229	305	350	305	350	432
125	254	356	400	381	400	508
150	267	394	480	403	480	559
200	292	457	600	419 *	600	660
250	330	533	730	457 *	730	787
300	356	610	850	502 *	850	838

* See ISO 5752 : 1982 Table 6 for special details.

PRESSURE/TEMPERATURE RATINGS FOR CAST IRON AND CARBON STEEL BALL VALVES

Nominal Pressure	Material	Flanged end valves only	Maximum Permissible Gauge Working Pressures * at Temperatures (° C) of:									
PN		BS 4504	– 10 to 120	150	180	200	220	250	260	300	350	400
(bar)		Table No.	bar	bar	bar	bar	bar	bar	bar	bar	bar	bar
10	Cast Iron	10 / 11	10	9.2	8.5	8	8	7	6.8	6	–	–
16	Cast Iron	16 / 11	16	14.8	13.9	13	13	11	10.8	10	–	–
	Carbon steel	16 / 1	16	–	–	16	–	15	–	13	11	9
25	Cast Iron	25 / 11	25	23	21.2	20	19	18	17.5	16	–	–
	Carbon steel	25 / 1	25	–	–	25	–	24	–	21	17	14
40	Carbon steel	40 / 1	40	–	–	40	–	38	–	35	28	23

* See BS 5159 : Table 1 for special details † See BS 5159: Table 5 for special details

MATERIALS OF CONSTRUCTION

Components	Cast Iron Valves	Carbon steel Valves	
	Material	Material	
Body	Cast iron to BS 1452 grade 220	Carbon steel	
		BS	*Grade*
Body		1504 (161)	B
connector		1503 (161)	28
cover		1501 (151)	26
ball		BS 970 :	
insert		Pt. 1 070M20 †	
Bolting	Carbon steel; min. tensile strength 390N/mm²(=MPa) †		
Seals Gaskets	Manufacturer's standard; suitable for duty		

VALVES 8.1.9

Wedge and parallel slide gate valves: Construction, selection and use

TYPICAL APPLICATIONS: On/off control of water and other fluid supplies, large sluice operation, domestic water control, uses where high reliability and low flow resistance are needed.

DEFINITION:

A screw down stop valve where the seat face is axial to the stem and where contact between the sliding disc and the seat create the seal.

CONSTRUCTION:

Main materials of body construction are: copper alloys, cast iron and steel with variations of these materials for the main internal and external components. Of particular importance is the need to minimise wear and corrosion on the screw, disc and seat but at the same time avoid electrolytic action between materials. Discs and seats may be made in plastic, rubber or composite materials. In some cases metal wedges and/or seats are coated in a resilient rubber or plastic to reduce friction and wear. Almost universally, gate valve bodies are castings or mouldings. Pipe connections are by screw thread, bolted or welded flange or compression joint.

NOTES ON SELECTION AND USE:

The gate valve is by far the most widely used of all stop valves and is available in the greatest range of sizes. The principal of the wedge disc not only gives full through flow when fully open, it also provides dual closure of the seats when in the shut position. It is ideally suited for applications calling for infrequent 'open' or 'close' operations, since its use in a partly closed condition can give rise to vibration and subsequent damage to seating faces. A variant on the wedge valve has a parallel sliding disc which is spring loaded to minimise vibration. This latter valve also has the advantage of needing less force to open and close it, but does have more component parts in its design and therefore may suffer more maintenance problems. Rubber and plastics may be specified with both types of gate valve, the flexible disc and seat providing better sealing with less sticking and corrosion damage. For smaller valves inside rising stems are most commonly used, being the cheapest but suffering a headroom limitation above the valve as it is opened. This feature does, however, provide a quick visual indicator of gate position. Sliding valves are generally best suited for *infrequent* use.

REFERENCES:

BS 21 : 1985	Specification for pipe threads for tubes and fittings where pressure-tight joints are made on the threads (metric dimensions) ≈ ISO 7/1, ISO 7/2
BS 970 :	Specification for wrought steels for mechanical and allied engineering purposes Part 4: 1970 (1987) Valve steels ≠ ISO 683/13, 15, 17
BS 1414 : 1975 (1991)	Specification for steel wedge gate valves (flanged and butt-welding ends) for the petroleum, petrochemical and allied industries
BS 4504 :	Circular flanges for pipes, valves and fittings: (PN Designated)
BS 5150 : 1990	Specification for cast iron gate valves
BS 5151 : 1974 (1991)	Specification for cast iron gate (parallel slide) valves for general purposes
BS 5157 : 1989	Specification for steel gate (parallel slide) valves
BS 5163 : 1986 (1991)	Specification for predominantly key-operated cast iron gate valves for waterworks purposes
BS 5353 : 1989	Specification for steel plug valves
BS 5041 : 1987 Pt 2	Specification for landing valves for dry risers
ISO 5752 : 1982	Metal valves for use in flanged pipe systems – face to face and centre to face dimensions
ISO 7259 : 1988	Predominantly key-operated cast iron gate valves for underground use

VALVES 8.1.10

Gate valves: Sectional details, sizes and pressure ratings

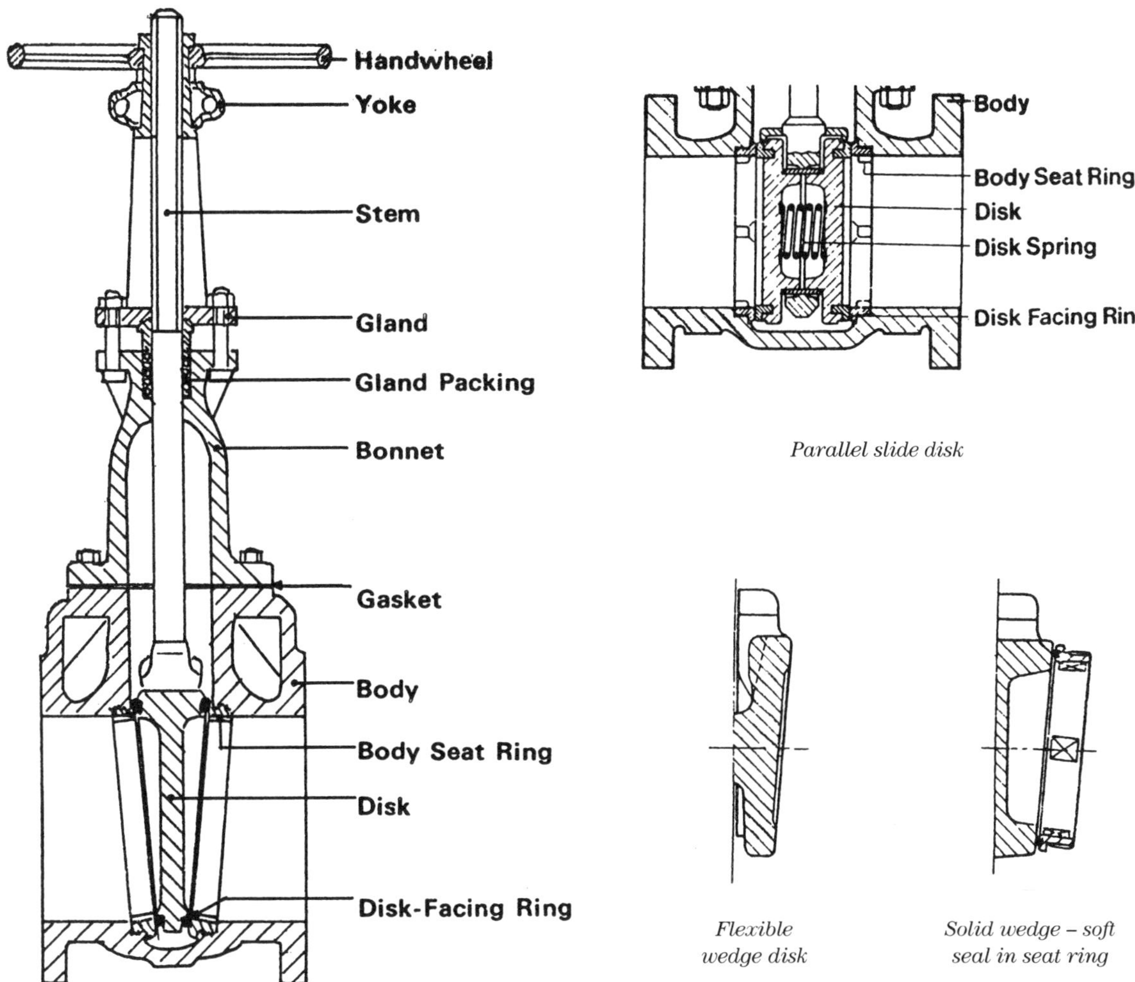

Parallel slide disk

Flexible wedge disk

Solid wedge – soft seal in seat ring

DIMENSIONS OF GATE VALVES AT NOMINAL PRESSURE RATINGS

Bore Diameter Nominal size (DN)	Face to face dimensions of short & long series valves at the following nominal pressures (PN) at an operating temperature of 20° C *					
	PN 10 / 16 bar (Imperial Class 125 / 150)		PN 25 / 40 bar (Imp. Class 300)	Alternative for PN 25 only	(Imp. Class 250) cast iron	(Imp.Class 600)
mm	**A short** (mm)	**A long** (mm)	**A** (mm)	**A** (mm)	**A** (mm)	**A** (mm)
10	102	–	–	–	–	–
15	108	–	140	–	140	165
20	117	–	152	–	152	190
25	127	–	165	–	165	216
32	140	–	178	–	178	229
40	165	240	190	240	190	241
50	178	250	216	250	216	292
65	190	270	241	270	241	330
80	203	280	283	280	283	356
100	229	300	305	300	305	432
125	254	325	381	325	381	508
150	267	350	403	350	403	559
200	292	400	419	400	419	660
250	330	450	457	450	457	787
300	356	500	502	500	502	838
350	381	550	762	550	572	889

* See overleaf for pressure / temperature tables and basic materials.

VALVES 8.1.11

Copper alloy gate valves: Pressure / temperature ratings and materials

PRESSURE / TEMPERATURE RATINGS FOR COPPER ALLOY GATE VALVES WITH FLANGED OR THREADED ENDS

***Series A Valves*: Upper working limit of 260° C with metallic wedge / seat.**

***Series B Valves*: Working limits as shown in the table below.**

	Maximum permissible gauge working pressure (bar) [note: 1 bar = 10^5 N/m^2 = 10^2 kPa]										
	PN 16 (bar)		PN 20 (bar)			PN 25 (bar)		PN 32 (bar)		PN 40 (bar)	PN 50 (bar)
Service temperature	Flanged or threaded		Flanged	Flanged	Threaded	Flanged or threaded		Threaded		Flanged or threaded	Flanged
° C	Series A	Series B	Series A	Series B	Series B	Series A	Series B	Series A	Series B	Series A	Series A
– 10 to 66	16.0	16.0	15.5	15.5	20.0	25.0	25.0	32.0	32.0	40.0	34.5
100	16.0	16.0	14.5	14.3	20.0	25.0	25.0	32.0	32.0	40.0	32.3
120	16.0	13.5	13.9	13.5	17.2	25.0	21.8	32.0	28.3	40.0	31.1
150	16.0	9.5	13.2	12.4	13.0	25.0	16.5	31.4	22.8	38.5	29.2
170	16.0	7.0	12.6	11.7	10.3	25.0	12.8	29.3	19.2	35.5	28.0
180	16.0	–	12.4	11.3	9.0	25.0	11.3	27.5	17.4	34.0	27.4
186	15.3	–	12.2	11.1	–	24.1	10.5	26.7	16.2	32.8	27.0
198	13.7	–	11.9	–	–	21.7	–	24.0	14.0	30.4	26.2
200	13.5	–	11.8	–	–	21.2	–	23.0	–	30.0	26.1
220	11.3	–	11.3	–	–	17.5	–	19.6	–	25.5	24.9
250	8.0	–	10.6	–	–	12.2	–	15.5	–	19.5	23.0
260	7.0	–	10.3	–	–	10.5	–	14.0	–	17.5	22.4

VALVES 8.1.11

Copper alloy gate valves: Pressure / temperature ratings and materials *(contd.)*

MATERIALS FOR SERIES A VALVES

Component	Material.	BS reference	Grade or designation
Body Bonnet Cover	Gunmetal	1400	LG 2 LG 4
Disk Wedge Piston Ball Body seat and disk facing ring where renewable	Gunmetal	1400	LG 2 LG 4
	Nickel copper alloy		32 % Ni minimum
		3071 3076	NA 1 NA 2 NA 3 NA 13
	Stainless steel	Martensitic stainless steel complying with BS 970 or austenitic stainless steel complying with BS 1503 or BS 1504.	
Stem Hinge Hinge pin Disk stem nut Stem bush Belt ring Stuffing box Gland Union nut Disk nut	Brass	2872 2874	CZ 112 CZ 114 CZ 116
	Aluminium bronze	2872	DGS 8453 DGS 1044 CA 103 CA 104 AB 2
	Stainless steel	Martensitic stainless steel complying with BS 970 or austenitic stainless steel complying with BS 1503 or BS 1504.	
	Gunmetal (continously cast when used for stems)	1400	LG 2 LG 4
Internal fasteners (where applicable)	Brass	2870 2873	CZ 106, CZ 107 CZ 108
	Phosphor bronze	2870 2873 2874 2875 1400	PB 102 PB 1
Handwheel	Grey cast iron	1452	Grade 180
	Steel		Any grade
	Aluminium alloy	1490	LM 6
	Zinc alloy	1004	Grade A
	Malleable iron	6681	B 290 / 6
	Ductile iron	2789	500 / 7, 420 / 12 370 / 17
Bolting	Carbon steel except free cutting	1506 (contained in 1502-6)	111

MATERIALS FOR SERIES B VALVES

Component	Material	BS reference	Grade or designation
Body Bonnet Cover Stuffing box Gland Union nut Disk Wedge Piston Ball Body seat where renewable	Brass	1400	DCB 1 DCB 3 PCB 1
		2872 2874	CZ 121 * CZ 122 * CZ 132 *
			A metal †
Stem Hinge Hinge pin Stem bush Belt ring Stem nut	Brass	2872 2874	CZ 121 CZ 122 CZ 132 A metal †

* Limited to size DN 50 or smaller. † See BS 5154 for specification.

VALVES 8.1.12

Cast iron gate valves: Pressure / temperature ratings and materials

PRESSURE / TEMPERATURE RATINGS FOR CAST IRON GATE VALVES.

Note: 1.6 to 25 bar for wedge and double disk types,
10 to 25 bar for parallel slide types.

Nominal pressure	For flanged end valves only:	Maximum permissible gauge working pressures * at temperatures (°C) of:				
PN	BS 4504 table number	– 10 to 120° C	150° C	180° C	200° C	220° C
(bar)		bar	bar	bar	bar	bar
1.6	6 / 11	1.6	–	–	–	–
2.5	6 / 11	2.5	–	–	–	–
4	6 / 11	4	–	–	–	–
6	6 / 11	6	5.6	–	–	–
10	10 / 11	10	9.2	8.5	–	–
16	16 / 11	16	14.8	13.9	13	–
25	25 / 11	25	23	21.2	20	19

* Note: 1 bar = 10^5 N/m^2 = 10 kPa

MATERIALS FOR PARALLEL SLIDE GATE VALVES

Component		Copper alloy faced			Nickel alloy faced or stainless steel faced		
		Material	BS	Grade or designation	Material	BS	Grade or designation
Body, bonnet, yoke, stuffing box		Cast Iron	1452	220, 180 *	Cast Iron	1452	220, 180 *
Disks	With integral faces	Gunmetal	1400	G1 LG 2 LG 4	Nickel alloy Stainless steel	Manufacturer's standard	Suitable for duty
	With separate facing rings	Cast iron not inferior to body material			Cast iron not inferior to body material		
Disk facing rings and body seat rings		Gunmetal	1400	G1 LG 2 LG 4	Nickel alloy Stainless steel	Manufacturer's standard	Suitable for duty
		Aluminium bronze	1400	AB2			
Stem		Gunmetal	1400	LG 2 *	Gunmetal	1400	LG 2 *
					Carbon steel †	970: Part 1	070M20
		Aluminium bronze	2872 2874	CA 103 CA 104 CA 106	Stainless steel	970: Part 4	410S21 302S25 431S29
		Stainless steel	970 : Pt. 4	410S21 302S25 431S29			
Bolting		Carbon steel; tensile strength 390 N/mm^2 (= MPa) *			Carbon steel; tensile strength 390 N/mm^2 (= MPa) *		
Gland		Brass	2872 2874	CZ 114 CZ 116 CZ 121 CZ 122	Brass	2872 2874	CZ 114 CZ 116 CZ 121 CZ 122
		Aluminium bronze	2872 2874	CA 103 CA 104 CA 106	Aluminium bronze	2872 2874	CA 103 CA 104 CA 106
			1400	AB 2		1400	AB 2
		Gunmetal	1400	LG 2	Gunmetal	1400	LG 2
		Cast Iron	1452	180	Cast Iron	1452	180
Hand wheel		Cast Iron	1452	180	Cast Iron	1452	180
Seals & gaskets		Manufacturer's standard; suitable for duty			Manufacturer's standard; suitable for duty		

* See BS 5151: 1974 (1983) , Table 4 for special details.

VALVES 8.1.12

Cast iron gate valves: Pressure / temperature ratings and materials *(contd.)*

MATERIALS FOR WEDGE AND DOUBLE DISK GATE VALVES

Component		Copper alloy faced			Resilient seated			All iron		
		Material	**BS**	**Grade or designation**	**Material**	**BS**	**Grade or designation**	**Material**	**BS**	**Grade or designation**
Body, Bonnet, Yoke Stuffing box	PN 1.6 PN 2.5, 4	Cast Iron	1452	12	Cast Iron	1452	12	Cast Iron	1452	12
	PN 6, 10 PN 16, 25	Cast Iron	1452	14	Cast Iron	1452	14	Cast Iron	1452	14
Disks or wedge	With integral faces	Gunmetal	1400	G1 LG 2 LG 4	Same as copper alloy faced or all iron			Cast iron not inferior to body material		
	With separate facing rings	Cast iron not inferior to body material								
Disk or wedge facing rings and/or body seat rings		Gunmetal	1400	G1 LG 2 LG 4	Resilient material, e.g. nitrile rubber			If separate not inferior to body or wedge materials		
		Aluminium bronze	1400	AB2						
Stem		Brass	2872 2874	CZ 114 CZ 116 CZ 121 CZ 122	Same as copper alloy faced or all iron depending on wedge & body seat material			Carbon steel	BS 970: Part 1	220M07
		Aluminium bronze	2872 2874	CA 103 CA 104 CA 106				Stainless steel	BS 970: Part 4	410S21 302S25 431S29
		Gunmetal	1400	LG 2 *						
		Stainless steel	970 Pt. 4	410S21 302S25 431S29	Stainless steel	970 Pt. 4	410S21 302S25 431S29			
Bolting		Carbon steel; tensile strength 390 N/mm^2 (=MPa) *			Carbon steel; tensile strength 390 N/mm^2 (=MPa) *			Carbon steel; tensile strength 390 N/mm^2 (=MPa) *		
Disk stem nut Back seat bushing Gland		Brass	2872 2874	CZ 114 CZ 116 CZ 121 CZ 122	Same as copper alloy faced or all iron depending on wedge & body seat material			Cast iron not inferior to body material		
		Aluminium bronze	2872 2874	CA 103 CA 104 CA 106				Carbon steel	970: Pt. 1	220M07
			1400	AB 2						
		Gunmetal	1400	LG 2						
Hand wheel		Cast Iron	1452	12	Cast Iron	1452	12	Cast Iron	1452	12
Seals, Gaskets		Manufacturer's standard; suitable for duty			Manufacturer's standard; suitable for duty			Manufacturer's standard; suitable for duty		

* Refer to BS 5152, Table 5 for special details.

VALVES 8.1.13

Screw down diaphragm valves: Construction, selection and use

TYPICAL APPLICATIONS: Low pressure food and chemical regulation, abrasive and hazardous gas / fluid control, industrial pneumatic systems.

DEFINITION:

A screw down valve in which the axis of the stem is at right angles to the sealing face and in which the closure member incorporates a flexible diaphragm. In all circumstances the diaphragm isolates the operating mechanism from the fluid passageway of the valve.

CONSTRUCTION:

Main materials of body construction are castings or mouldings of: cast iron, steel, copper and aluminium alloys with, in recent years, a growth in the use of thermosetting and thermoplastics. Variations on these materials are used for main internal parts such as stem, bush nut and compressor, taking into account the need to minimise wear and corrosion. Diaphragms are commonly made from natural, butyl or neoprene rubbers and a variety of fluorinated hydrocarbon plastics, and may be composites or incorporate fibrous or similar reinforcement. The flexible diaphragms are injection or compression mouldings often including a preformed contour to limit stretching during operation.

NOTES ON SELECTION AND USE:

Diaphragm valves are found in most commonly in low pressure applications where the fluid being transported is aggressive or abrasive or must be kept at a high level of purity (ie. food, pharmaceuticals). The use of a diaphragm as a means of totally isolating the fluid from the operating mechanism is unique amongst designs of screw down valves and offers the additional advantage of making repair and maintenance simple and fast. Unlike the globe valve, for instance, there is no need for precision seats to be cut during repair. All that is necessary is for the diaphragm to be renewed in situ, which means simply unbolting the bonnet top and replacing the old membrane. The position of the bonnet in relation to the body need not be as precise as that for gate or globe valves and because the diaphragm physically separates the two components, less precision is necessary in finished parts. Limitations centre mostly around the material of the sealing membrane which, during opening and closing, suffers distortion and therefore there is a risk of failure from wear and fatigue, especially at extreme temperatures and pressures. Standard valve designs incorporate a 'weir' against which the seal is made and this offers resistance to free flow. 'Straight-through' designs reduce flow losses, but rely much more on heavy distortion of the diaphragm. These find favour for handling difficult fluids but because of the long strokes needed, diaphragm material choice is usually limited to elastomers.

REFERENCES:

BS 21: 1985	Specification for pipe threads for tubes and fittings where pressure-tight joints are made on the threads (metric dimensions) ≈ ISO 7/1, ISO 7/2
BS 970 :	Specification for wrought steels for mechanical and allied engineering purposes Part 4: 1970 (1987) Valve steels ≠ ISO 683/13, 15, 17
BS 4504 :	Circular flanges for pipes, valves and fittings (PN Designated)
BS 5156 : 1985 (1990)	Specification for diaphragm valves
ISO 5752 : 1982	Metal valves for use in flanged pipe systems – face to face and centre to face dimensions
BS 5041 : 1987 Pt 1	Specification for landing valves for wet risers
BS 3016 : 1989	Specifications for pressure regulators (etc) for liquified gas
BS 1212 : 1990 Pt 2	Specification for float operated diaphragm valves

VALVES 8.1.14

Diaphragm valves: Sizes, pressure ratings and materials

WEIR-TYPE SCREW DOWN DIAPHRAGM VALVE.

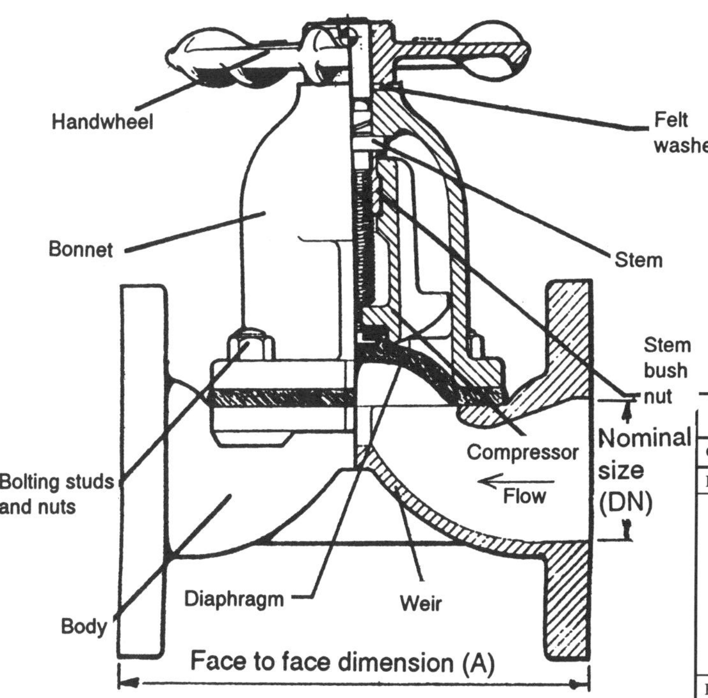

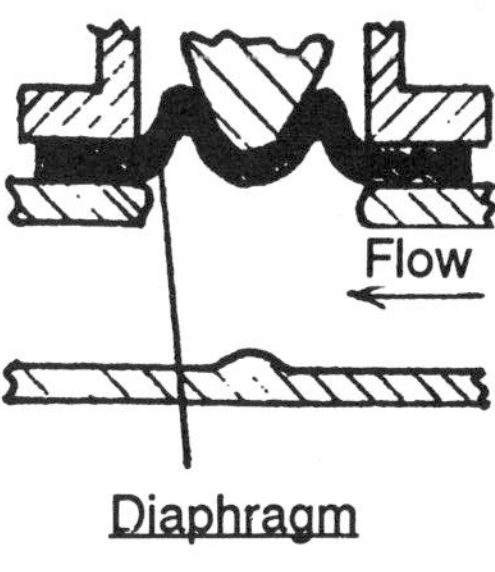

ALTERNATIVE STRAIGHT THROUGH PATTERN

DIMENSIONS OF DIAPHRAGM VALVES FOR NOMINAL PRESSURES				
Bore Diameter Nominal size (DN)	Face to face dimensions at the following nominal pressures (PN) at an operating temperature of 20°C *			
	PN 6 bar	PN 10 / 16 bar (Imp. Class 125 / 150)		PN 25 / 40 (Imperial Class 300)
		A short	A long	
mm	(mm)	(mm)	(mm)	(mm)
10	108	108	130	130
15	108	108	130	130
20	117	117	150	150
25	127	127	160	160
32	146	146	180	180
40	159	159	200	200
50	190	190	230	230
65	216	216	290	290
80	254	254	310	310
100	305	305	350	350
125	356	356	400	400
150	406	406	480	480
200	521	521	600	600
250	635	635	730	730
300	749	749	850	850

* Temperature/pressure ratings to be confirmed with supplier.

ACKNOWLEDGEMENT:

The main valve body diagrams shown on pages 127, 131, 133 and 139 are reproduced from 'Valve Users Manual' MEP Publications Ltd. by kind permission of the BVMA.

MATERIALS OF CONSTRUCTION FOR DIAPHRAGM VALVES			
Component	**Material**	**BS**	**Grade or designation**
Body	Grey cast iron	1452	220, 180*
	Malleable cast iron	6681	BS 310/10 W 410/4
	Gunmetal	1400	LG 2, LG 4, G 1
	Carbon steel	1504-161	B
	Stainless steel	3100	BM, CM, DM
	Aluminium	1490	LM 6, LM 25
	Spheroidal graphite cast iron	2789	420/12, 370/17
Bonnet	Grey cast iron	1452	180
	Malleable iron	6681	BS 310/10 W 410/4
	Gunmetal	1400	LG 2, LG 4, G 1
	Carbon steel	1504-161	B
	Stainless steel	3100	BM, CM, DM
	Aluminium	1490	LM 6, LM 25
	Plastics		Manufacturer's standard
Handwheel	Grey cast iron	1452	180
	Malleable cast iron	6681	BS 310/10 W 410/4
	Gunmetal	1400	LG 2, LG 4, G 1
	Carbon steel	1504-161	B
	Stainless steel	3100	BM, CM, DM
	Aluminium	1490	LM 6, LM 25
	Plastics		Manufacturer's standard
Compressor	Grey cast iron	1452	150 or 180
	Malleable cast iron	6681	BS 310/10 W 410/4
	Gunmetal	1400	LG 2, LG 4, G 1
	Carbon steel	1504-161	B
	Stainless steel	3100	BM, CM, DM
	Aluminium	1490	LM 6, LM 25
	Zinc alloy	1004	A
	Plastics		Manufacturer's standard
Stem Bush Nut	Copper alloy	1400, 2870 2872, 2874 2874, 2874	LG 2 *, CZ 108 CZ 112, CZ 114 CZ 121, PB 102
	Mild steel	970: Pt.1	220M07, 230M07, 240M07
	Stainless steel	970: Pt.4	325S21, 431S29
Bolting studs and nuts	Carbon steel Stainless steel Copper alloy	Minimum tensile strength 390 N/mm² (= MPa) *	
Diaphragm (basic polymer)	Natural rubber Butyl Neoprene Nitrile Fluorinated hydrocarbon		Manufacturer's standard

* Refer to BS 5156 Table 3 for special details.

SUPPLIERS

VALVES: Manually operated

COMPANY	ADDRESS	TELEPHONE	FAX
British Fittings Co (EM) Ltd	Highfields Science Park University Boulevard NOTTINGHAM Notts NG7 2RG	0602 789362	0602 420690
Crane Fluid Systems Ltd	Nacton Road IPSWICH Suffolk IP3 9QH	0473 77222	
Gemu Valves Ltd	9 Grosvenor Grange Woolston WARRINGTON WA1 4SF	0925 812622	
Guest & Chrimes Ltd	Don Street ROTHERHAM S Yorks S60 1AH	0709 2035	
Hattersley Heaton Ltd	Bradley Road TROWBRIDGE Wilts BS14 0RH	0225 763721	0225 769010
Keystone Valve (UK) Ltd	9 Meiklewood Road Drumoyne GLASGOW Strathclyde G51 4DU	041 810 3121	041 810 4724
Pegler Ltd	Hattersley Valve Works Hopwood Lane HALIFAX W Yorks HX1 4EZ	0422 67783	
Rotork Controls Ltd	Brassmell Lane Lower Weston BATH BA1 3JQ	0225 428451	0225 333467
Shipham & Co Ltd	Hawthorne Avenue HULL HU3 5JX	0482 23163	
Unival Controls Ltd	Hollins Works Hollins Lane Sowerby Bridge HALIFAX W Yorks HX6 2RS	0422 835977	

USEFUL ADDRESSES

VALVES

ADDRESS	TELEPHONE
British Metal Castings Council 121 Smallbrook Queensway BIRMINGHAM B5 4JP	021 643 3377
BVAMA British Valve & Actuator Manufacturers Association 8th Floor 121 Smallbrook Queensway BIRMINGHAM B5 4JP	021 643 3377

HYDRAULIC CYLINDERS 8.2.1

Single and double acting hydraulic cylinders: Construction, selection and use

TYPICAL APPLICATIONS: Automotive, railway and aerospace actuating and braking systems, jacks, presses, control systems for ships, mechanical handling machinery, test rigs, assembly lines, robotics, pit props, sluices, weirs, lock gates, suspension systems.

DEFINITION:

A device which converts fluid power into linear mechanical force and motion.

CONSTRUCTION:

The cylinder is a pressure vessel with the body or barrel made from internally honed, seamless, steel tubing with end caps of steel joined to it by screwthread, welding (one end only), or longitudinal tie rods. The piston is normally cast iron or steel with one or more piston rings making a fluid tight sliding seal with the cylinder bore. The rod is high tensile steel with a highly polished (often hard chromed) surface. Plastics and/or elastomers are comonly used for wiper seals between the rod and the end cap, and 'o' ring seals on the inlet and outlet ports.

NOTES ON SELECTION AND USE:

Single acting types can provide force in one direction only and need additional force (spring, counterweight) to return the rod. A typical application is a vehicle jack or upstroking press where there is a constant deadweight opposing the hydraulic force. Double acting cylinders are in much more common use, providing powered forward and retract strokes and can be operated in any position. The incompressibility of the water and oil-based liquids used in hydraulic systems gives these cylinders the advantage of higher power over air or gas powered ones, and permits constant linear force and precise positional control. The most popular double acting cylinder is the differential type for which a wide range of rod end and cylinder body fixings are available. Note that on the retract stroke the same fluid pressure results in a lower output force because the effective area of the piston is reduced by the area of the piston rod. All standard hydraulic cylinders are designed to transmit tensile or compressive forces but care must be taken to avoid eccentric or side loads on the piston rod. The tie rod type of cylinder is the most economic for general engineering because manufacturers can easily modify the stroke by changing barrel and tie rod lengths to meet customer needs. For high pressure applications, welded or threaded end types are used which, because of their higher performance, are more expensive. Universal standardization does not yet apply to threads and connectors for hydraulic systems especially between European and American components. Great care must therefore be taken when selecting fittings. Contaminated hydraulic fluid accounts for most system failures and so the highest standards of cleanliness must be observed during their assembly.

REFERENCES:

BS 4575 :	Fluid power transmission and control systems Part 1: 1979 Guide for hydraulic equipment and systems
BS 5200 : 1986	Specification for dimensions of hydraulic connectors and adaptors
BS 5380 : 1984	Spec. for hydraulic port & stud coupling using 'O'-ring sealing & 'G' series fastening threads
BS 5755 : 1986	Specification for dimensions of basic features of fluid power cylinders
BS 6276 : 1987	Specification for dimensions and identification code for mounting flanges and shaft ends for hydraulic fluid power pumps and motors
BS 6331 :	Mounting dimensions of single rod double acting hydraulic cylinders Part 1 : 1983 Specification for 160 bar medium series ≈ ISO 6020/1 Part 2 : 1983 Specification for 160 bar compact series ≈ ISO 6020/2 Part 3 : 1983 Specification for 250 bar series ≈ ISO 6022 Part 4 : 1985 Specification for 63 bar series, including associated components
BS 6984 : 1988	Specification for dimensions of housings for elastomer-energized plastic-faced hydraulic seals in reciprocating applications

HYDRAULIC CYLINDERS 8.2.2

Sectional details and types available

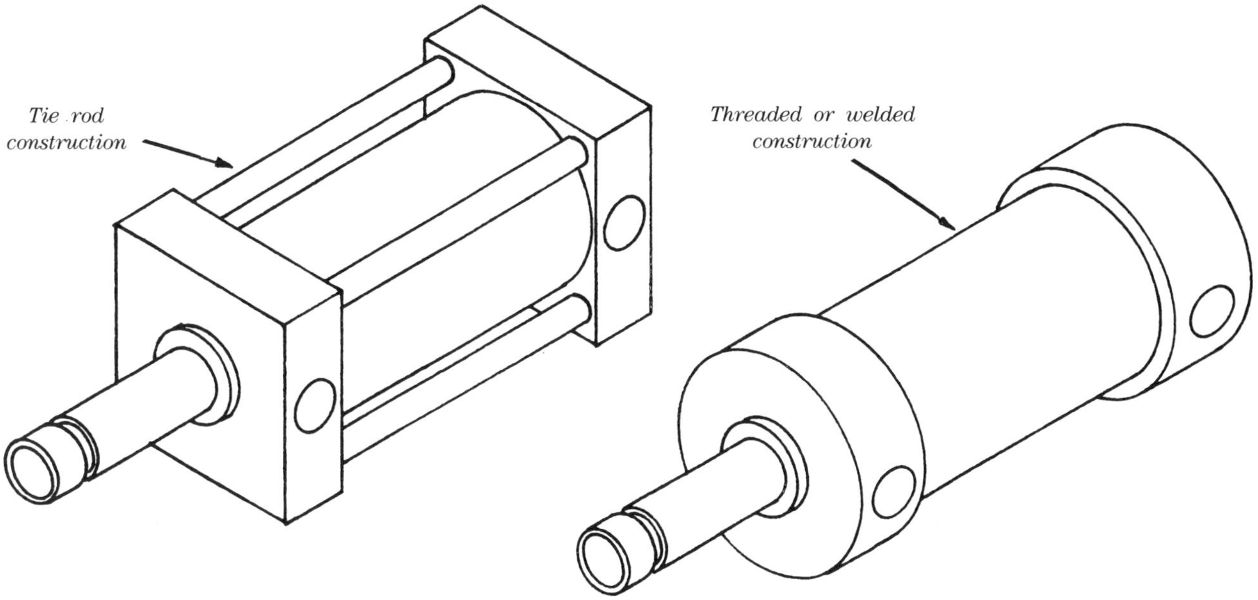

Tie rod construction

Threaded or welded construction

DOUBLE ACTING CYLINDERS

Single Acting

Single Acting (Spring return)

Double Acting (Differential)

Double Acting (synchronous)

SYMBOLS SHOWING MAIN TYPES OF CYLINDER

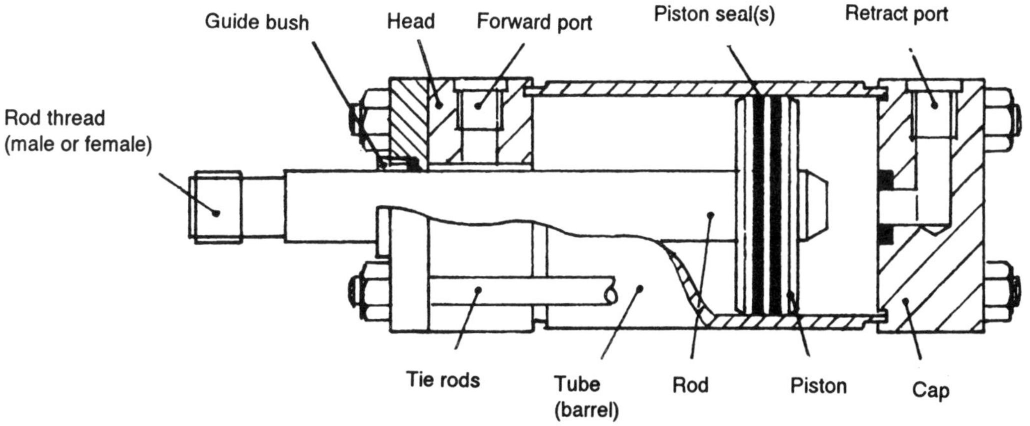

Guide bush

Head

Forward port

Piston seal(s)

Retract port

Rod thread (male or female)

Tie rods

Tube (barrel)

Rod

Piston

Cap

SECTIONAL VIEW OF TIE ROD TYPE OF DOUBLE ACTING (DIFFERENTIAL) CYLINDER

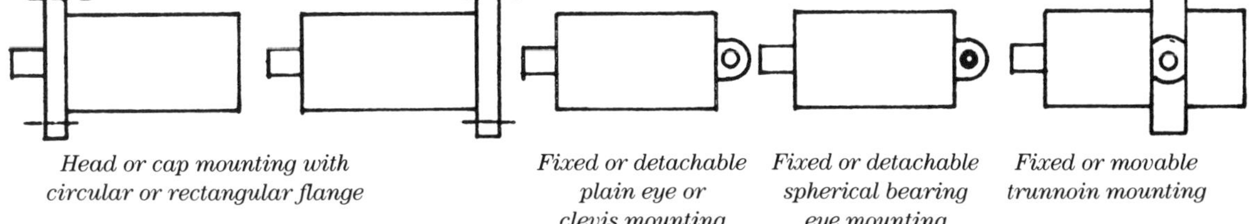

Head or cap mounting with circular or rectangular flange

Fixed or detachable plain eye or clevis mounting

Fixed or detachable spherical bearing eye mounting

Fixed or movable trunnoin mounting

COMMON TYPES OF CYLINDER MOUNTING

HYDRAULIC CYLINDERS 8.2.3 — Design notes and general dimensions

DESIGN NOTES FOR CYLINDER SELECTION

Maximum cylinder force is dependent on effective area and maximum safe working pressure of the fluid;

$$F = p.A,$$

and is constant throughout the stroke.

Volume of fluid used is: $V = S.A$ *for a full stroke.*

An important value with double acting cylinders is the area ratio between d_1 *and* d_2*:*

$$\text{Area ratio} = \frac{\text{piston area}}{\text{piston annulus area}}$$

where: piston annulus area = piston area – rod area

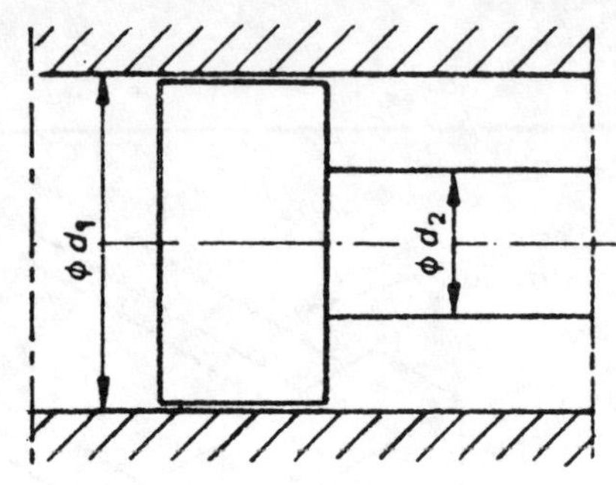

d_1 = *cylinder bore* d_2 = *piston rod diameter*

TABLE 1. CYLINDER BORES (Dimensions in mm)

d_1	8	10	12	16	20	25	32	40	50
	63	80	100	125	160	200	250	320	400

TABLE 2. PISTON ROD DIAMETERS (Dimensions in mm)

d_2	4	5	6	8	10	12	14	16	18	20	22	25
	28	32	36	40	45	50	56	63	70	80	90	100
	110	125	140	160	180	200	220	250	280	320	360	

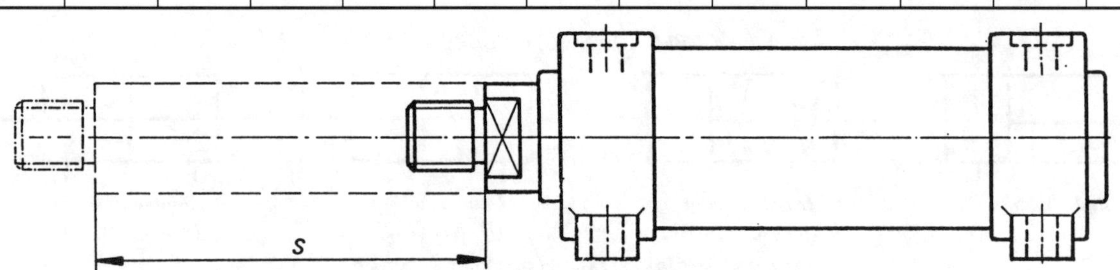

TABLE 3. PISTON STROKES (Dimensions in mm)

s	25	50	80	100	125	160	200	250	320	400	500

TABLE 4. PISTON ROD THREADS (Dimensions in mm)

Thread sizes	Thread length, L	
	Short type	**Long type**
M3 x 0.35	6	9
M4 x 0.5	8	12
M5 x 0.5	10	15
M6 x 0.75	12	16
M8 x 1	12	20
M10 x 1.25	14	22
M12 x 1.25	16	24
M14 x 1.5	18	28
M16 x 1.5	22	32
M18 x 1.5	25	36
M20 x 1.5	28	40
M22 x 1.5	30	44
M24 x 2	32	48
M27 x 2	36	54
M30 x 2	40	60
M33 x 2	45	66
M36 x 2	50	72
M42 x 2	56	84
M48 x 2	63	96
M56 x 2	75	112
M64 x 3	85	128
M72 x 3	85	128
M80 x 3	95	140
M90 x 3	106	140
M100 x 3	112	–

TYPES OF THREADED ENDS ON PISTON RODS

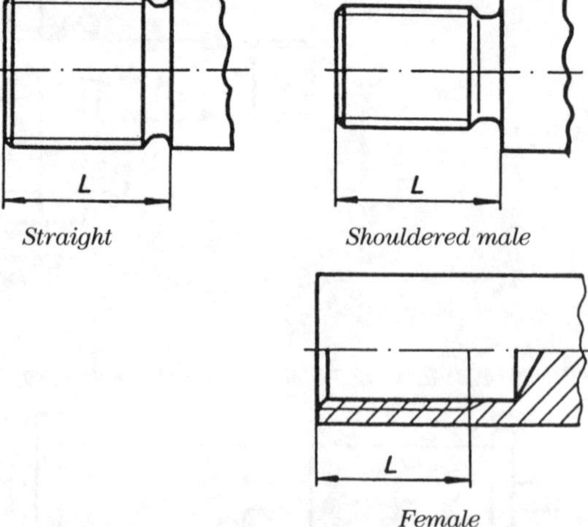

Straight *Shouldered male* *Female*

WORKING LOADS ON PISTON RODS:
Slender rods may be subjected to bending / buckling forces when in compression and therefore additional calculations should be done to check this.
If in doubt, consult suppliers.

HYDRAULIC CYLINDERS 8.2.4

160 bar double acting cylinders: Detailed dimensions

Basic Cylinder Dimensions *for 160 bar (medium series) single rod double acting hydraulic cylinders.*

This type is particularly suitable for applications requiring higher piston velocities and rapid decelerations.

Detailed dimensions of different mounting styles can be found in BS 6331 Part 1 1983.

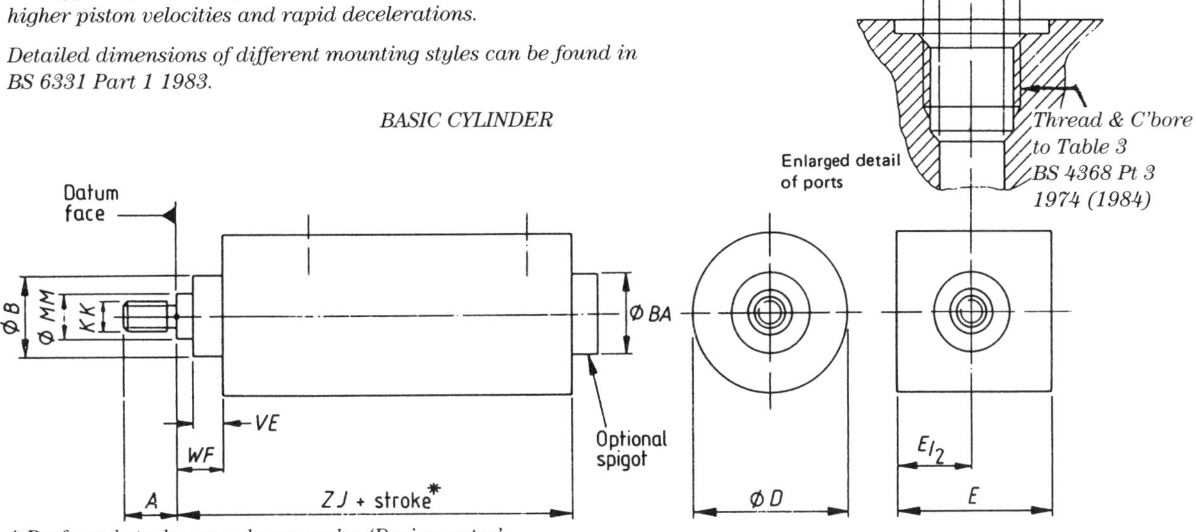

* *Preferred strokes are shown under 'Design notes'.*

DIMENSIONS OF BASIC CYLINDER FOR 160 BAR OPERATING PRESSURE

Cylinder						*Threaded piston rod end* (Selected from BS 5755)			*Entry ports* (see diag.) Additional to ISO 6020/1	
Nominal bore (BS 5755)	Diameters BA and B	Diameter D & E max. (Add to ISO 6020)	VE	WF	ZJ	Piston rod dia.MM	Thread designation KK to BS 3643	Thread length A	Thread designation FF to BS 2779	Diameter EE min.
25	32	||	15	28	150	14	M12 x 1.25	16	G ¼	6
						18	M14 x 1.5	18		
32	40	||	19	32	170	18	M14 x 1.5	18	G ¼	10
						22	M16 x 1.5	22		
40	50	75	19	32	190	22	M16 x 1.5	22	G ½	12
						28	M20 x 1.5	28		
50	60	95	24	38	205	28	M20 x 1.5	28	G ½	12
						36	M27 x 2	36		
63	70	115	29	45	224	36	M27 x 2	36	G ¾	16
						45	M33 x 2	45		
80	85	135	36	54	250	45	M33 x 2	45	G ¾	16
						56	M42 x 2	56		
100	106	165	37	57	300	56	M42 x 2	56	G 1	20
						70	M48 x 2	63		
125	132	200	37	60	325	70	M48 x 2	63	G 1	20
						90	M64 x 3	85		
160	160	245	41	66	370	90	M64 x 3	85	G 1¼	25
						110	M80 x 3	95		
200	200	295	45	75	450	110	M80 x 3	95	G 1¼	25
						140	M100 x 3	112		
250	250	365	64	96	550	140	M100 x 3	112	G 1½	32
						180	M125 x 4	125		
320	320	455	71	108	660	180	M125 x 4	125	G 1½	32
						220	M160 x 4	160		
400	400	560	90	130	740	220	M160 x 4	160	G 2	38
						280	M200 x 4	200		

HYDRAULIC CYLINDERS 8.2.5

160 bar (compact) double acting cylinders: Detailed dimensions

Basic Cylinder Dimensions for 160 bar (compact series) single rod double acting hydraulic cylinders. This type relates to a compact series of cylinders having square heads. Detailed dimensions of different mounting styles can be found in BS 6331: Part 2 1983.

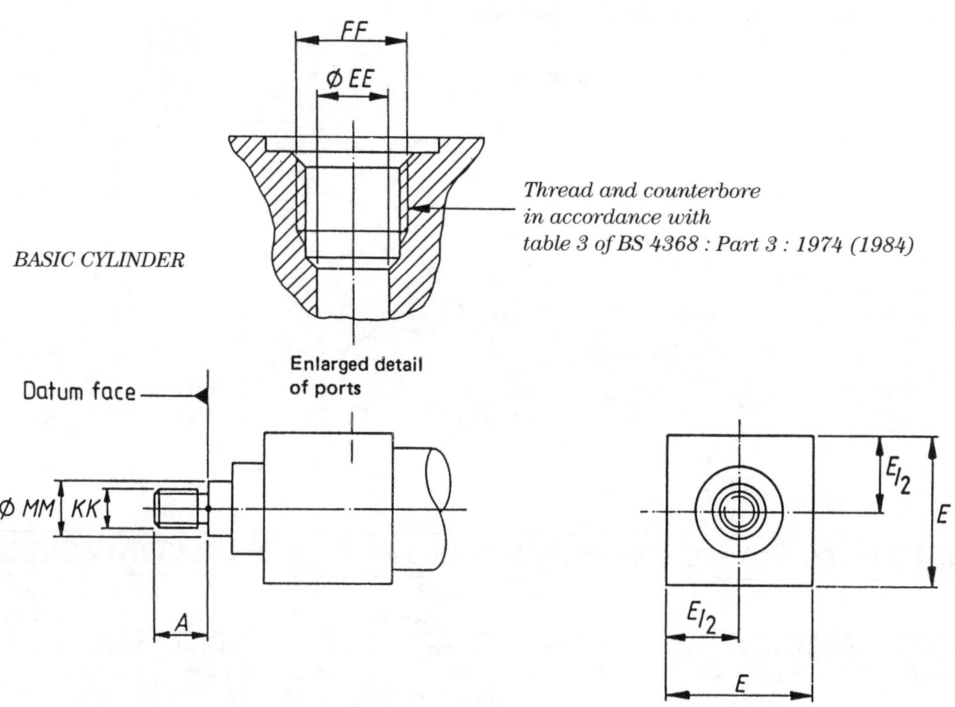

DIMENSIONS OF BASIC CYLINDER (COMPACT SERIES) FOR 160 BAR OPERATING PRESSURE						
Cylinder		**Threaded piston rod end (Selected from BS 5755)**			**Entry ports (see diag.) (Additional to ISO 6020/1)**	
Nominal bore	**E max.**	**Piston rod Diameter MM**	**Thread designation KK (to BS 3643)**	**Thread length A**	**Thread designation FF (to BS 2779)**	**Diameter EE min.**
25	42	12	M10 x 1.25	14	G ¼	6
		18	M14 x 1.5	18		
32	50	14	M12 x 1.25	16	G ¼	10
		22	M16 x 1.5	22		
40	68	18	M14 x 1.5	18	G ½	12
		28	M20 x 1.5	28		
50	80	22	M16 x 1.5	22	G ½	12
		36	M27 x 2	36		
63	95	28	M20 x 1.5	28	G ¾	16
		45	M33 x 2	45		
80	120	36	M27 x 2	36	G ¾	16
		56	M42 x 2	56		
100	132	45	M33 x 2	45	G 1	20
		70	M48 x 2	63		
125	170	56	M42 x 2	56	G 1	20
		90	M64 x 3	85		
160	210	70	M48 x 2	63	G 1¼	25
		110	M80 x 3	95		
200	250	90	M64 x 3	85	G 1¼	25
		140	M100 x 3	112		

250 bar (compact) double acting cylinders: Detailed dimensions

Basic Cylinder Dimensions for 250 bar single rod double acting hydraulic cylinders. Detailed dimensions of different mounting styles can be found in BS 6331: Part 3 1983.

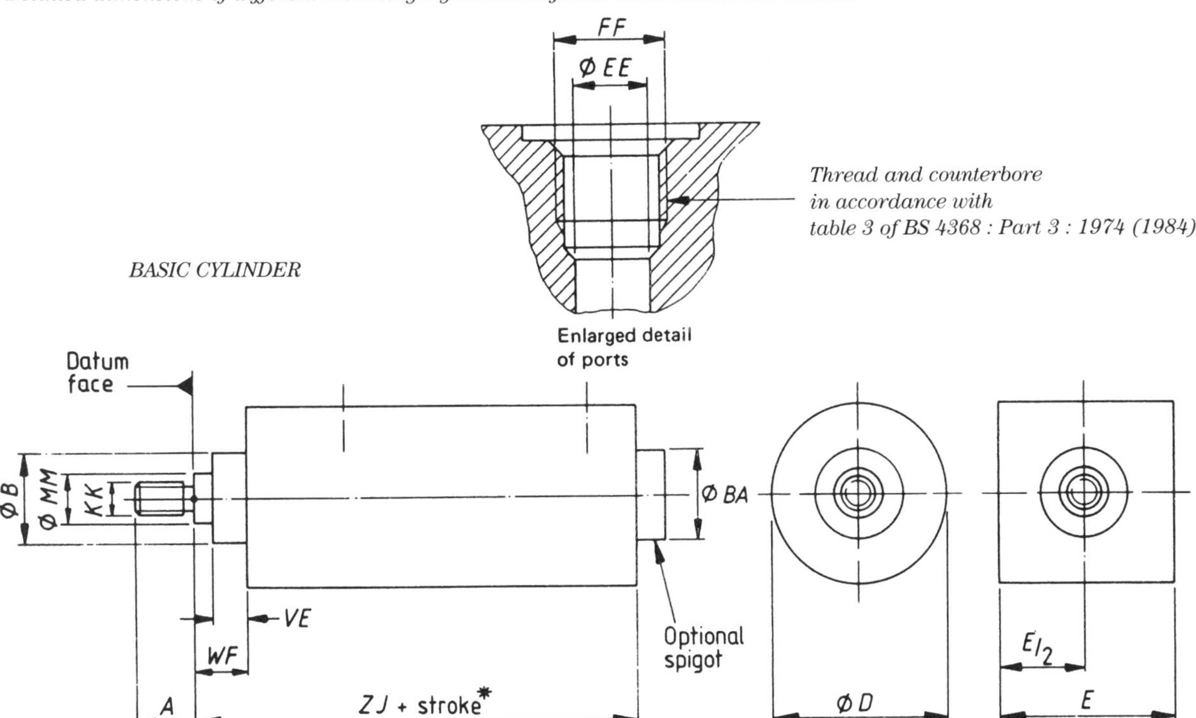

* *Preferred strokes are shown under 'Design Notes'.*

DIMENSIONS OF BASIC CYLINDER FOR 250 BAR OPERATING PRESSURE

Cylinder						***Threaded piston rod end*** **(Selected from BS 5755)**			***Entry ports*** **(see diag.) Additional to ISO 6020/1**	
Nominal bore (BS 5755)	**Diameters BA and B**	**Diameter D & E max. (Add to ISO 6022)**	**VE**	**WF**	**ZJ**	**Piston rod dia.MM**	**Thread designation KK (BS 3643)**	**Thread length A**	**Thread designation FF (BS 2779)**	**Diameter EE min.**
50	63	115	29	47	240	32 36	M27 x 2	36	G ½	12
63	75	135	32	53	270	40 45	M33 x 2	45	G ¾	16
80	90	155	36	60	300	50 56	M42 x 2	56	G ¾	16
100	110	180	41	68	335	63 70	M48 x 2	63	G 1	20
125	132	220	45	76	390	80 90	M64 x 3	85	G 1	20
160	160	275	50	85	460	100 110	M80 x 3	95	G 1¼	25
200	200	335	61	101	540	125 140	M100 x 3	112	G 1¼	25
250	250	415	70	113	640	160 180	M125 x 4	125	G 1½	32
320	320	535	88	136	750	200 220	M160 x 4	160	G 1½	32
400	400	630	110	163	755	250 280	M200 x 4	200	G 2	38

SUPPLIERS

FLUID ENGINEERING: Hydraulic cylinders

COMPANY	ADDRESS	TELEPHONE	FAX
Air Power & Hydraulics Ltd	Erskine Square Hillington Ind Estate GLASGOW Strathclyde G52 4PQ	041 810 4511	041 883 3825
British Engineering Productions Ltd West Group Ltd	Arnside Road Waterlooville PORTSMOUTH Hants PO7 7UP	0705 268733	0705 251104
Elram International Actuators Ltd	Moorfield Road Yeadon LEEDS W Yorks LS19 7BN	0532 504941	0532 506641
Helipebs Controls Ltd	Premier Works Sissons Road GLOUCESTER Glos GL2 0RE	0452 423201	0452 307665
Johnston Fluid Power Ltd	Dominion Way WORTHING W Sussex BN14 8PR	0903 31631	0903 38619
Lucas Fluid Power Ltd	Unit 1 Torrington Avenue COVENTRY W Midlands CV4 9AJ	0203 694000	0203 694019
P & A Hydraulics Ltd	Ashingdon Road ROCHFORD ST13 5QF	0538 372444	0538 399604
Rota Engineering Ltd	Wellington Street BURY Lancs BL8 2BD	061 764 0424	061 762 9729

USEFUL ADDRESSES

FLUID ENGINEERING

ADDRESS	TELEPHONE
British Fluid Power Association 235–237 Vauxhall Bridge Road LONDON SW1V 1EJ	071 233 7044
High Pressure Technology Association Holly Cottage Clay Lane Beenham READING RG7 5PA	0734 713722

FLUID EQUIPMENT

PIPES 8.3.1

Rigid, semi-rigid and flexible hydraulic tubing: Construction, selection and use

TYPICAL APPLICATIONS: Liquid and gas transport, fluid waste, heating and cooling plant, hydraulic and pneumatic systems, petrochemical processing and supply, remote control systems for vehicle, ship and aircraft actuators, power supplies to robotic, materials handling and construction equipment.

DEFINITION: A hollow conveyance which provides a leakproof carrier for fluids and gases.

CONSTRUCTION:

Rigid and semi-rigid hydraulic tubing is commonly made from carbon, alloy and stainless steels, with copper and aluminium alloys used for some applications. Manufacture is by hot or cold finished seamless drawing or electric resistance or induction welding. Flexible hoses consist of a seamless oil and water resistant synthetic rubber tube, one or more layers of high tensile steel wire and oil and weather resistant synthetic rubber cover.

NOTES ON SELECTION AND USE:

Rigid tubing is used in straight lines between components or fittings. Semi-rigid tubing may be bent on site to connect components permanently in different positions and planes. Flexible tubing allows one component to move, either component to be portable, or allows quick manual disconnection. Tubing systems should be leakproof, vibration-free, internally and externally temperature and corrosion resistant, environmentally stable and abuse resistant. Although high internal stresses are normal for pressurized tubing, external stresses (e.g. from bad clamping or misaligned fittings), should be avoided. All components (including valves) should be rigidly mounted with the fixings provided so that tubing and fittings take no external operating loads. Tubing installations should permit the freest possible flow of fluid by optimising internal bore sizes and minimizing sharp bends. Symmetry and neatness of layout for ease of assembly and maintenance is important, avoiding short straight line runs between components. A straight portion of at least twice the length of a coupling nut should be allowed after all bends before connection to a component. The most common causes of tube failures are: wall thicknesses inadequate for operating pressures, fastenings insecure, sudden restrictions to free flow and mismatching of external diameters with fittings and components. Tubing materials are available to suit extreme environmental conditions. Special care must be taken for systems which may experience cyclic temperature variations. Tubes may be joined by welding (tube to tube or tube to fitting or flange), threading, compression fittings or swaged-on couplings. Outside diameter is now almost universally used to specify tube size, with wall thickness and materials determining pressure rating. Some imperial sizes are still common, especially from American manufacturers, so tube specifications must be carefully checked because differences in equivalent sizes may make joints ineffective or dangerous.

REFERENCES:

BS 3600 : 1976 (1988)	Specification for dimensions and masses per unit length of welded and seamless steel pipes and tubes for pressure purposes
BS 3601 : 1987	Specification for carbon steel pipes and tubes with specified room temperature properties for pressure purposes
BS 3602 :	Specification for steel pipes and tubes for pressure purposes: carbon and carbon manganese steel with specified elevated temperature properties
BS 3603 : 1991	Specification for carbon and alloy steel pipes and tubes with specified low temperature properties for pressure purposes
BS 3604 :	Steel pipes and tubes for pressure purposes: ferritic alloy steel tubes with specified elevated temperature properties
BS 3605 :	Austenitic stainless steel pipes & tubes for pressure purposes
BS 3832 : 1991	Spec. for wire reinforced rubber hoses & hose assemblies for hydraulic installations
BS 4772 : 1988	Specification for ductile iron pipes and fittings
BS 5173 :	Methods of test for rubber and plastics hoses & hose assemblies
BS 6501 :	Flexible metallic hose assemblies
BS 4749 : 1991	Specification for textile reinforced rubber hydraulic hose and hose assemblies
BS 4983 : 1992	Specification for textile reinforced thermoplastics hydraulic hoses and hose assemblies
BS 5244 : 1986 (1991)	Application, storage, life and layout of hydraulic hoses and hose assemblies (etc)
BS 4586 : 1992	Specification for spiral wire reinforced rubber covered hydraulic hoses and hose assemblies
BS 1306 : 1975 (1990)	Specification for copper and copper alloy pressure piping systems
BS 7416 : 1991	Precision finished seamless steel tubes for hydraulic pressure purposes (etc)

PIPES 8.3.2

Semi-rigid and flexible tubing: Sectional details and types available

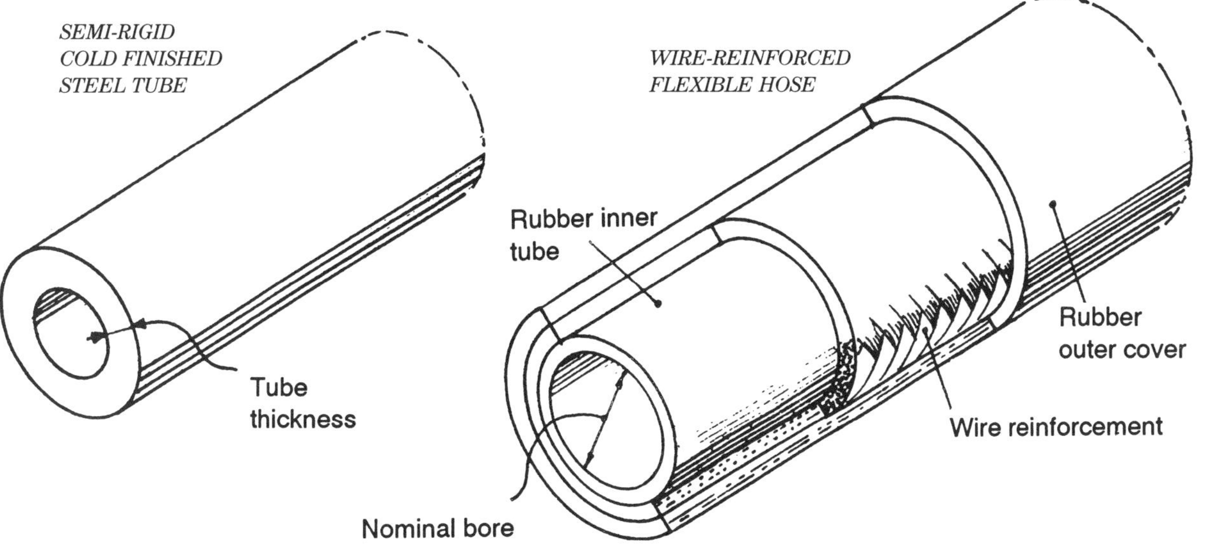

GENERAL APPEARANCE OF SEMI-RIGID AND FLEXIBLE TUBING

N.B. The terms 'tube' and 'pipe' are interchangeable, 'hose' means the same as 'flexible tubing' and none of these terms has definitive meaning. 'Semi-rigid' tube can be cold bent on site and is commonly used for hydraulic systems. 'Rigid' tubing is supplied and used in straight runs.

STEEL TUBING – TYPES OF CONSTRUCTION

Method of Manufacture	Reference	Methods of Manufacture	Code
Hot finished seamless	HFS	Seamless	
Cold finished seamless	CFS *	Cold finished	CFS *
Electric resistance welded & induction welded	ERW	Hot finished	HFS
Cold finished electric resistance welded		Hot finished and machined	HFM
& induction welded	CEW	Longitudinally welded	
		As welded	LW
		Welded and heat treated	LWHT
		Welded,cold finished and heat treated	LWCF
		Spirally welded	
		As welded	SW
		Welded and heat treated	SWHT
		Welded,cold finished and heat treated	SWCF

* Note: The term 'CDS' (Cold drawn seamless) was in common usage until recently, and has been replaced by 'CFS'.

FLEXIBLE TUBING – TYPES OF CONSTRUCTION

FLEXIBLE TUBING – TYPES OF CONSTRUCTION
Synthetic rubber with single or double textile braid reinforcement. (Note: This type is limited to low pressures only – maximum approximately 100 bar.)
Synthetic rubber with single or double wire braid reinforcement. (Note: This type is commonly available for pressures up to 350 bar.
Temperature range for flexible hose is normally between – 40°C to + 100°C.

APPLICATION OF SEMI-RIGID AND FLEXIBLE TUBING

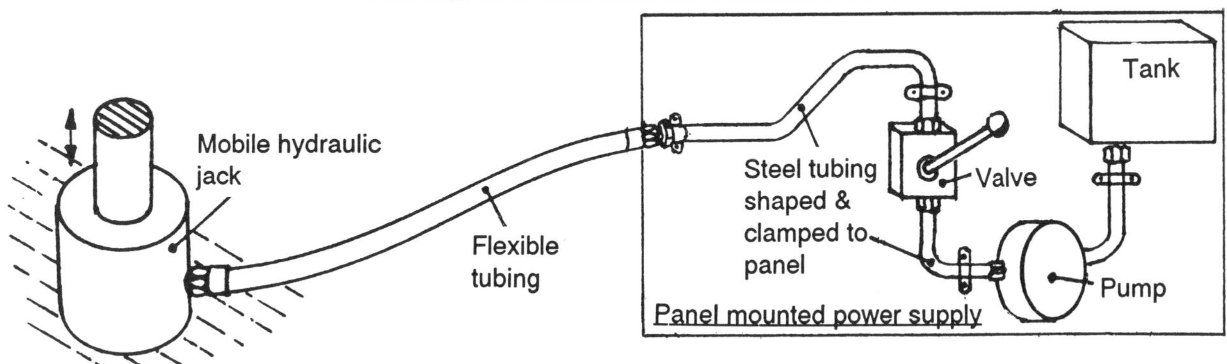

PIPES 8.3.3

Wire reinforced flexible hose: Sizes

The tables below give dimensions (internal and external), pressure rating and minimum bend radius for commonly available flexible hose. Note that the U.K. accepted standard is based on U.S.A. – (SAE) hoses which are used throughout the world. End fittings for these hoses may be specified from the metric series so that they are compatible.

DIMENSIONAL DETAILS OF WIDELY USED HOSES — Dimensions in mm.

Nominal bore	Type 1				Type 2			
	Diameter over wire		Outside diameter of finished hose		Diameter over wire		Overall diameter of finished hose	
	min.	max.	min.	max.	min.	max.	min.	max.
5	8.9	10.1	11.9	13.5	10.6	11.7	15.1	16.7
6.3	10.6	11.7	15.1	16.7	12.1	13.3	16.7	18.3
8	12.1	13.3	16.7	18.3	13.7	14.9	18.3	19.8
10	14.5	15.7	19.1	20.6	16.1	17.3	20.6	22.2
12.5	17.5	19.1	22.2	23.8	19.1	20.6	23.8	25.4
16	20.6	22.2	25.4	27	22.2	23.8	27	28.6
19	24.6	26.2	29.4	31	26.2	27.8	31	32.5
22	27.8	29.4	32.5	34.1	29.4	31	34.1	35.7
25	32.5	34.1	36.9	39.3	34.1	35.7	38.5	40.9
31.5	39.3	41.7	44.5	47.6	43.3	45.6	49.2	52.4
38	45.6	48	50.8	54	49.6	52	55.6	58.7
51	58.7	61.9	65.1	68.3	62.3	64.7	68.3	71.4

The above dimensions are based on specifications SAE 100 RI, SAE 100 R2A, and SAE 100 R2B (U.S.A.) which are in wide use in numerous countries throughout the world.

DIMENSIONS

Nominal bore	Permitted range	
	minimum	maximum
5	4.5	5.4
6.3	6.1	6.9
8	7.7	8.5
10	9.3	10.1
12.5	12.3	13.5
16	15.4	16.7
19	18.6	19.8
22	21.8	23.0
25	25.0	26.4
31.5	31.3	33.0
38	37.7	39.3
51	50.4	52.0

PRESSURE REQUIREMENTS *

Nominal bore	Design working pressure	
	Type 1	Type 2
mm	bar (MPa)	bar (MPa)
5	210 (21.0)	350 (35.0)
6.3	200 (20.0)	350 (35.0)
8	175 (17.5)	300 (30.0)
10	160 (16.0)	280 (28.0)
12.5	140 (14.0)	250 (25.0)
16	105 (10.5)	200 (20.0)
19	90 (9.0)	160 (16.0)
22	80 (8.0)	140 (14.0)
25	70 (7.0)	140 (14.0)
31.5	44 (4.4)	110 (11.0)
38	35 (3.5)	90 (9.0)
51	26 (2.6)	80 (8.0)

MINUMUM BEND RADIUS & CHANGE IN LENGTH AT DESIGN WORKING PRESSURE * *

Nominal bore	Bend radius	Change in length
mm	mm	%
5	90	+ 0 – 6
6.3	100	+ 0 – 6
8	115	+ 2 – 4
10	130	+ 2 – 4
12.5	180	+ 2 – 4
16	205	+ 2 – 4
19	240	+ 2 – 4
22	280	+ 2 – 4
25	300	+ 2 – 4
31.5	420	+ 2 – 4
38	500	+ 2 – 4
51	630	+ 2 – 4

* Based on a 4 : 1 safety factor.

* * Minimum radius is measured on the inside of the curve.

PIPES 8.3.4

Cold finished and welded tube: Materials, sizes and pressure ratings

The tables below give composition, preferred sizes and pressure ratings at a range of common safety factors. Note that the table of dimensions and performance covers the '360' grade of tubing only as this is the most popular for general purpose use.

SEAMLESS AND ELECTRIC RESISTANCE WELDED TUBES FOR PRESSURE PURPOSES

Chemical composition and mechanical properties at room temperature

		Chemical composition (ladle analysis) (See BS 3602: Part 1: 1987)										Mechanical properties at room temp.					
		C	Si		Mn		P	S	Al (total)	Nb		Tensile strength		Yield strength min. for thickness in mm			A*
Steel	Method of manufacture	max.	min.	max.	min.	max.	max.	max.	max.	min.	max.	min.	max.	≤ 16	>16≤ 40	>40≤ 65	min.
		%	%	%	%	%	%	%	%	%	%	N/mm²		N/mm²			%
360	Seamless	0.17	0.10	0.35	0.30	0.80	0.035	0.035	0.06	–	–	360	500	235	225	215	25
	Welded	0.17	–	0.35	0.30	0.80	0.035	0.035	0.06	–	–	360	500	235	–	–	25
430	Seamless	0.21	0.10	0.35	0.40	1.20	0.035	0.035	0.06	–	–	430	570	275	265	255	22
	Welded	0.21	–	0.35	0.40	1.20	0.035	0.035	0.06	–	–	430	570	275	–	–	22
500 Nb	Seamless	0.22	0.15	0.35	1.00	1.50	0.035	0.030	0.06	0.015	0.10	500	650	355	345	335	21

* A is the percentage elongation after fracture on a gauge length of $L_o = 5.65\sqrt{S_o}$ (where S_o is the original cross-sectional area of the gauge length).

TABLE OF SIZE AND PERFORMANCE FOR CFS 360 TUBING

Steel tube to BS 3602: Pt.1 CFS 360 Cat.2 **		Maximum Working Pressure (bar)		
Nominal size	Wall thick	@ Safety Factor		
Tube Outside Diameter (mm)		2.5 : 1	3 : 1	4 : 1
6	1.0	480	400	300
	1.5	720	600	450
8	1.0	360	300	230
	1.5	540	450	340
	2.5	900	750	560
10	1.0	290	240	180
	1.5	430	360	270
	2.0	580	480	360
	3.5	1000	840	630
12	1.5	360	300	230
	2.0	480	400	300
	2.5	600	500	380
14	1.5	290	240	180
	2.5	510	430	320
15	1.5	290	240	180
	2.5	480	400	300
16	1.5	270	230	170
	2.0	360	300	230
	2.5	450	380	280
	3.0	540	450	340
	3.5	630	530	390
18	1.5	240	200	150

Data continued in adjacent table

Steel tube to BS 3602: Pt.1 CFS 360 Cat.2 **		Maximum Working Pressure (bar)		
Nominal size	Wall thick	@ Safety Factor		
Tube Outside Diameter (mm)		2.5 : 1	3 : 1	4 : 1
20	1.5	220	180	140
	2.0	290	240	180
	2.5	360	300	230
	3.0	430	360	270
	4.0	580	480	360
22	1.5	200	160	120
	2.0	260	220	160
	2.5	330	270	210
	3.0	390	330	250
25	2.0	230	190	140
	2.8	320	270	200
	3.0	350	290	220
	4.0	460	380	290
	4.5	520	430	320
28	1.0	100	90	60
	2.0	210	170	130
	3.0	310	260	190
	4.0	410	340	260
30	2.5	240	200	150
	3.0	290	240	180
	4.0	380	320	240
	5.0	480	400	300
35	2.5	200	170	130
38	3.0	230	190	140
	4.0	300	250	190
	5.0	380	320	240

* * Nearest equivalent European standard is ISO 2604 Parts II & III TS 5 Cat. 2 (CFS)
A useful German equivalent is DIN 2391 / C

NOTE: Compression, screw, flanged or welded joints may be used with these pipes. See Pipe Fittings Section 8.4.

PIPES 8.3.5

Tubing for compression fittings: Weights and measures

The following weights and measures have two main uses for the engineer: firstly, systems intended for application in high cost transport, such as aircraft, carry a severe weight penalty – (it may be necessary to refer to BS Aerospace series for alternatives), secondly, the cost of tube is related directly to weight and these tables will be useful as a ready reckoner.

Note that tube is usually supplied in straight lengths of 4 to 6 metres.

WEIGHTS AND MEASURES FOR STEEL TUBING FOR COMPRESSION FITTINGS

Dimensions and masses per unit length of welded and seamless carbon steel tubes for use with compression couplings

Outside diameter	Thickness (mm)															
	0.5	**0.6**	**0.8**	**1.0**	**1.2**	**1.6**	**1.8**	**2.0**	**2.3**	**2.6**	**2.9**	**3.2**	**3.6**	**4.0**	**4.5**	**5.0**
mm	**Mass per unit length** (kg/m)															
6	0.068	0.080	0.103	0.123	0.142											
8	0.092	0.109	0.142	0.173	0.201	0.253										
10		0.139	0.182	0.222	0.260	0.331	0.364	0.395	0.437							
12		0.169	0.221	0.271	0.320	0.410	0.453	0.493	0.550	0.603	0.651	0.694	0.746			
15		0.213	0.280	0.345	0.408	0.529	0.586	0.641	0.720	0.795	0.865	0.931	1.01	1.09	1.17	
16			0.300	0.370	0.438	0.538	0.630	0.691	0.777	0.859	0.937	1.01	1.10	1.18	1.28	
18			0.339	0.419	0.497	0.647	0.719	0.789	0.891	0.987	1.08	1.17	1.28	1.38	1.50	1.60
20			0.379	0.469	0.556	0.726	0.808	0.888	1.00	1.12	1.22	1.33	1.46	1.58	1.72	1.85
22			0.418	0.518	0.616	0.805	0.897	0.986	1.12	1.24	1.37	1.48	1.63	1.78	1.94	2.10
25			0.477	0.592	0.704	0.923	1.03	1.13	1.29	1.44	1.58	1.72	1.90	2.07	2.28	2.47
28			0.537	0.666	0.793	1.04	1.16	1.28	1.46	1.63	1.80	1.96	2.17	2.37	2.61	2.84
30			0.576	0.715	0.852	1.12	1.25	1.38	1.57	1.76	1.94	2.11	2.34	2.56	2.83	3.08
35				0.838	1.00	1.32	1.47	1.63	1.85	2.08	2.30	2.51	2.79	3.06	3.38	3.70
38				0.912	1.09	1.44	1.61	1.78	2.02	2.27	2.51	2.75	3.05	3.35	3.72	4.07
42				1.01	1.21	1.59	1.78	1.97	2.25	2.53	2.80	3.06	3.41	3.75	4.16	4.56
50				1.21	1.44	1.91	2.14	2.37	2.71	3.04	3.37	3.69	4.12	4.54	5.05	5.55

Dimensions and masses per unit length of welded and seamless austenitic stainless steel tubes for use with compression couplings

Outside diameter	Thickness (mm)															
	0.5	**0.6**	**0.8**	**1.0**	**1.2**	**1.6**	**1.8**	**2.0**	**2.3**	**2.6**	**2.9**	**3.2**	**3.6**	**4.0**	**4.5**	**5.0**
mm	**Mass per unit length** (kg/m)															
6	0.069	0.081	0.104	0.125	0.144											
8	0.094	0.111	0.144	0.175	0.204	0.256										
10		0.141	0.184	0.225	0.264	0.336	0.369	0.401	0.443							
12		0.171	0.224	0.275	0.324	0.417	0.460	0.501	0.559	0.612	0.661	0.705	0.757			
15		0.216	0.284	0.350	0.415	0.537	0.595	0.651	0.731	0.807	0.878	0.945	1.03	1.10	1.18	
16			0.304	0.376	0.445	0.577	0.640	0.701	0.789	0.872	0.951	1.03	1.12	1.20	1.30	
18			0.344	0.426	0.505	0.657	0.730	0.801	0.904	1.00	1.10	1.19	1.30	1.40	1.52	1.62
20			0.385	0.476	0.565	0.737	0.820	0.901	1.02	1.13	1.24	1.35	1.48	1.60	1.75	1.88
22			0.425	0.526	0.625	0.817	0.910	1.00	1.13	1.26	1.39	1.51	1.66	1.80	1.97	2.13
25			0.485	0.601	0.715	0.937	1.05	1.15	1.31	1.46	1.60	1.75	1.93	2.10	2.31	2.50
28			0.545	0.676	0.805	1.06	1.18	1.30	1.48	1.65	1.82	1.99	2.20	2.40	2.65	2.88
30			0.585	0.726	0.865	1.14	1.27	1.40	1.59	1.78	1.97	2.15	2.38	2.60	2.87	3.13
35				0.851	1.02	1.34	1.50	1.65	1.88	2.11	2.33	2.55	2.83	3.10	3.44	3.75
38				0.926	1.11	1.46	1.63	1.80	2.06	2.30	2.55	2.79	3.10	3.40	3.77	4.13
42				1.03	1.23	1.62	1.81	2.00	2.29	2.56	2.84	3.12	3.46	3.80	4.22	4.63
50				1.23	1.47	1.94	2.17	2.40	2.75	3.08	3.42	3.75	4.18	4.61	5.13	5.63

PIPES 8.3.6

Tube/hose assemblies: Installation notes

The installation of flexible and semi-rigid tubing requires a high degree of care and cleanliness – the following points should be noted:

- *Avoid short, straight runs*
- *Eliminate stress*
- *Never twist*
- *Clip or support on long runs*
- *Allow for access and maintenance*
- *Always inspect before assembly*
- *Protect hoses from heat*
- *Protect from rubbing / abrasion*
- *Protect from accidental damage*

Note that, for semi-rigid tubing, bending is usually done on site as it is not normally advisable to predetermine exact sizes of cut lengths.

INSTALLATION OF SEMI-RIGID TUBING BETWEEN TWO FIXED COMPONENTS

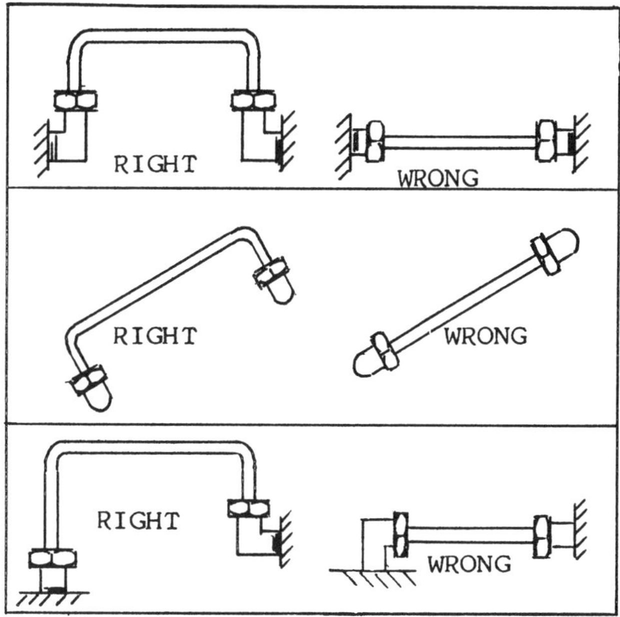

FLEXIBLE WIRE REINFORCED TUBES FOR FIXED AND MOVING ASSEMBLIES

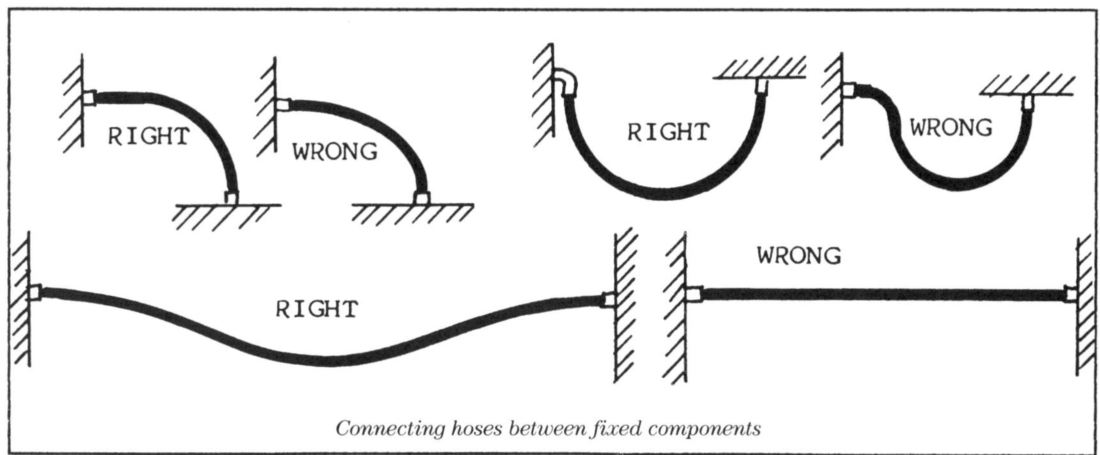

Connecting hoses between fixed components

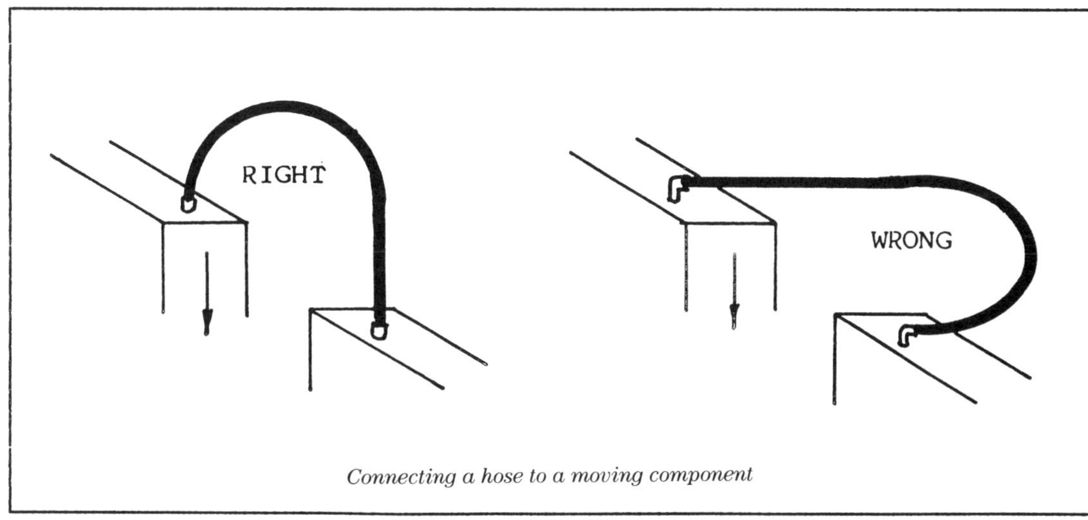

Connecting a hose to a moving component

PIPES 8.3.7

Ductile iron pipes and fittings

The tables and information on this page are derived from BS 4772: 1988 'Ductile iron pipes and fittings' which gives full details of requirements for materials, dimensions, mechanical properties, hardness, heat treatment, condition, tolerances and surface protection of ductile iron pipes and fittings.

TABLE 1. CLASS DESIGNATIONS OF DUCTILE IRON PIPES AND FITTINGS

PIPE / FITTING TYPE	CLASS DESIGNATION from BS 4772 & ISO 2531	TABLES IN BS 4772
Pipes with flexible joints	K9	21
Pipes with screwed-on flanges	K9 * or K12	22
Pipes with welded-on flanges	K9	23
Pipes with cast-on flanges	K12	24
Pipes with spigot pieces with screwed or welded flanges	K9 or K12	42
Fittings without branches	K12	25–28, 31, 32, 39–41, 47–52, 55, 62–65
Fittings with branches (i.e. tees)	K14 to K18	29, 30, 53, 54, 66, 67
Change fittings	see BS 4772	33–35
Plugs	K12	37
Caps	–	36
Double socket condensate receivers	–	38
Blank flanges	–	43–46

* Pipes with screwed-on flanges will be supplied to class K9 unless otherwise specified.

MAXIMUM HYDRAULIC WORKING PRESSURES:

General Ductile Iron Pipe:

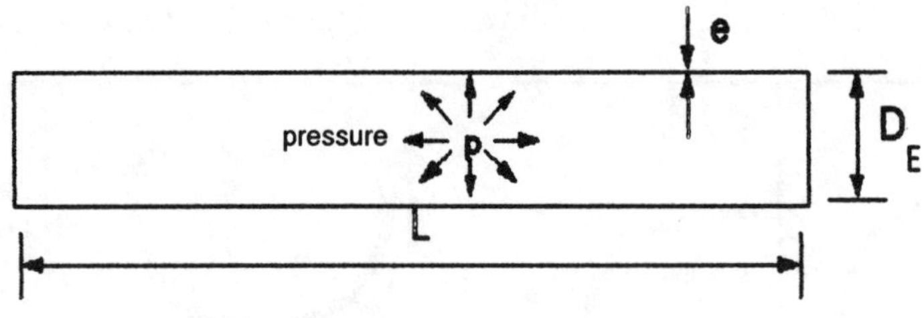

TABLE 2. MAXIMUM HYDRAULIC WORKING PRESSURES

Exclusive of surge, for ductile iron pipes and fittings (specified in Table 1) and flanged joints.

NOM. SIZE	PIPE DIMENSIONS			MAXIMUM HYDRAULIC WORKING PRESSURES					
		e		Centrifugally cast pipes class K9 Fittings class K12 * *	Fittings (i.e. tees) class K14 & thicker	Flanged Joints			
DN	D_E	K9	K12			PN 10	PN 16	PN 25	PN 40
mm	mm	mm	mm	bar	bar	bar	bar	bar	bar
80	98	6.0	7.0	60	60	10	16	25	40
100	118	6.1	7.2	60	60	10	16	25	40
150	170	6.3	7.8	60	60	10	16	25	40
200	222	6.4	8.4	60	50	10	16	25	40
250	274	6.8	9.0	53	40	10	16	25	40
300	326	7.2	9.6	47	40	10	16	25	40
350	378	7.7	10.2	43	25	10	16	25	40

* * Includes flanged pipes with integrally cast flanges. (See 8.4.11–8.4.13)

PN 16 is the preferred flange.

BS 4772 : 1988 Appendix K introduces a new concept for the design of fittings which are designated 'unified design'. Because of the large number of these their introduction to general use will be phased over a long period of time.

The object of the new designs is to minimize the number of component parts of foundry tackle and so optimize efficiency and at the same time extend the range of fittings made available.

BS 4772: 1988 includes the new 'unified design' fittings and the corresponding fittings from BS 4772: 1980.

PIPES 8.3.8

Ductile iron pipes and fittings: Methods of joining pipes

The following show the variety of standard methods of joining pipes together. Class designations are according to BS 4772 and ISO 2531.

For standard fittings associated with these pipes, such as : bends, spigots, sockets and collars, see BS 4772: 1988.

METHODS OF JOINING PIPES :

a. Pipes with flexible joints, Class K9.

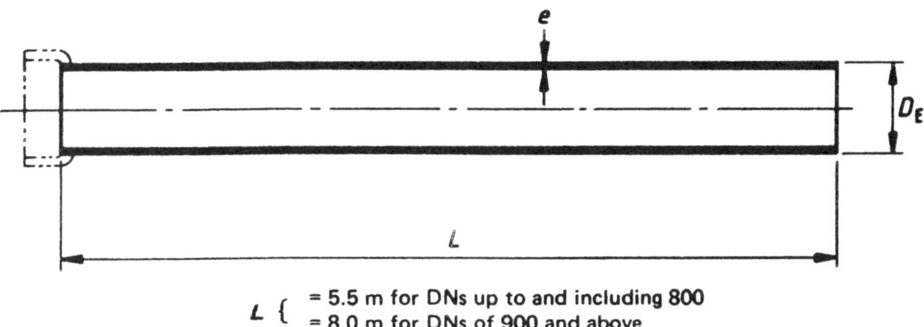

b. Pipes with screwed - on flanges, Classes K9 and K12.

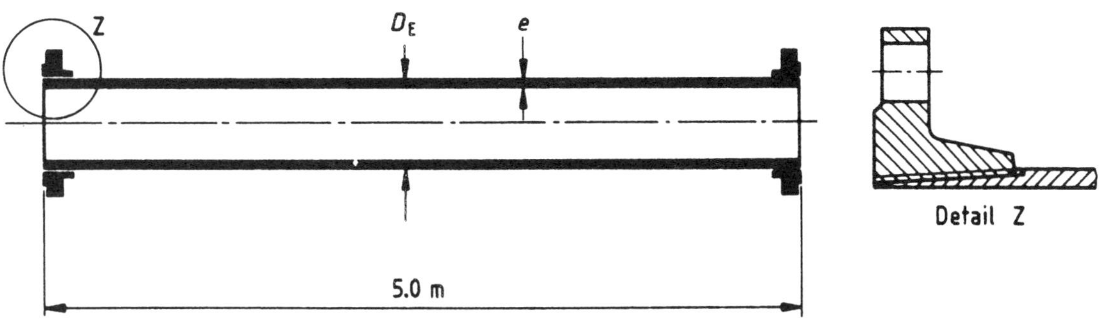

c. Pipes with welded - on flanges, Class K9.

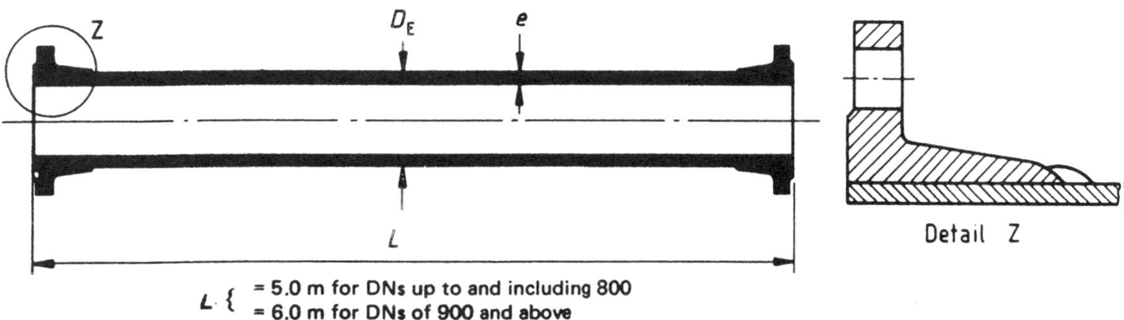

d. Pipes with cast - on flanges, Class K12.

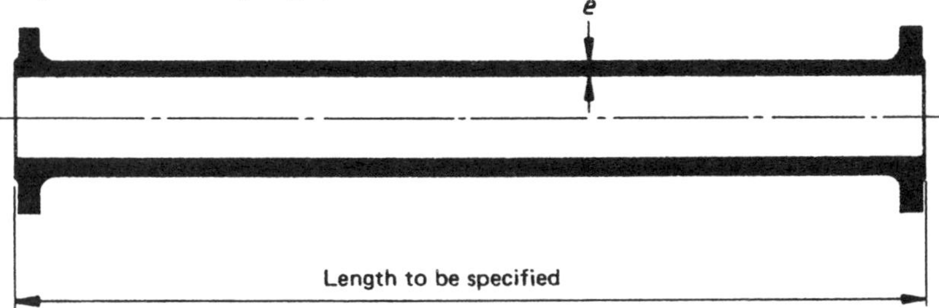

SUPPLIERS

HYDRAULIC TUBING: Hydraulic tubing and hose

COMPANY	ADDRESS	TELEPHONE	FAX
BTR Hose Ltd	PO Box 3 Centurion Way Farlington, Leyland PRESTON Lancs PR5 2RE	0772 421711	0772 436610
Dunlop Hiflex Ltd	PO Box 2 SALISBURY Wilts SP2 7PQ	0722 336231	0722 323914
Dunlop Hydraulic Hose Ltd	Earlsway Team Valley Trading Est GATESHEAD Tyne & Wear NE11 0RQ	091 487 8899	091 482 6933
Europower Hydraulics Ltd	Southgate Market Weighton YORK N Yorks YO4 3BG	0430 872361	0430 872230
Gates Hydraulics Ltd	Station Road ST NEOTS Cambs PE19 1QF	0480 75333	0480 215048
Hydrapower Dynamics Ltd	37/39 Hampton St BIRMINGHAM B19 8LS	021 233 1988	021 236 5071
Norgen Martonair Ltd	PO Box 22 Eastern Avenue LICHFIELD Staffs WS13 6SB	0543 414333	0543 268052
Pressure-Flex (Wakefind) Ltd	Fazely Street BIRMINGHAM B5 5RE	021 643 2631	021 643 2637
Tubesales (UK) Ltd	Majestic Rd Nursling Industrial Estate SOUTHAMPTON Hants SO1 9YX	0703 739333	
Yarl Ltd	Sowerby Wood Ind Est BARROW-IN-FURNESS Cumbria LA14 8RF	0229 836922	0229 870364

ADDRESS	TELEPHONE
British Fluid Power Association 235–237 Vauxhall Bridge Road LONDON SW1V 1EJ	071 233 7044
High Pressure Technology Association Holly Cottage Clay Lane Beenham READING RG7 5PA	0734 713722

PIPE FITTINGS 8.4.1

Couplings for hydraulic tube and components: Construction, selection and use

TYPICAL APPLICATIONS: Connecting domestic and industrial heating systems, hydraulic and pneumatic circuits, automotive, ship and aircraft hydraulic systems, fluid engineering assemblies, industrial presses, moulding forming and forging machines, off-the-road construction machinery, railway engineering, mining equipment.

DEFINITION: Coupling: a positive mechanical assembly for making a pressure tight joint between rigid or flexible tubing and hydraulic components which permits dismantling.

CONSTRUCTION:

Bodies and nuts are typically made from copper alloy, carbon or stainless steel with chromium, zinc, phosphate or cadmium plating on materials which may tarnish or corrode. Sleeves, rings or ferrules are non-corrosive materials which permit high fluid or mechanical pressures without cracking or splitting. Metal, plastic or elastomeric fluid seals may also be used both internally and externally. Quick-release couplings often incorporate a valve in the body which automatically seals the hydraulic line or component to prevent fluid leakage during disconnection.

NOTES ON SELECTION AND USE:

Couplings are pressure vessels and should therefore be selected to operate safely at the same maximum pressure as all other parts of the system considering maximum temperature range and long-term working conditions. Couplings onto flexible tube are often factory assembled using special crimping tools and therefore fixed lengths of tube with a coupling on each end must be specified beforehand, unless suitable standard lengths are available off the shelf. Flexible tubing is commonly used where elements of the system undergo controlled movement such as the excavator arms of earth moving equipment. They may be fitted with hand-operated, quick release, self-sealing couplings for situations where, for instance, a portable hydraulic pump is used to serve a number of different jacks. Semi-rigid tube compression couplings are generally based on three different designs: those where the joint is made and the tube held by the compression of a ring or ferrule on the tube, those where the tube itself is swaged at its end and compressed inside the coupling, and those where the joint is made by compressible seals within the assembly. Semi-rigid tube couplings are used whenever a hydraulic system and its various components are to be permanently located and, as they can be site assembled without special tools, they permit the maximum variability for layout design. The compression ring or ferrule coupling is very popular because it does not rely on special tube preparation and because the ring becomes 'captive' on the tube when compressed, so minimising the chance of error or loss of vital parts of the joint. It is crucially important with all hydraulic couplings to ensure that tube outside diameters and thread sizes are compatible throughout. Imperial tube sizes are still used both in the UK and overseas, and the smallest difference in an equivalent diameter will render a compression ring coupling ineffective or even dangerous. Thread sizes on hydraulic components are not internationally standardized and great care is needed when specifying a system with a mixture of American and metric sizes. American threads such as NPT are not generally compatible with the ISO metric series and therefore adaptors are needed which convert to the most common thread used in the system. Cleanliness during supply, fitting and use of couplings is crucially important to maintain a safe and efficient system.

REFERENCES:

BS 864 : Capillary and compression tube fittings of copper and copper alloy
BS 1740 : Specification for wrought steel pipe fittings (screwed BS 21 R-series thread)
BS 2779 : 1986 Specification for pipe threads for tubes and fittings where pressure-tight joints are not made on the threads (metric dimensions)
BS 4368 : (1984) Compression couplings for tubes Pt 1 : heavy series Pt 3 : light series Pt 4 : type test rqmts
BS 5200 : 1986 Specification for dimensions of hydraulic connectors and adaptors
BS 5380 : 1984 Spec. for hydraulic port & stud coupling using 'O'-ring sealing & 'G' series fastening threads
BS 7198 : Hydraulic fluid power quick-action couplings

PIPE FITTINGS 8.4.2

Hydraulic couplings: Sectional details, types available and pressure ratings

Couplings for semi-rigid tubing and flexible hoses are included in the following diagrams and tables. Note that the data on compression couplings refers only to TYPE A HEAVY SERIES as these are the most readily available and more suitable for higher pressure systems.

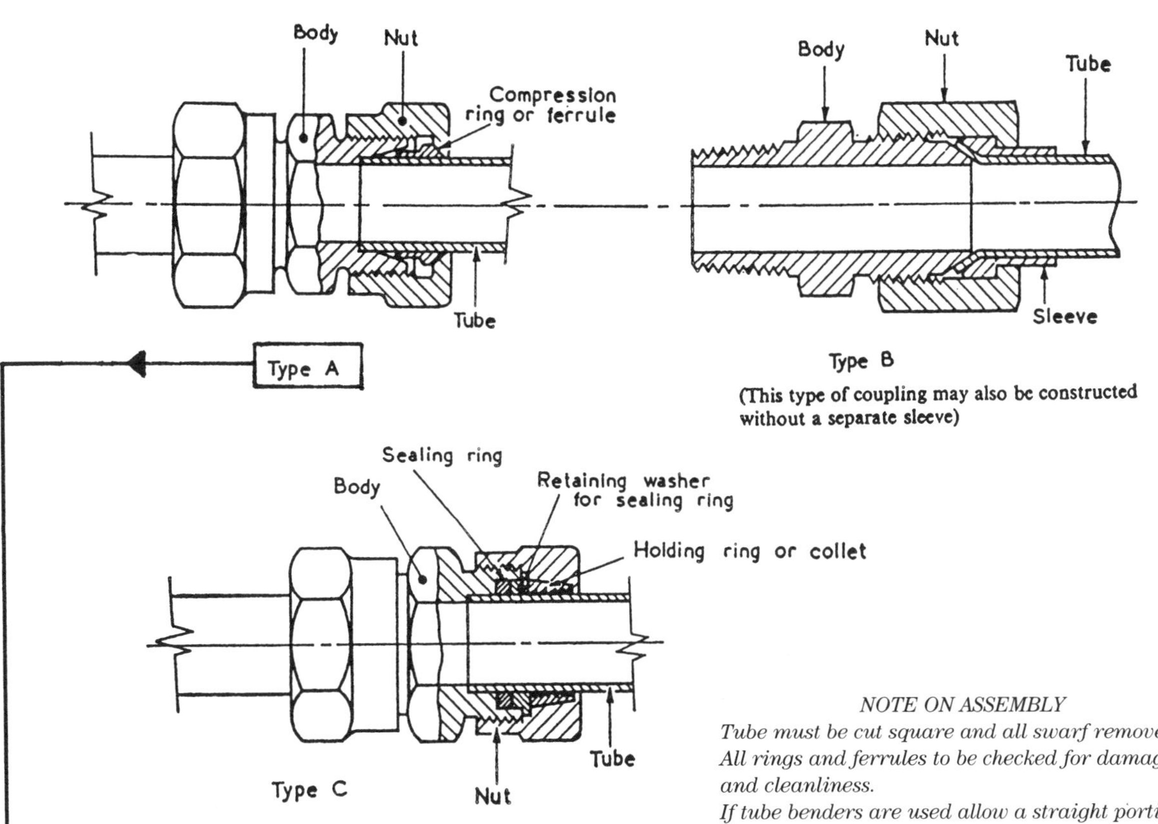

NOTE ON ASSEMBLY
Tube must be cut square and all swarf removed. All rings and ferrules to be checked for damage and cleanliness. If tube benders are used allow a straight portion equal to twice the nut length for insertion into coupling.

Type testing. Testing shall be in accordance with BS 4368 : Part 4.

NOMINAL WORKING PRESSURE RATINGS OF TYPE A HEAVY SERIES COUPLINGS

COPPER ALLOY COUPLINGS

Designation (tube o.d.)	Working Pressure at temp. range – 10°C to + 60°C
mm	bar (1 bar = 10^5 N/mm^2)
6 up to and including 12	400
16 up to and including 25	250
30 up to and including 38	160

CARBON AND STAINLESS STEEL COUPLINGS

Designation (tube o.d.)	Working Pressure at temp. range – 10°C to + 60°C
mm	bar (1 bar = 10^5 N/mm^2)
6 up to and including 12	640
16 up to and including 25	400
30 up to and including 38	250

* All carbon steel bodies and nuts shall be given a protective coating to BS 3382, BS 3189 or BS 1706

COUPLING BODY TYPES COMMONLY AVAILABLE

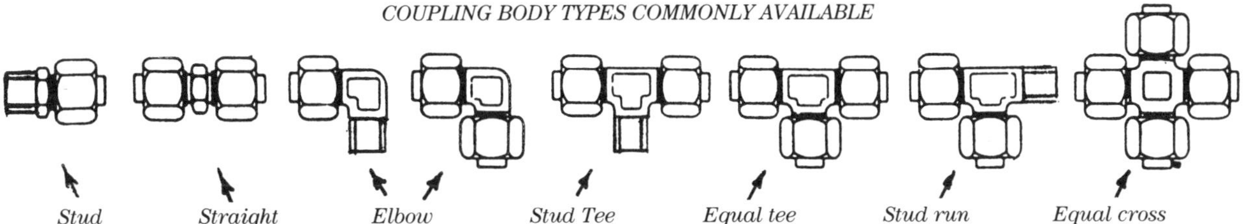

TABLE OF RECOMMENDED TUBE SIZES

Outside Diameter		6	8	10	12	16	20	25	30	38
Limits of Size	*Maximum*	6.1	8.1	10.1	12.1	16.1	20.1	25.1	30.1	38.15
	Minimum	5.9	7.9	9.9	11.9	15.9	19.9	24.9	29.9	37.85

PIPE FITTINGS 8.4.3

Equal elbow, equal cross and equal tee compression fittings: Sizes

COUPLING DETAILS – COMPRESSION TYPE FITTINGS ONLY

Equal Elbow – Assembly

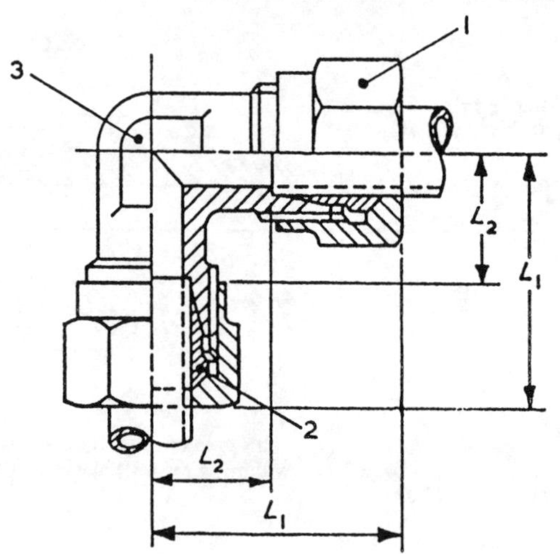

1	2	3
Designation (tube o.d.)	Nominal installed length L_1	Tube abutment distance L_2
6	31	16
8	32	17
10	34	17.5
12	38	21.5
16	43	24.5
20	48	26.5
25	54	30
30	62	35.5
38	72	41

Equal Cross – Assembly

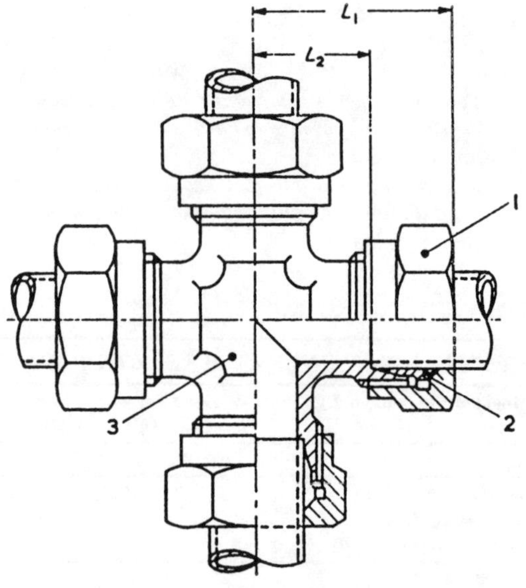

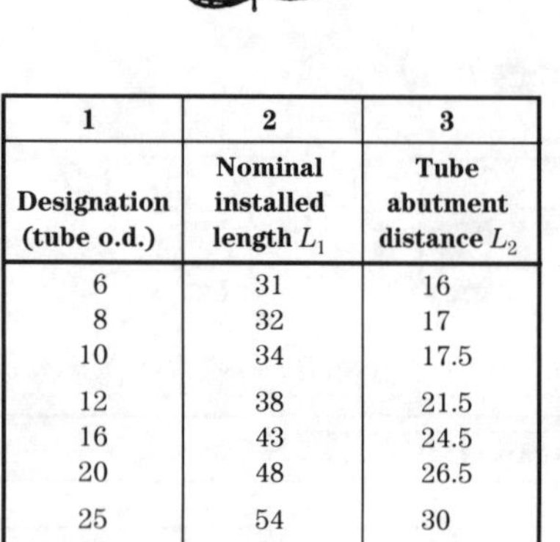

1	2	3
Designation (tube o.d.)	Nominal installed length L_1	Tube abutment distance L_2
6	31	16
8	32	17
10	34	17.5
12	38	21.5
16	43	24.5
20	48	26.5
25	54	30
30	62	35.5
38	72	41

Equal Tee – Assembly

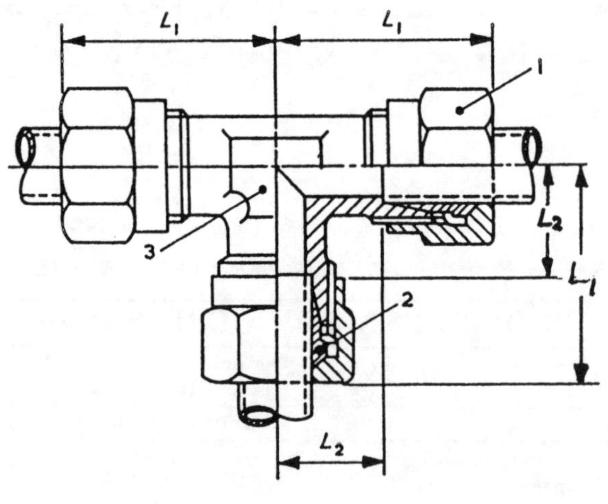

1	2	3
Designation (tube o.d.)	Nominal installed length L_1	Tube abutment distance L_2
6	31	16
8	32	17
10	34	17.5
12	38	21.5
16	43	24.5
20	48	26.5
25	54	30
30	62	35.5
38	72	41

PIPE FITTINGS 8.4.4

Stud, stud elbow and straight coupling compression fittings: Sizes

COUPLING DETAILS – COMPRESSION TYPE FITTINGS ONLY

Male Stud Coupling – Assembly

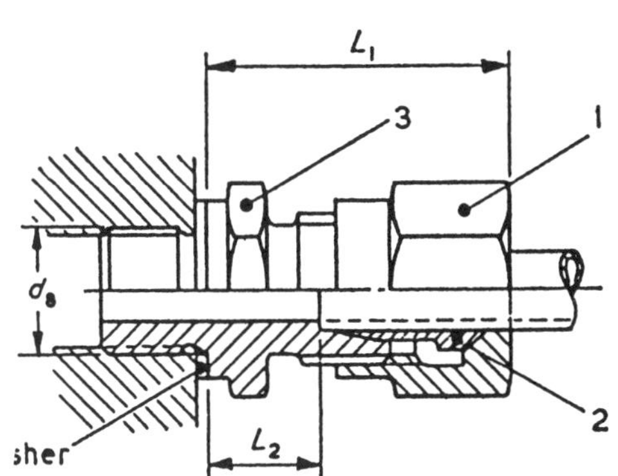

1	2	3	4
Designation (tube o.d.)	Stud end Series G thread. (BS 2779) d_s	Nominal installed length L_1	Tube abutment distance L_2
	in		
6	¼	28	13
8	¼	30	15
10	⅜	31	15
12	⅜	33	17
16	½	37	18.5
20	¾	42	20.5
25	1	47	23
30	1¼	50	23.5
38	1½	57	26

Straight Coupling – Assembly

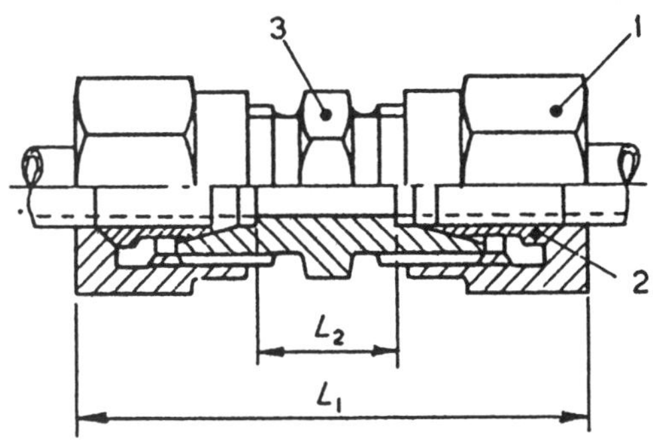

1	2	3
Designation (tube o.d.)	Nominal installed length L_1	Tube abutment distance L_2
6	45	16
8	47	18
10	49	17
12	51	19
16	57	21
20	66	23
25	74	26
30	80	27
38	90	29

Male Stud Elbow – Assembly

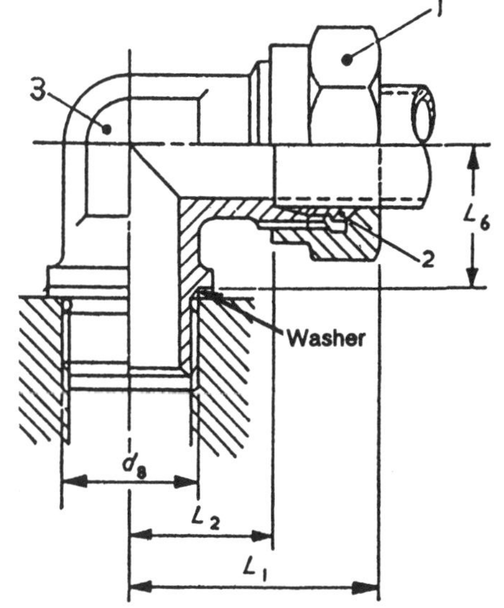

1	2	3	4	5
Designation (tube o.d.)	Stud end Series G thread. (BS 2779) d_s	Nominal installed length L_1	Tube abutment distance L_2	Centre line height L_6
	in			
6	¼	31	16	18
8	¼	32	17	18
10	⅜	34	17.5	20
12	⅜	38	21.5	20
16	½	43	24.5	26
20	¾	48	26.5	26
25	1	54	30	30
30	1¼	62	35.5	34
38	1½	72	41	39

PIPE FITTINGS 8.4.5

Male stud tees (branch and run) compression fittings: Sizes

COUPLING DETAILS – COMPRESSION TYPE FITTINGS ONLY
Male Stud Tee (Stud Run) – Assembly

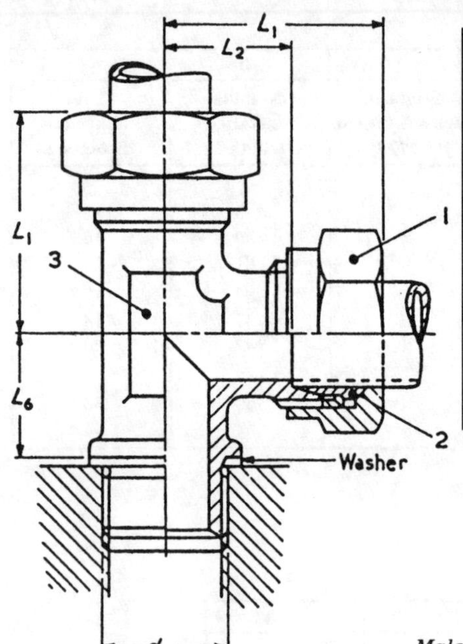

1	2	3	4	5
Designation (tube o.d.)	Stud end Series G thread. (BS 2779) d_s	Nominal installed length L_1	Tube abutment distance L_2	Centre line height L_6
	in			
6	¼	31	16.0	18
8	¼	32	17.0	18
10	⅜	34	17.5	20
12	⅜	38	21.5	20
16	½	43	24.5	26
20	¾	48	26.5	26
25	1	54	30.0	30
30	1¼	62	35.5	34
38	1½	72	41.0	39

Male Stud Tee (Stud Branch) – Assembly

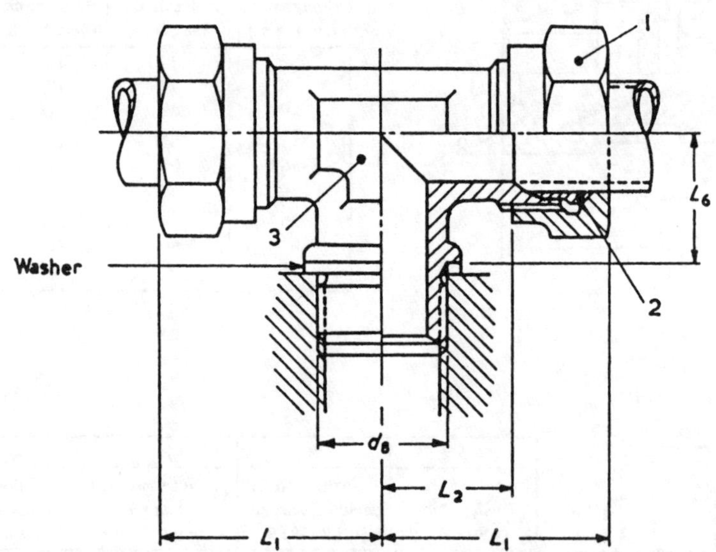

1	2	3	4	5
Designation (tube o.d.)	Stud end Series G thread. (BS 2779) d_s	Nominal installed length L_1	Tube abutment distance L_2	Centre line height L_6
	in			
6	¼	31	16.0	18
8	¼	32	17.0	18
10	⅜	34	17.5	20
12	⅜	38	21.5	20
16	½	43	24.5	26
20	¾	48	26.5	26
25	1	54	30.0	30
30	1¼	62	35.5	34
38	1½	72	41.0	39

PIPE FITTINGS 8.4.6

Couplings for flexible tubing: interface details

This type of coupling is suitable where some relative motion is expected between the fluid supply and the component it serves. The seal is made by the connection of a male and female conical or spherical surface and therefore cleanliness on assembly is essential. A permanent joint is made (usually offsite) between the hose and the fitting and details of : Pressure rating / internal and external diameters / temperature rating must be specified beforehand (see BS 3832). The flexibility of the tubing will permit a degree of reusability but if frequent connect / disconnect is required a quick release coupling is recommended. Sharp bending or twisting of tubing should be avoided by the use of angled couplings. The adaptor shown for connection to components will need either an 'O' ring, washer, or bonded seal to effect a pressure tight joint. Special applications for this type of coupling may call for some differences in materials and design, for example, equipment to be used in hazardous environments such as coal mines.

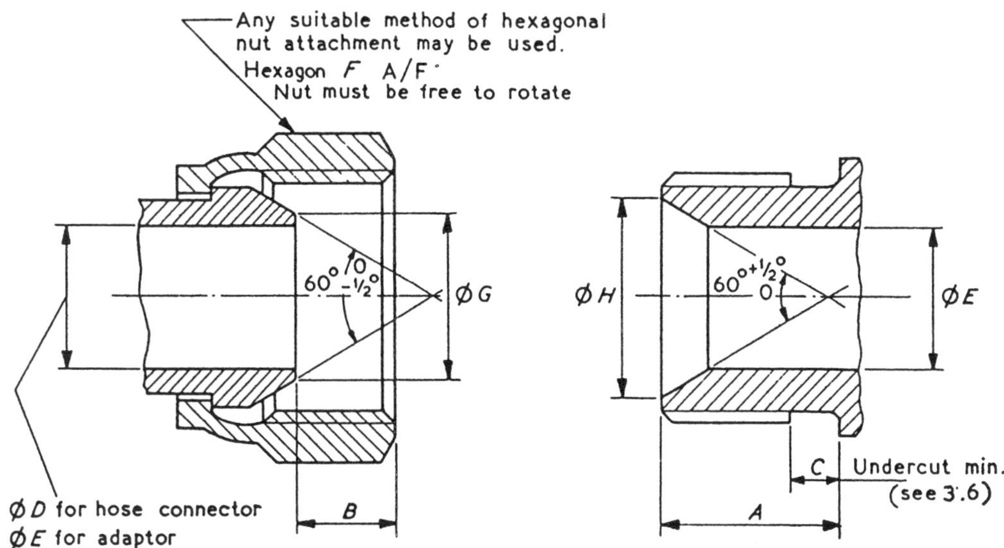

Dimensions for hose connectors and female adaptors

Dimensions for male adaptors

INTERFACE DETAILS OF MALE AND FEMALE CONNECTIONS

All dimensions in millimetres

Thread designation	A min.	B nom.	C min.	D min.	E min.	F nom.	G ± 0.12	H ± 0.15	Hose i.d. nom.
G ⅛	10	6.4	2	3.5	3.5	14	5.6	7.5	5.0
G ¼	10	4.2	3	4.5	4.7	19	7.2	10.4	6.3
G ⅜	12	6.0	3	7.0	7.9	22	10.4	13.9	10.0
G ½	14	6.5	4	10.0	11.1	27	13.5	17.5	12.5
G ⅝	16	9.7	4	12.5	14.3	30	16.7	19.3	16.0
G ¾	16	8.7	4	15.5	16.7	32	19.0	22.8	19.0
G 1	19	10.5	5	20.0	22.2	41	24.5	28.7	25.0

Note: It is an acceptable alternative for the conical seating surface of the female adaptor to be replaced by a spherical seating surface, provided the same limiting dimensions are maintained.

PIPE FITTINGS 8.4.7

Straight and tubular elbow couplings for flexible tubing

COUPLING DETAILS – FLEXIBLE TUBING ASSEMBLIES ONLY

NOTE : Pressure ratings are dependent on tubing – see BS 3832

All dimensions in mm

Hose i.d. nom.	Thread designation (BS 2779)	J_4 max.
5.0	G ⅛	47
6.3	G ¼	53
10.0	G ⅜	57
12.5	G ½	63
16.0	G ⅝ *	68
19.0	G ¾	73
25.0	G 1	86

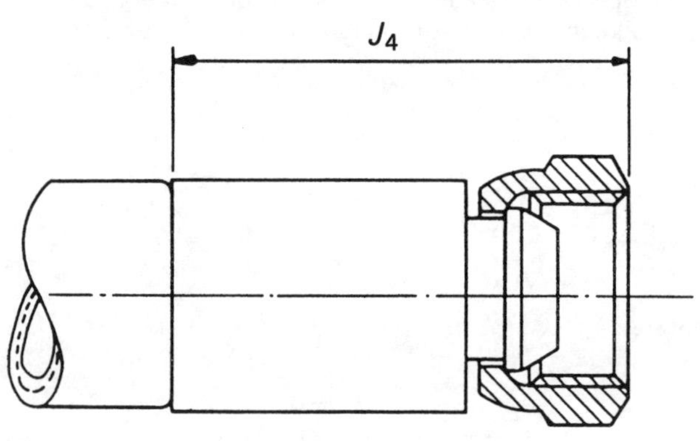

Straight hose end fitting

All dimensions in mm

Hose i.d. nom.	Thread designation (BS 2779)	J_2 max.	K_2 max.
5.0	G ⅛	60	27.5
6.3	G ¼	64	32.5
10.0	G ⅜	74	38.0
12.5	G ½	83	43.5
16.0	G ⅝ *	92	53.0
19.0	G ¾	102	56.0
25.0	G 1	124	69.5

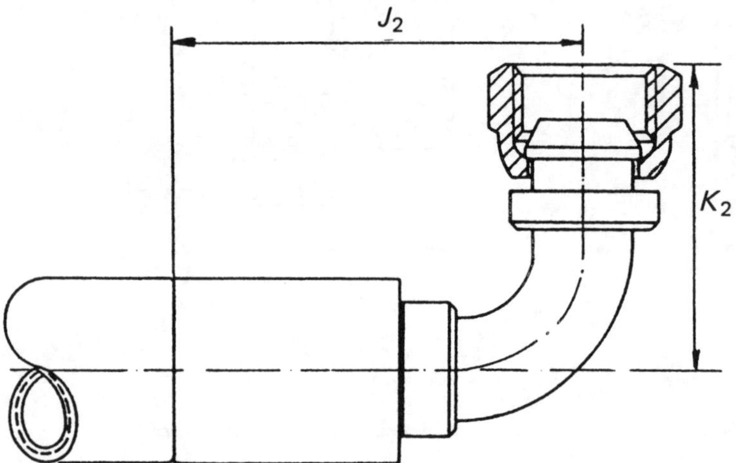

90° tubular elbow : maximum envelope dimensions

All dimensions in mm

Hose i.d. nom.	Thread designation (BS 2779)	J_3 max.	K_3 max.
5.0	G ⅛	75.5	22.5
6.3	G ¼	74.0	21.0
10.0	G ⅜	86.5	24.5
12.5	G ½	95.0	26.0
16.0	G ⅝ *	102.0	32.0
19.0	G ¾	112.0	31.0
25.0	G 1	132.5	35.5

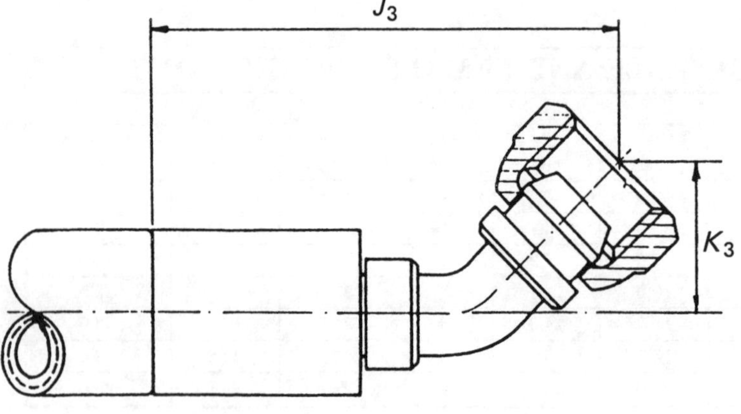

135° tubular elbow : maximum envelope dimensions

* Non-preferred size

PIPE FITTINGS 8.4.8

Block elbow couplings and adaptors for flexible tubing

COUPLING DETAILS – FLEXIBLE TUBING ASSEMBLIES ONLY

In addition to the tubular fittings shown on the facing page, another type called a block fitting is commonly available. It serves the same purpose, but there may be advantages of compactness, cost and stock sizes to be considered when selecting.

Two examples of block fittings are shown below, and detailed dimensions of these are shown in BS 5200.

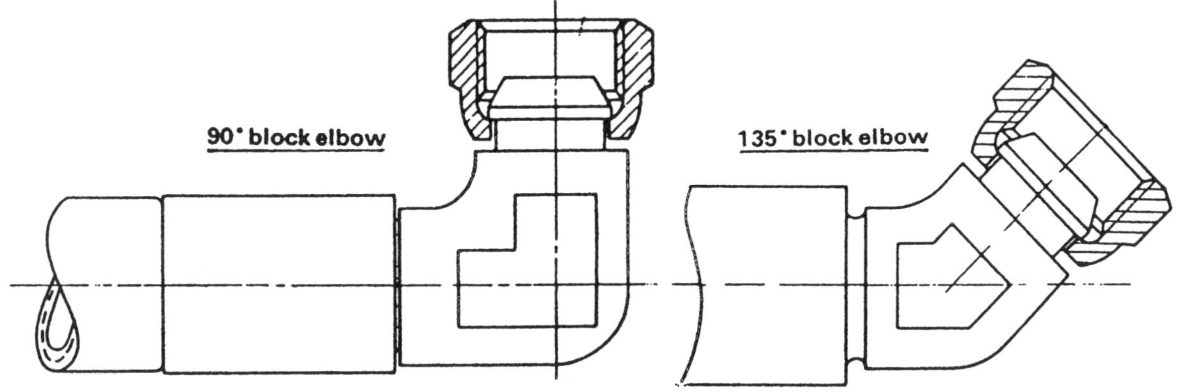

ADAPTORS FOR CONNECTING COUPLING / COUPLING OR COUPLING / COMPONENT

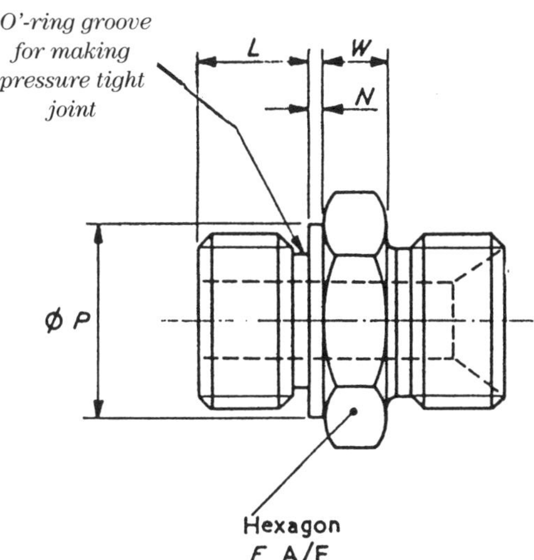

Dimensions for male-male adaptor with single 'O'-ring groove

All dimensions in mm

Thread designation	*L* max.	*N* min.	*P* nom.	*W* (td $^{+0.5}_{-0}$)	*F* nom.
G ⅛	7.4	1.0	14	5	14
G ¼	11.0	1.5	18	7	19
G ⅜	11.4	2.0	22	8	22
G ½	15.0	2.5	26	9	27
G ⅝ *	16.3	2.5	30	9	30
G ¾	16.3	2.5	32	10	32
G 1	19.1	2.5	39	12	41

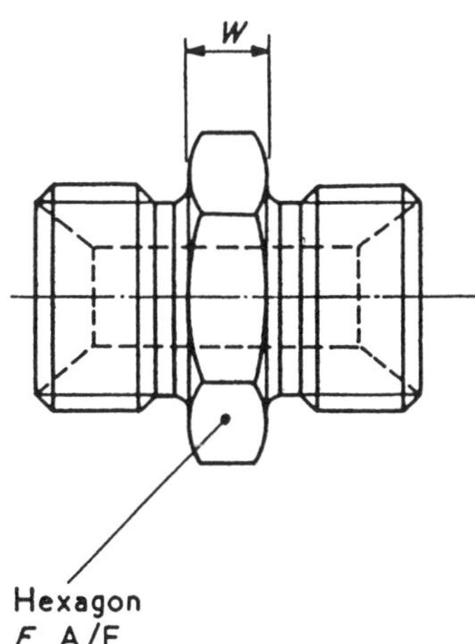

Dimensions for male-male adaptor e.g. coupling to coupling

All dimensions in mm

Thread designation	*W* (td $^{+0.5}_{-0}$)	*F* nom.
G ⅛	5	14
G ¼	7	19
G ⅜	8	22
G ½	9	27
G ⅝ *	9	30
G ¾	10	32
G 1	12	41

* Non-preferred size

PIPE FITTINGS 8.4.9

Port and stud couplings with 'O'-ring seals: Sizes and details

BASIC DIMENSIONS FOR PORT CONNECTION AND STUD COUPLING USING 'O'-RING SEALING

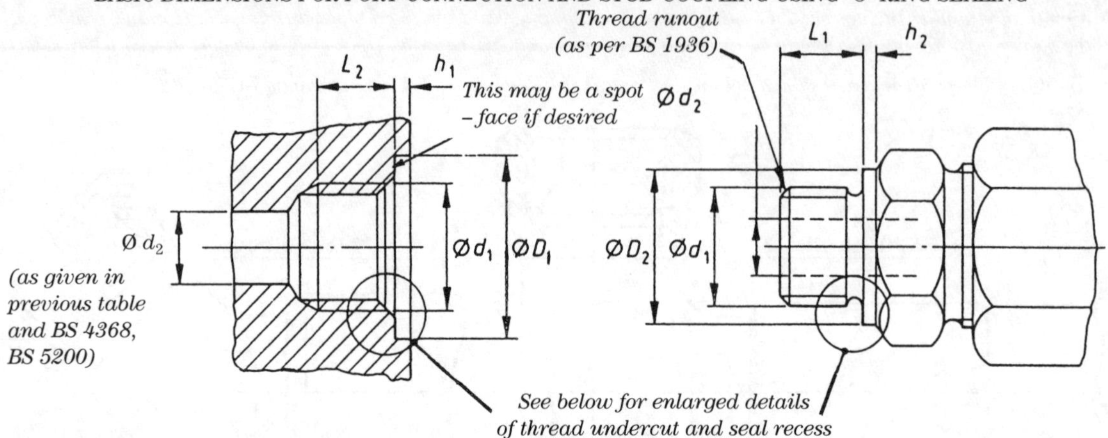

Thread designation (to BS 2779) d_1	Thread length L_1 (stud) max. L_2 (port) min.	Counterbore Ø D_1 min.	h_1 max.	h_2 min.	Spigot Ø D_2 max.
G ⅛	10.5	15	0.6	1.0	14
G ¼	11.0	19	0.6	1.5	18
G ⅜	12.5	23	0.6	2.0	22
G ½	15.0	27	0.8	2.5	26
G ⅝ (non-preferred)	16.3	31	0.8	2.5	30
G ¾	16.3	33	1.1	2.5	32
G 1	19.1	40	1.1	2.5	39

UNDERCUT, RECESS AND SEAL DIMENSIONS

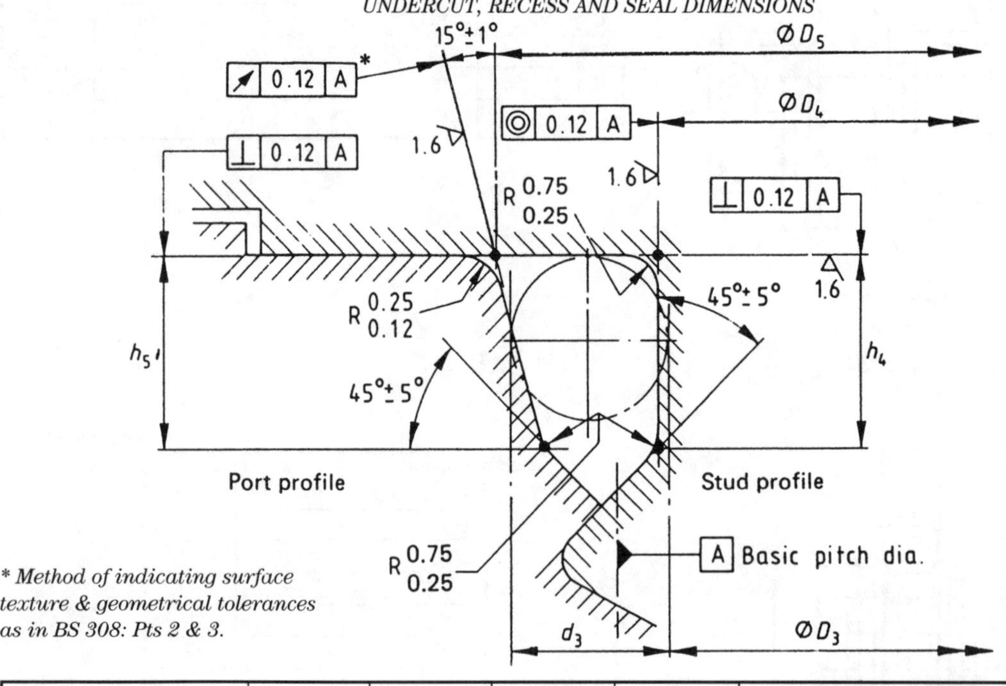

* *Method of indicating surface texture & geometrical tolerances as in BS 308: Pts 2 & 3.*

Thread designation (to BS 2779) d_1	D_4 + 0.12 0	h_4 + 0.12 0	D_5 + 0.12 0	h_5 + 0.12 0	Toroidal sealing ring (to BS 4518)		
					D_3 nom.	d_3 nom.	Ref. no.
G ⅛	8.00	2.1	11.24	1.3	8.1	1.6	0081-16
G ¼	11.00	2.0	14.16	1.2	10.1	1.6	0101-16
G ⅜	14.28	3.1	18.86	1.9	13.6	2.4	0136-24
G ½	17.72	3.1	22.40	1.9	17.6	2.4	0176-24
G ⅝ (non-preferred)	20.18	3.9	26.00	2.4	19.5	3.0	0195-30
G ¾	23.20	3.9	28.92	2.4	22.5	3.0	0225-30
G 1	29.78	3.9	35.50	2.4	29.5	3.0	0295-30

PIPE FITTINGS 8.4.10

Threaded studs for couplings: Sizes and details

THREADED STUD ENDS USED ON HYDRAULIC COUPLINGS

There are two different threads used on compression couplings: those which join the nut to the body and effect the compression of the ring or ferrule, and those which connect the body of the coupling to a component (such as a valve). The latter thread may be tapered or straight – if it is straight then an 'O'-ring or sealing washer is needed to made a pressure tight joint. the old 'Imperial' (BSP) thread has been selected as an ISO standard connection thread and hence the fractional sizes which appear in the following tables.

SCREWTHREADS

Compression ends. *The screw threads on the compression ends of the couplings shall be ISO metric threads in accordance with BS 3643 Part 2 and for Type A couplings the actual threads and the lengths of thread shall be in accordance with the details specified in the tables in Section 2, BS 4368 Part 1.*

External and internal threads shall be chamfered at the face of the coupling to an included angle of 90°. The diameter of the chamfer shall be equal to the minor or major diameter of the thread as appropriate.

Stud ends (connector ends). *The preferred thread for stud ends (connector ends)(of couplings shall be Series G Class A, in accordance with BS 2779. The dimensions of the stud ends shall comply with the requirements shown below. Other threads shall be by agreement between the purchaser and the manufacturer.*

The faces designated A and B (below) – shall have a smooth finish at right angles to the threads to take suitable sealing washers or compounds. For 'O'-ring sealing of stud ends see facing page.

Thread undercuts and recesses. Thread undercuts shall be in accordance with BS 1936.

STANDARD THREADED STUD ENDS (CONNECTOR ENDS)

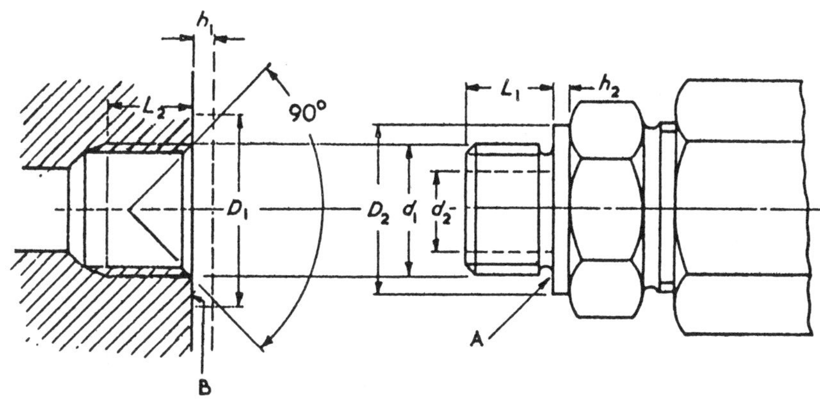

Note. These illustrations are diagrammatic only; they do not purport to indicate forms or shapes and are solely for the purpose of indicating where the specified dimensions are to be measured.

Thread size Series G (BS 2779, Class A) d_1 (in)	*Max.* bore d_2	*Thread length* L_1 Male max. L_2 Female min.	D_1 *Min.*	h_1 *Max.* h_2 *Min.*	*Spigot* D_2 max.
⅛	4	7.4	15	1	14
¼	5	11.0	19	1.5	18
⅜	8	11.4	23	2	22
½	12	15.0	27	2.5	26
¾	16	16.3	33	2.5	32
1	20	19.1	40	2.5	39
1 ¼	25	21.4	50	2.5	49
1 ½	32	21.4	56	2.5	55
2	40	25.7	69	3	68

PIPE FITTINGS 8.4.11

Flanges: Construction, selection and use

TYPICAL APPLICATIONS: Joining of water, oil, steam and chemical pipework above and below ground or water. Permanent joining of valves, pressure vessels, tanks and other equipment to pipework and components. Ductile iron pipes and flanges are used for liquid / gas transport for low cost and ease of assembly, such as in building services and industrial heating systems.

DEFINITION: A projecting flat rim, collar or rib used to join two parts together by means of continous face contact between them.

CONSTRUCTION:

Ferrous and non-ferrous steel and alloy plates, forgings and castings with or without provision for welding or screwing to existing pipework. Can be supplied as blanks or machined complete with boltholes. Plastic flanges can be screwed, welded, solvent or adhesive bonded to pipework. Flanges may be integrally machined, moulded or formed in any material. Ductile iron pipes may have screwed, welded or cast-on flanges and fittings and these may be readily assembled on site using thread cutting and pipe bending equipment and suitable gaskets and jointing compounds.

NOTES ON SELECTION AND USE:

The most widely used method of joining lengths of large diameter pipework together or to other components or assemblies. Flanges may be fitted to pipe on site or ready supplied on the ends of tailor-made sections. Flange faces must always be square at the centreline of the pipe end and therefore site wel. .g, bonding or threading of flanges should always be done in clean dry conditionsl Proper jigs and tools are needed and site inspection equipment is often necessary to check flange joints before and after assembly and during trials under working conditions. Site drilling of flange bolt holes should be avoided and under no circumstances should machining of faces be done on site. All types of flange conforming to current international standards must have pre-machined faces finished according to their pressure rating and these faces should be suitably protected from corrosion and accidental damage until ready for assembly. Where bolted or studded flanges are used, both flanges, gasket and washer thicknesses are to be taken into account when calculating thread length. If flanges and / or threads are surface coated then hole sizes for thread clearance should allow for this.

To avoid undue stresses and potential leaks, specify a tightening sequence for bolts during which pipes / components both sides of the flange should be supported. For long pipe runs and heavy components permanent methods of supporting them may be needed to minimise working stresses on flange joints. High levels of vibration, shock and temperature can also increase stresses, and localised electro-chemical corrosion may occur if dissimilar metallic materials are used for bolts, flanges and gaskets. Flanges must be clearly marked with the material reference if alloy steels are used and for some copper alloy flanges full face gaskets are required to make a satisfactory joint.

Both imperial and metric sizes are currently available and therefore great care is needed if metric pipework is required to join to existing imperial flanges.

REFERENCES:

BS 10 : 1962 — (obsolescent) Specification for flanges and bolting for pipes, valves, and fittings
BS 1560 : — Circular flanges for pipes, valves and fittings (Class designated)
BS 3063 : 1965 — (obsolescent) Specification for dimensions of gaskets for pipe flanges
BS 4504 : — Circular flanges for pipes, valves and fittings: (PN designated)
BS 4772 : 1988 — Specification for ductile iron pipes and fittings
BS 8010 : Sect.2.1 1987 — Ductile iron for pipelines
BS 4515 : 1984 — Welding of steel pipelines on land and offshore
PD 6438 : 1969 — Review of present methods for design of bolted flanges for pressure vessels
ISO 7005-2 : 1988 — Metallic flanges

PIPE FITTINGS 8.4.12

Selecting a flange

SELECTING A FLANGE:

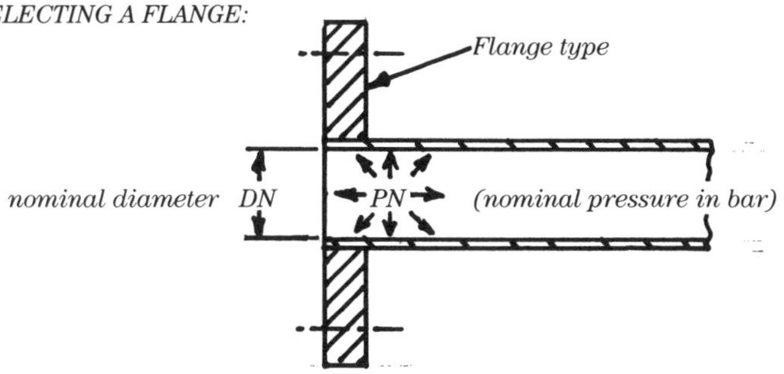

Flange type

nominal diameter DN

PN *(nominal pressure in bar)*

TYPICAL APPEARANCE OF:

Weld Neck Flange *Loose Flange*

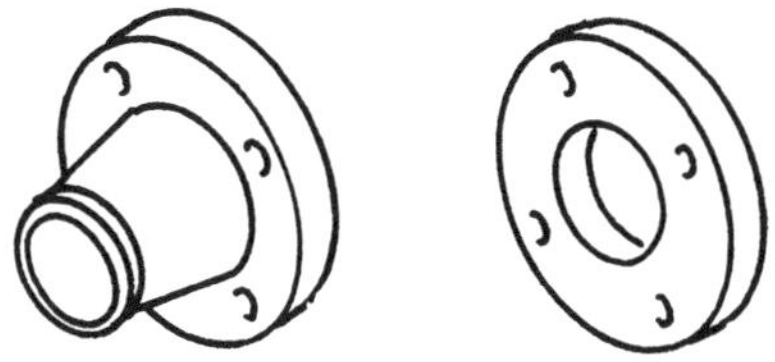

Flanges are selected by a combination of DN, PN and flange type.

Use Table A to select a flange table reference number according to flange type, pressure and material. These flange table reference numbers (such as 25/3 , 16/4) are taken from BS 4504 which must be referred to as it gives detailed information not shown here.

Refer to Table B for preferred range of nominal sizes. Refer to 8.3.7–8.3.8 for Ductile Iron Pipes.

TABLE A: GUIDE TO APPROPRIATE FLANGE TABLES IN BS 4504.

	TABLES TO REFER TO IN BS 4504							
TYPE OF FLANGE	**Material:** STEEL				CAST IRON			
Pressure:	**PN10**	**PN16**	**PN25**	**PN40**	**PN10**	**PN16**	**PN25**	**PN40**
1. Integral flanges 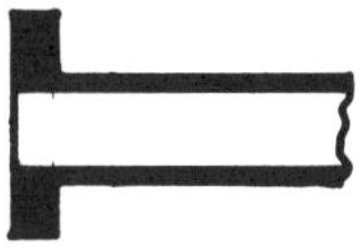		16/1	25/1	40/1	10/11	16/11 16/12	25/11 25/12	
2. Welding neck flanges 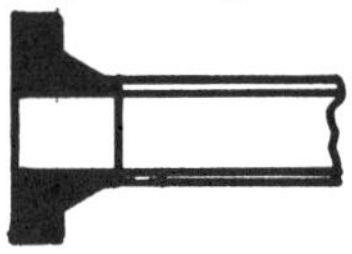	10/2	16/2	25/2	40/2				
3. Steel plate flanges for welding 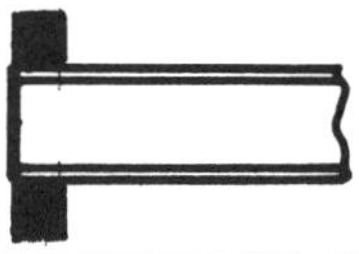	10/3	16/3	25/3	40/3				
4. Screwed boss flanges 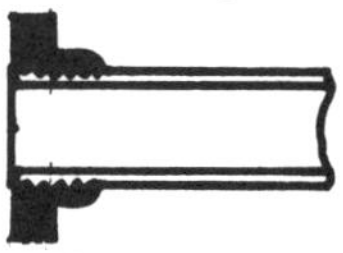		16/4		40/4		16/13	25/13	
5. Slip-on boss flanges for welding 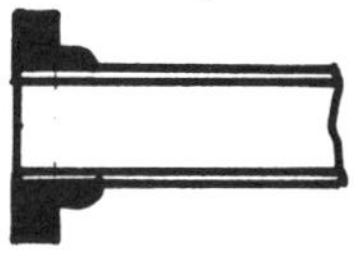	10/5	16/5	25/5	40/5				
6. Loose flanges for welded on lapped pipe ends 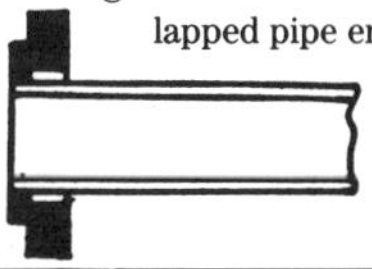	10/6							
7. Steel plate blank flanges	10/8	16/8	25/8	40/8				

PIPE FITTINGS 8.4.12

Selecting a flange *(contd)*

The following table is a guide to the preferred flange sizes and pressures shown in detail in BS 4504.

TABLE B. RANGE OF FLANGES DETAILED IN THE TABLES IN BS 4504

NOMINAL PRESSURES IN : bar , (N/m^2) , [psi] for flanges at 20°C.

PN10 (1.0x10^6) [145] (Non-preferred)

Nom Size mm	TABLES 10 / 2	3	5	6	8	11
6			↑			
8						
10	↑	↑		◊	↑	↑
15				◊		
20				◊		
25			Use table 16/5	◊		
32				◊		
40				◊		
50				◊		
65			↓	◊		
80	Use table 16/2	Use table 16/3	◊	◊	Use table 16/8	Use table 16/11
100			◊	◊		
125			◊	◊		
150			◊	◊		
175	↓	↓			↓	↓
200	◊	◊	◊	◊	◊	◊
250	◊	◊	◊	◊	◊	◊
300	◊	◊	◊	◊	◊	◊
350	◊	◊			◊	◊

PN16 (1.6x10^6) [232]

Nom Size mm	TABLES 16 / 1	2	3	4	5	8	11	12	13
6				◊	◊				◊
8				◊	◊				◊
10	↑	◊	◊	◊	◊	◊	◊	◊	◊
15		◊	◊	◊	◊	◊	◊	◊	◊
20		◊	◊	◊	◊	◊	◊	◊	◊
25	Use table 40/1	◊	◊	◊	◊	◊	◊	◊	◊
32		◊	◊	◊	◊	◊	◊	◊	◊
40		◊	◊	◊	◊	◊	◊	◊	◊
50	↓	◊	◊	◊	◊	◊	◊	◊	◊
65	◊	◊	◊	◊	◊	◊	◊	◊	◊
80	◊	◊	◊	◊	◊	◊	◊	◊	◊
100	◊	◊	◊	◊	◊	◊	◊	◊	◊
125	◊	◊	◊	◊	◊	◊	◊	◊	◊
150	◊	◊	◊	◊	◊	◊	◊	◊	◊
175	◊	◊	◊			◊	◊		
200	◊	◊	◊		◊	◊	◊		
250	◊	◊	◊		◊	◊	◊		
300	◊	◊	◊		◊	◊	◊		
350	◊	◊	◊			◊	◊		

PN25 (2.5x10^6) [362.5]

Nom Size mm	TABLES 25 / 1	2	3	5	8	11	12	13
6				◊				◊
8				◊				◊
10	↑	↑	↑	◊	↑	◊	◊	◊
15				◊		◊	◊	◊
20				◊		◊	◊	◊
25				◊		◊	◊	◊
32				◊		◊	◊	◊
40				◊		◊	◊	◊
50	Use table 40/1	Use table 40/2	Use table 40/3	◊	Use table 40/8	◊	◊	◊
65				◊		◊	◊	◊
80				◊		◊	◊	◊
100				◊		◊	◊	◊
125				◊		◊	◊	◊
150	↓	↓	↓	◊	↓	◊	◊	◊
175	◊	◊	◊		◊	◊		
200	◊	◊	◊	◊	◊	◊		
250	◊	◊	◊	◊	◊	◊		
300	◊	◊	◊	◊	◊	◊		
350	◊	◊	◊		◊	◊		

PN40 (4.0x10^6) [580]

Nom Size mm	TABLES 40 / 1	2	3	4	5	8
6	◊	◊				
8	◊	◊				
10	◊	◊	◊	◊	◊	◊
15	◊	◊	◊	◊	◊	◊
20	◊	◊	◊	◊	◊	◊
25	◊	◊	◊	◊	◊	◊
32	◊	◊	◊	◊	◊	◊
40	◊	◊	◊	◊	◊	◊
50	◊	◊	◊	◊	◊	◊
65	◊	◊	◊	◊	◊	◊
80	◊	◊	◊	◊	◊	◊
100	◊	◊	◊	◊	◊	◊
125	◊	◊	◊	◊	◊	◊
150	◊	◊	◊	◊	◊	◊
175	◊	◊	◊			◊
200	◊	◊	◊		◊	◊
250	◊	◊	◊		◊	◊
300	◊	◊	◊		◊	◊
350	◊	◊	◊			◊

(For flanges operating at other temperatures see BS 4504 Tables A1 and A2.)

DETAILS TO BE SUPPLIED WHEN ORDERING FLANGES :

1. Nominal size (DN), nominal pressure (PN), type of flange and material.
2. Whether test certificates of the material are required.
3. Details of bolting (if required). (See BS 4504: Part 1: Clause 5.)
4. Details of the machining for the attachment of flanges. (See BS 4504: Part 1: Clause 6.)
5. Whether taper or parallel screwing is required. (See BS 4504: Part 1: Clause 6.2.)
6. Whether flanges are to be machined. (See BS 4504: Part 1: Clauses 4.2 and 4.3.)

FLANGE FINISHES: The finish of jointing surfaces up to & including PN 40 shall not be coarser than given in the following table.

Method of machining	Ra µm	Ra µin	Rz µm	BS 1134 Grade ref.
Turning	12.5	500	50 to 87.5	N.10
Other than turning	3.2	125	12.5 to 21.85	N. 8

Note: The term 'turning' includes any method of machining producing concentric or spiral grooves.

FLANGE TOLERANCES: Flanges shall be subject to the following tolerances on flange diameter, thickness, and length of welding necks.

Outside Diameter (D):	M/c'd	Not m/c'd
Up to 200 inclusive	± 1	± 2
Over 200 to 300 incl.	± 1.5	± 2
Over 300 to 400 incl.	± 2	± 3
Over 400	± 2	± 5

Length of Welding Neck Flange	M/c'd
Up to 80 nom. size inclusive	± 1.5
Over 80 to 250 nom. size incl.	± 2.0
Over 250 nom. size incl.	± 3.0

THICKNESS (B):

	M/c'd at back	Not m/c'd at back	
Up to 10	+ 1.5 − 0	+ 2.5 − 0	For flanges integral with valves and fittings (other than forged steel).
Over 10, up to 20 incl.	+ 2.0 − 0	+ 3.5 − 0	
Over 20, up to 30 incl.	+ 2.5 − 0	+ 4.5 − 0	
Over 30, up to 50 incl.	+ 3.0 − 0	+ 6.5 − 0	
Over 50, up to 70 incl.	+ 3.0 − 0	+ 8.5 − 0	
Over 70, up to 100 incl.	+ 5.0 − 0	+ 10.5 − 0	
Over 100	+ 7.0 − 0	+ 14.5 − 0	
Up to 35 inclusive	+ 1.5 − 0	+ 3.0 − 0	Flanges not integral with valves & fittings & forged steel flanges with integral valves & fittings
Over 35	+ 3.0 − 0	+ 5.0 − 0	

For notes on BOLTING of flanges see BS 4504: Part 1 Clause 5.

(Copper, stainless steel and other alloys are also used for pipes and flanges. BS 4504: Part 2 covers Copper alloy and Composite flanges.)

Notes

SUPPLIERS

COUPLINGS: Couplings for hydraulic tube and components

COMPANY	ADDRESS	TELEPHONE	FAX
AP Precision Hydraulics (Bolton) Ltd	Great Bank Road Wingates Industrial Park West Loughton BOLTON Lancs BL5 3XN	0942 813314	0942 812014
Europower Hydraulics Ltd	Southgate Market Weighton YORK N Yorks YO4 3BG	0430 872361	0430 872230
Fluidrive Engineering Co Ltd	Broad Lane BRACKNELL Berks RG12 3BH	0344 424789	0344 53531
James Lister & Sons Ltd	Sandwell Ind Est Spon Lane South Smethwick WARLEY W Midlands B66 1QJ	021 525 7733	
Lucas Fluid Power Ltd	Unit 1 Torrington Ave COVENTRY W Midlands CV4 9AJ	0203 694000	0203 694019
Tom Parker (Hydraulics and Pneumatics) Ltd	PO Box 36 Marsh Lane PRESTON Lancs PR1 1HY	0772 51405	0772 827088
Sterling Hydraulics Ltd Coupling Division	Sterling House CREWKERNE Somerset TA18 8LL	0460 72222	0460 72334

USEFUL ADDRESSES

FLUID ENGINEERING

ADDRESS	TELEPHONE
British Fluid Power Association 235–237 Vauxhall Bridge Road LONDON SW1V 1EJ	071 233 7044
High Pressure Technology Association Holly Cottage Clay Lane Beenham READING RG7 5PA	0734 713722

Notes

SECTION 9 – MECHANICAL COMPONENTS

SEALS 9.1.1

'O'-rings and their housings: Construction, selection and use (Toroidal seals)

TYPICAL APPLICATIONS: Domestic and industrial heating, ventilating and plumbing systems, hydraulics and pneumatics, valves, pressure vessels, pipe joints and couplings, vehicle transmission and braking systems, pumps and compressors, fluid and powder handling equipment, aerospace fluid and electro-mechanical devices, static and dynamic sealing for special purpose machinery.

DEFINITION: A toroidal shaped seal made from a resilient material which prevents ingress or egress of fluids under static or dynamic conditions.

CONSTRUCTION:

'O'-rings are moulded from nitrile rubber for most general applications, polyurethane for abrasion resistance and silicone rubber for extreme temperatures. A number of other plastic and elastomeric materials are also available to cope with a variety of special environmental conditions. The housing material and finish has a direct effect on the life of the seal and therefore soft metals such as aluminium, brass and some stainless steels should be avoided for high pressure dynamic applications. Housing grooves should accurately match the required seal geometry, be made to close tolerances and have smooth surface finishes.

NOTES ON SELECTION AND USE: 'O'-rings are one of the most widely used seals because of their relatively low cost, ease of use and high performance in service. They rely on a confined housing which elastically deforms the cross section of the ring so creating an initial seal and then, as fluid pressure is applied, the ring deforms against the housing so increasing its effectiveness. They can be guaranteed completely leakproof as a static seal up to extremely high pressures and are satisfactorily leakproof under dynamic conditions. Commonly available 'O'-rings in various materials will operate at up to 100 bar pressure in standard form and up to 350 bar if a back-up washer is used to prevent extrusion of the ring through the clearance in the housing. In dynamic use, for instance as a rotary seal, peripheral speeds of up to 7.5m/sec can be easily accommodated. Higher speeds, especially if clearances are large, can cause extrusion and localized 'nibbling' damage to the ring surface. It should be noted that as dynamic seals, 'O'-rings are best suited for small diameter, short stroke, medium pressure applications, but if there is *very slow* reciprocating motion the high friction can cause premature failure. As a general rule, seals should be arranged so that the direction of pressure and any rubbing friction are in opposition. Although 'O'-rings of suitable materials can operate over a temperature range of −40 °C to +250 °C, contraction or expansion of metal housings can make significant changes to original machined sizes and corrections may be necessary to avoid extrusion occurring. In static housings, for instance a pressure vessel end cap, stretching of assembly bolts may also change ring clearances. Groove finish is important as it affects the wear and life of the seal, although for some static uses a rougher finish than that needed for compression gaskets can often be tolerated as long as all edges are deburred. Great care is needed during ring handling and assembly to ensure no premature damage occurs and protective tubes or cones are often used, especially if a ring has to pass over a threaded part to be fitted into its housing. Lubricants are recommended for rings and housings, and greases with wide temperature ranges are usually specified for this purpose. Always wear protective gloves when handling 'O'-rings that have perished due to overheating as in some circumstances highly toxic chemicals may be released. If in doubt, check with the manufacturer. Absolute cleanliness at all stages of supply and assembly is crucial.

REFERENCES:

BS 1134 : Assessment of surface texture
BS 1806 : 1989 Spec. for dimensions of toroidal sealing rings ('O'-rings) and their housings (inch series)
BS 4518 : 1982 Specification for metric dimensions of toroidal sealing rings ('O'-rings) and their housings
BS 5106 : 1988 Specification for dimensions of spiral anti-extrusion back-up rings and their housings
BS 6442 : 1984 Spec. for limits of surface imperfections on elastomeric toroidal sealing rings ('O'-rings)
BS 6984 : 1988 Spec. for dims. of housings for elastomer-energized plastic-faced hydr'lic seals in recip. appl'ns
ISO 3601-1 : 1988 (Edition 2) Fluid systems – Sealing devices – 'O'-rings
BS 6997 : 1990 Specification for elastomeric 'O'-rings manufactured from acrylonitrile butadiene rubber (etc.)
BS EN 279 : 1991 Specification for 'O'-ring seal materials for domestic gas appliances (etc.)

For Aero 'O'-rings: See BS M33, M48 and M63.

SEALS 9.1.2

'O'-rings and their housings (toroidal seals): Sectional details, materials and notes on fitting

COMMON USES FOR 'O'-RING SEALS

Diametral sealing may be static or dynamic and may accommodate both linear and rotary movements. In the diagrams shown, pressure can be applied on either or both sides of the seal. Static face sealing can be done with a groove or chamfer, and in the examples shown, the end cap must be retained by external fluid or mechanical pressure.

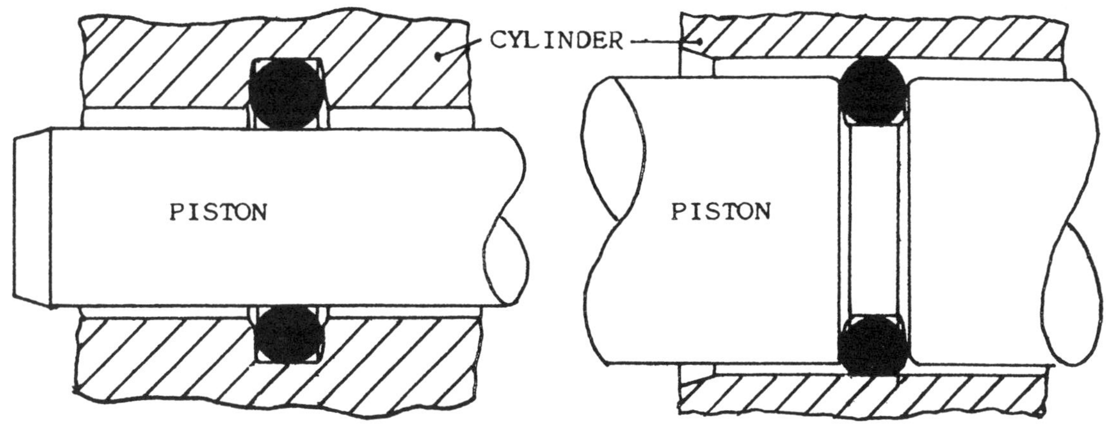

Groove in Cylinder *Groove in Piston*

DIAMETRAL SEALING (Note 'O'-ring taking up eccentricity)

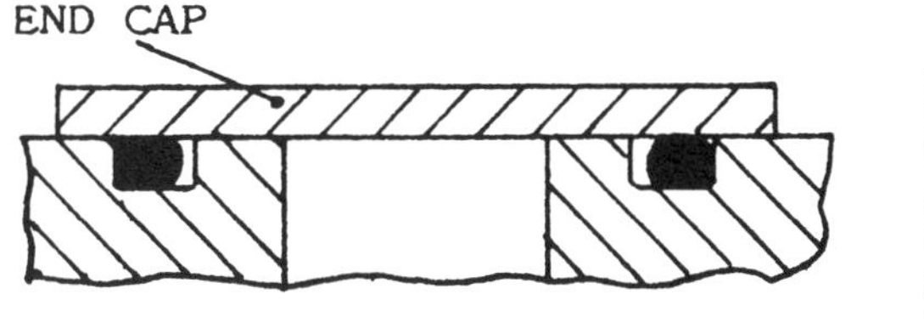

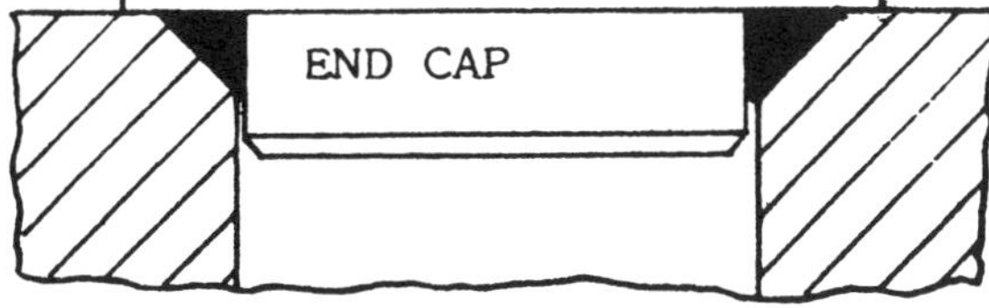

Grooved Housing *Triangular Housing*

STATIC FACE SEALING (Note distortion of 'O'-ring section)

'O' RING MATERIALS		
MATERIAL	**APPLICATIONS**	**TEMP. RANGE**
Nitrile rubber	Majority of uses	− 40 to + 130
Acrylate ester	Better heat resistance than Nitrile	− 10 to + 150
Butyl rubber	High resistance to synthetic fluids	− 35 to + 120
Polyurethane	High resistance to abrasion	− 50 to + 100
Ethylene propylene	Resistance to non-mineral synthetic fluid	− 55 to + 150
Fluorocarbon	High heat resistance	− 40 to + 230
Silicone	High temperature uses in static seals	− 40 to + 230
Chloroprene	Acid and ozone resistance	− 40 to + 120

FITTING OF 'O'-RINGS
Ring must be clean and free from dust
Check that housing finish is correct
Avoid twisting seal during assembly
Always lubricate before fitting
To avoid damage from sharp edges, a card cone may be used as illustrated.

RE-USE AND STORAGE
Rings are relatively cheap items and therefore reuse is normally unnecessary and is definitely inadvisable where high risk applications are concerned. Storage must be in clean, dry conditions and away from sharp edges and possible contaminants.

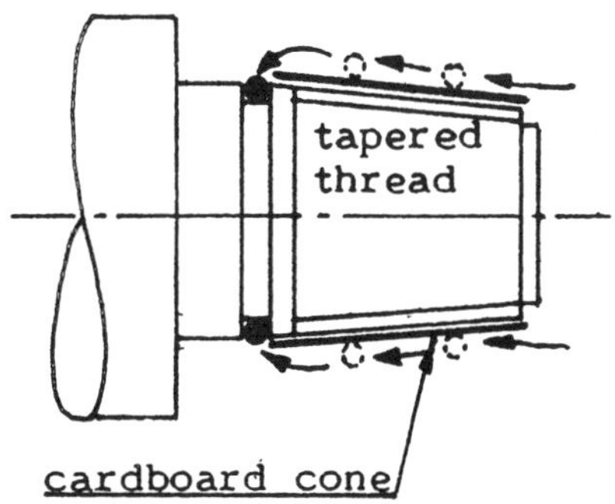

SEALS 9.1.3

Housings for diametral 'O'-ring sealing: Sizes

GROOVES FOR STATIC AND DYNAMIC DIAMETRAL SEALS @ UP TO 100 BAR

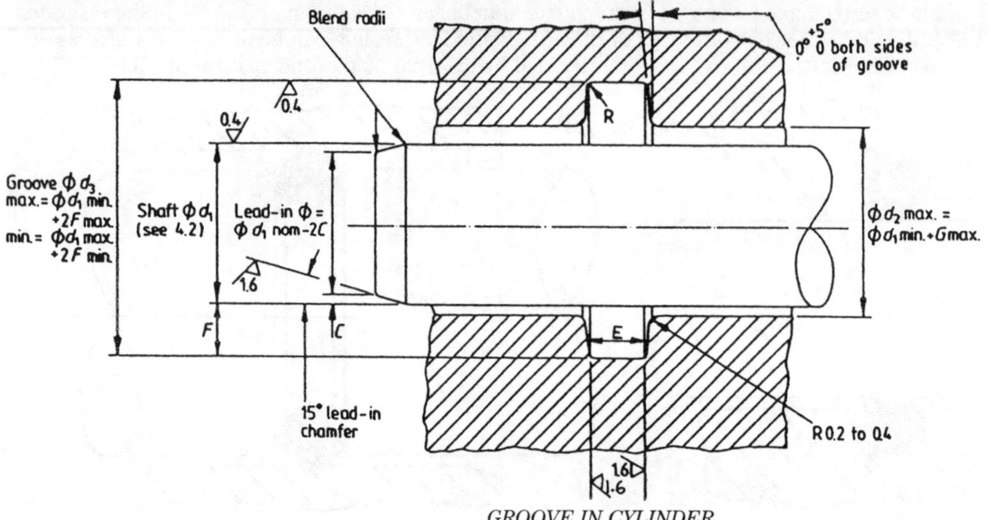

GROOVE IN CYLINDER

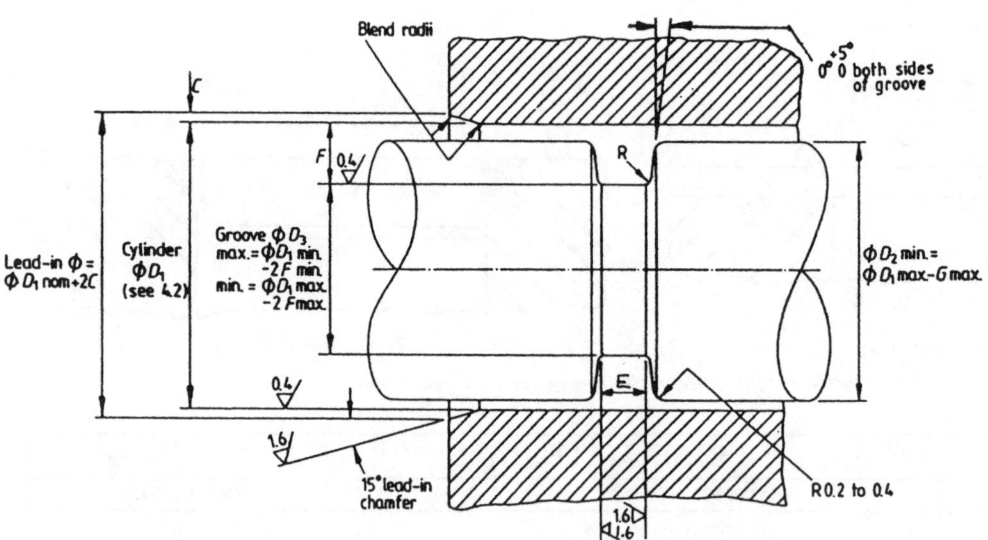

GROOVE IN PISTON

GROOVE DIMENSIONS FOR STATIC DIAMETRAL SEALING

'O'-ring ref. no.	Cross section diameter A	Radial depth F		Groove width E + 0.2 0	Total diametral clearance G (max.)	Lead-in chamfer C	Max. radius R
		max.	min.				
0031-16 to 0371-16	1.6	1.25	1.18	2.3	0.12	0.6	0.5
0036-24 to 0696-24	2.4	1.97	1.84	3.1	0.14	0.7	0.5
0195-30 to 2495-30	3.0	2.50	2.35	3.7	0.15	0.8	1.0
0443-57 to 4993-57	5.7	4.95	4.70	6.4	0.18	1.2	1.0
1441-84 to 2491-84	8.4	7.50	7.20	9.0	0.20	1.5	1.0

GROOVE DIMENSIONS FOR DYNAMIC DIAMETRAL SEALING IN PNEUMATICS AND HYDRAULICS

'O'-ring ref. no.	Cross section diameter A	Radial depth F for pneumatics		Radial depth F for hydraulics		Groove width E + 0.2 0	Total diametral clearance G (max.)	Lead-in chamfer C	Max. radius R
		max.	min.	max.	min				
0036-24 to 0176-24	2.4	2.20	2.13	2.09	1.97	3.2	0.14	0.6	0.5
0195-30 to 0445-30	3.0	2.77	2.70	2.65	2.50	4.0	0.15	0.7	1.0
0443-57 to 1443-57	5.7	5.38	5.22	5.18	4.95	7.5	0.18	1.0	1.0
1441-84 to 2491-84	8.4	7.96	7.75	7.75	7.50	11.0	0.20	1.2	1.0

DIMENSIONS OF 'O'-RINGS AND HOUSINGS FOR DIAMETRAL SEALING @ UP TO 100 BAR

Note : Reference number consists of ring internal diameter + section diameter (no decimal points).

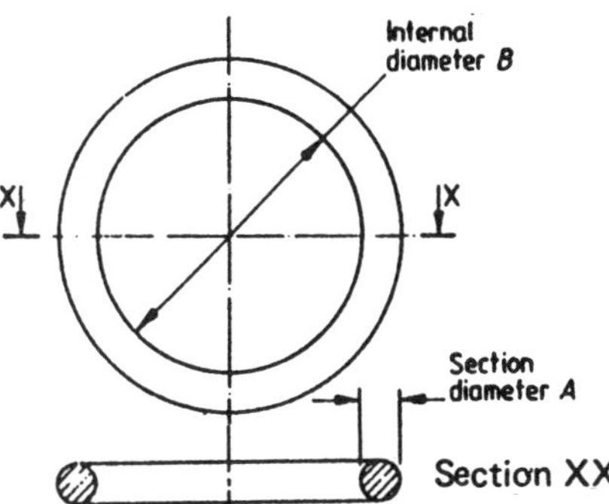

Toroidal Sealing Ring ('O'-ring)

'O'-ring ref. no (see note)	'O'-ring dimensions				Nominal housing dimensions (see figure 2 and 4.1)	
	Internal diameter $B_{(tolerance)}$		Section diameter $A_{(tolerance)}$		Shaft diameter d_1	Cylinder diameter D_1
0031-16	3.1		1.6		3.5	6
0041-16	4.1		1.6		4.5	7
0051-16	5.1		1.6		5.5	8†
0061-16	6.1	(± 0.15)	1.6	(± 0.08)	6.5	9
0071-16	7.1		1.6		7.5	10†
0081-16	8.1		1.6		8.5	11
0091-16	9.1		1.6		9.5	12†
0101-16	10.1		1.6		10.5	13
0111-16	11.1		1.6		11.5	14
0121-16	12.1		1.6		12.5	15
0131-16	13.1	(± 0.2)	1.6	(± 0.08)	13.5	16†
0141-16	14.1		1.6		14.5	17
0151-16	15.1		1.6		15.5	18
0161-16	16.1		1.6		16.5	19
0171-16	17.1		1.6		17.5	20†
0181-16	18.1		1.6		18.5	21
0191-16	19.1		1.6		19.5	22
0221-16	22.1	(± 0.25)	1.6	(± 0.08)	22.5	25†
0251-16	25.1		1.6		25.5	28
0271-16	27.1		1.6		27.5	30
0291-16	29.1		1.6		29.5	32†
0321-16	32.1		1.6		32.5	35
0351-16	35.1	(± 0.3)	1.6	(± 0.08)	35.5	38
0371-16	37.1		1.6		37.5	40†
0036-24 *	3.6		2.4		4†	8†
0046-24 *	4.6		2.4		5†	9
0056-24 *	5.6		2.4		6†	10†
0066-24 *	6.6	(± 0.15)	2.4	(± 0.08)	7	11
0076-24 *	7.6		2.4		8†	12†
0086-24 *	8.6		2.4		9	13
0096-24 *	9.6		2.4		10†	14
0106-24 *	10.6		2.4		11	15
0116-24 *	11.6		2.4		12†	16†
0126-24 *	12.6		2.4		13	17
0136-24 *	13.6	(± 0.2)	2.4	(± 0.08)	14†	18
0146-24 *	14.6		2.4		15	19
0156-24 *	15.6		2.4		16†	20†
0166-24 *	16.6		2.4		17	21
0176-24 *	17.6		2.4		18†	22
0186-24	18.6		2.4		19	23
0196-24	19.6		2.4		20†	24
0206-24	20.6		2.4		21	25†
0216-24	21.6	(± 0.25)	2.4	(± 0.08)	22†	26
0246-24	24.6		2.4		25†	29
0276-24	27.6		2.4		28†	32†
0296-24	29.6		2.4		30	34

'O'-ring ref. no (see note)	'O'-ring dimensions (continued)				Nominal housing dimensions (see figure opposite)	
	Internal diameter $B_{(tolerance)}$		Section diameter $A_{(tolerance)}$		Shaft diameter d_1	Cylinder diameter D_1
0316-24	31.6		2.4		32†	36
0346-24	34.6		2.4		35	39
0356-24	35.6		2.4		36†	40†
0376-24	37.6		2.4		38	42
0396-24	39.6	(± 0.3)	2.4	(± 0.08)	40†	44
0416-24	41.6		2.4		42	46
0446-24	44.6		2.4		45†	49
0456-24	45.6		2.4		46	50†
0476-24	47.6		2.4		48	52
0496-24	49.6		2.4		50†	54
0516-24	51.6		2.4		52	56
0546-24	54.6		2.4		55	59
0556-24	55.6		2.4		56†	60
0576-24	57.6		2.4		58	62
0586-24	58.6		2.4		59	63†
0596-24	59.6	(± 0.4)	2.4	(± 0.08)	60	64
0616-24	61.6		2.4		62	66
0626-24	62.6		2.4		63†	67
0646-24	64.6		2.4		65	69
0676-24	67.6		2.4		68	72
0696-24	69.6		2.4		70†	74
0195-30 *	19.5		3.0		20†	25†
0215-30 *	21.5		3.0		22†	27
0225-30 *	22.5		3.0		23	28
0245-30 *	24.5	(± 0.25)	3.0	(± 0.1)	25†	30
0255-30 *	25.5		3.0		26	31
0265-30 *	26.5		3.0		27	32†
0275-30 *	27.5		3.0		28†	33
0295-30 *	29.5		3.0		30	35
0315-30 *	31.5		3.0		32†	37
0325-30 *	32.5		3.0		33	38
0345-30 *	34.5		3.0		35	40†
0355-30 *	35.5		3.0		36†	41
0365-30 *	36.5		3.0		37	42
0375-30 *	37.5	(± 0.3)	3.0	(± 0.1)	38	43
0395-30 *	39.5		3.0		40†	45
0415-30 *	41.5		3.0		42	47
0425-30 *	42.5		3.0		43	48
0445-30 *	44.5		3.0		45†	50†
0495-30	49.5		3.0		50†	55
0545-30	54.5		3.0		55	60
0555-30	55.5		3.0		56†	61
0575-30	57.5		3.0		58	63†
0595-30	59.5		3.0		60	65
0625-30	62.5	(± 0.4)	3.0	(± 0.1)	63†	68
0645-30	64.5		3.0		65	70
0695-30	69.5		3.0		70†	75
0745-30	74.5		3.0		75	80†
0795-30	79.5		3.0		80†	85
0845-30	84.5		3.0		85	90
0895-30	89.5		3.0		90†	95
0945-30	94.5		3.0		95	100†
0995-30	99.5	(± 0.5)	3.0	(± 0.1)	100†	105
1045-30	104.5		3.0		105	110
1095-30	109.5		3.0		110†	115
1145-30	114.5		3.0		115	120
1195-30	119.5		3.0		120	125†

* Only 'O'-rings marked with an asterisk are recommended for dynamic sealing.

† Preferred size in accordance with BS 5755.

SEALS 9.1.5

'O'-rings and grooved housings for static face sealing: Sizes

GROOVE DIMENSIONS FOR STATIC FACE SEALING @ UP TO 100 BAR

'O'-ring ref. no.	Internal pressure			External pressure			H	R max.
	d (max.)	D	J	D (min.)	d	K		
0031-16	1.0	6.3		7.5	3.5			
0041-16	2.3	7.3		8.5	4.5	0.075		
0051-16	3.3	8.3	0.09	9.5	5.5			
0061-16	4.3	9.3		10.5	6.5			
0071-16	5.8	10.3		11.5	7.5			
0081-16	6.8	11.3		12.5	8.5	0.09		
0091-16	7.8	12.3		13.5	9.5			
0101-16	8.8	13.3		14.5	10.5			
0111-16	9.8	14.3	0.11	15.5	11.5			
0121-16	10.8	15.3		16.5	12.5			
0131-16	11.8	16.3		17.5	13.5			0.2
0141-16	12.8	17.3		18.5	14.5	0.11		
0151-16	14.0	18.3		19.5	15.5		$1.2^{+0.1}_{0}$	
0161-16	15	19.3		20.5	16.5			
0171-16	16	20.3		21.5	17.5			
0181-16	17	21.3	0.13	22.5	18.5			
0191-16	18	22.3		23.5	19.5			
0221-16	21	25.3		26.5	22.5			
0251-16	24	28.3		29.5	25.5	0.13		
0271-16	26	30.3		31.5	27.5			
0291-16	28	32.3		33.5	29.5			
0321-16	31	35.3	0.16	36.5	32.5			
0351-16	34	38.3		39.5	35.5	0.16		
0371-16	36	40.3		41.5	37.5			
0036-24	–	8.4		10	4			
0046-24	1.0	9.4	0.09	11	5	0.075		
0056-24	2.5	10.4		12	6			
0066-24	4.0	11.4		13	7			
0076-24	5.0	12.4		14	8			
0086-24	6.4	13.4		15	9	0.09		
0096-24	7.4	14.4		16	10			
0106-24	8.4	15.4		17	11			
0116-24	9.5	16.4	0.11	18	12			
0126-24	10.5	17.4		19	13			
0136-24	11.5	18.4		20	14	0.11		
0146-24	12.5	19.4		21	15			
0156-24	13.5	20.4		22	16			
0166-24	14.5	21.4		23	17			
0176-24	15.5	22.4		24	18			
0186-24	16.5	23.4		25	19			
0196-24	17.5	24.4	0.13	26	20			
0206-24	18.5	25.4		27	21			
0216-24	19.5	26.4		28	22	0.13		
0246-24	22.5	29.4		31	25		$1.7^{+0.1}_{0}$	0.5
0276-24	25.5	32.4		34	28			
0296-24	27.5	34.4		36	30			
0316-24	29.5	36.4		38	32			
0346-24	32.5	39.4		41	35			
0356-24	33.5	40.4		42	36			
0376-24	35.5	42.4	0.16	44	38			
0396-24	37.5	44.4		46	40			
0416-24	39.5	46.4		48	42	0.16		
0446-24	42.5	49.4		51	45			
0456-24	43.5	50.4		52	46			
0476-24	45.5	52.4		54	48			
0496-24	47.5	54.4		56	50			
0516-24	49.5	56.4		58	52			
0546-24	52.5	59.4		61	55			
0556-24	53.5	60.4		62	56			
0576-24	55.5	62.4		64	58			
0586-24	56.5	63.4		65	59			
0596-24	57.5	64.4	0.19	66	60			
0616-24	59.5	66.4		68	62	0.19		
0626-24	60.5	67.4		69	63			
0646-24	62.5	69.4		71	65			
0676-24	65.5	72.4		74	68			
0696-24	67.5	74.4		76	70			

GROOVE FORM

Note : The top plate shown in the diagram below will normally require additional mechanical fixing to hold it in place to prevent lifting or sliding when under pressure.

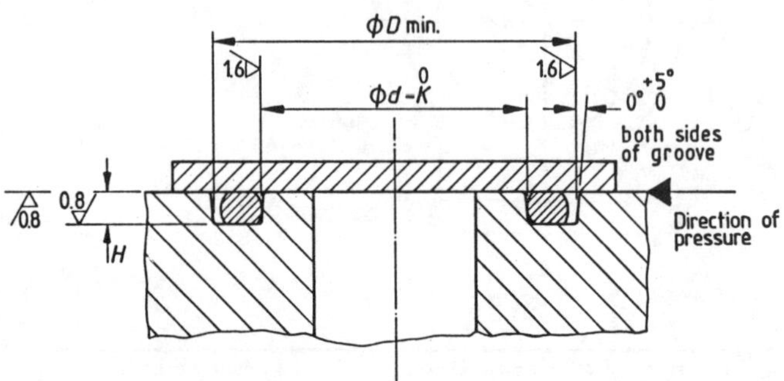

EXTERNALLY PRESSURIZED

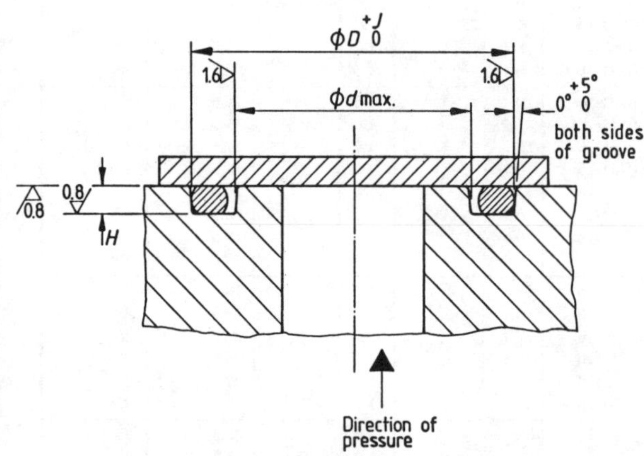

INTERNALLY PRESSURIZED

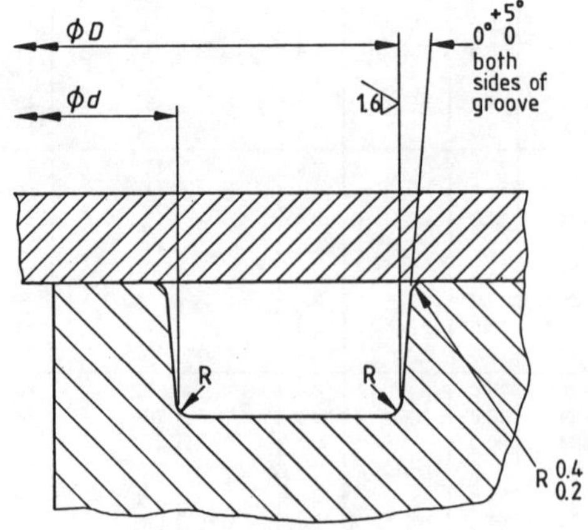

ENLARGED DETAIL OF 'O'-RING GROOVE

SEALS 9.1.6

'O'-rings and triangular housings for static face sealing: Sizes

TRIANGULAR STATIC FACE SEALING @ UP TO 100 BAR

Note that the spigot would normally need to be retained mechanically unless the greatest pressure is external and applied uniformly to its surface.

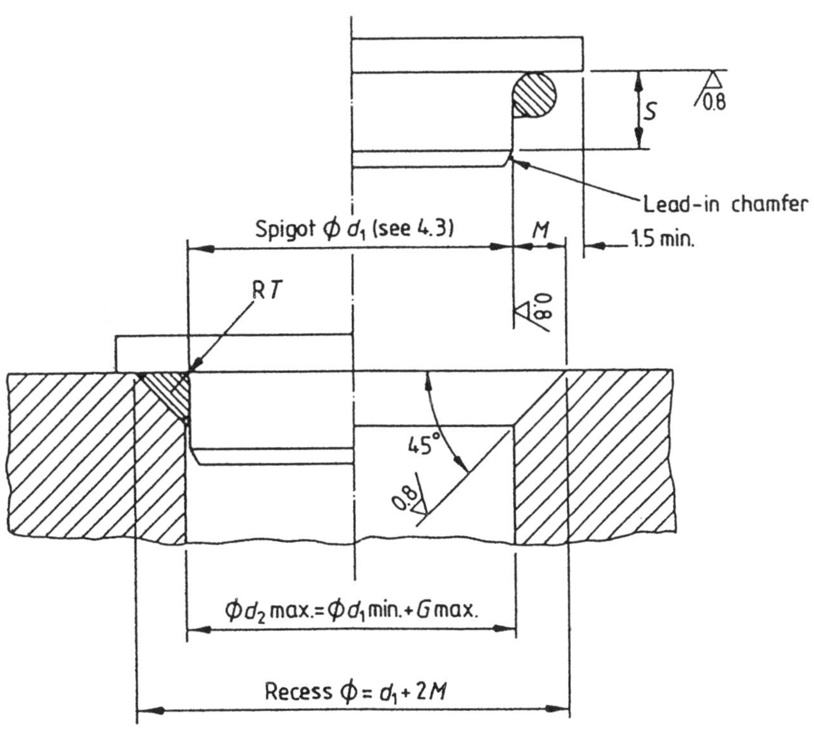

TRIANGULAR HOUSING PROFILE FOR STATIC SEALING

DIMENSIONS OF TRIANGULAR HOUSING PROFILE FOR STATIC SEALING

All dimensions in millimetres

'O'-RING		Spigot diameter	Total diametral clearance	Chamfer	Maximum radius on spigot	Spigot length
Reference no.	Cross section diameter A	d_1	G (max.)	$M^{+0.12}_{0}$		
T	S (min.)					
0031-16 to 0371-16	1.6		0.12	2.20	0.8	4.0
0036-24 to 0696-24	2.4	As in table	0.14	3.30	1.3	5.0
0195-30 to 2495-30	3.0	on 9.1.4	0.15	4.20	2.0	6.0
0443-57 to 4993-57	5.7		0.18	7.80	3.0	10.0
1441-84 to 2491-84	8.4		0.20	11.50	4.0	14.0

SEALS 9.1.7

'O'-rings for nominal shaft sizes: Sizes

The following tables are intended to aid selection of appropriate seals for given applications.

'O'-RING REFERENCE NUMBERS FOR NOMINAL SHAFT DIAMETERS

Nominal shaft diameter	Section diameter			
	1.6 mm	2.4 mm	3.0 mm	5.7 mm
mm				
3.5	0031-16			
4†		0036-24 *		
4.5	0041-16			
5†		0046-24 *		
5.5	0051-16			
6†		0056-24 *		
6.5	0061-16			
7		0066-24 *		
7.5	0071-16			
8†		0076-24 *		
8.5	0081-16			
9		0086-24 *		
9.5	0091-16			
10†		0096-24 *		
10.5	0101-16			
11		0106-24 *		
11.5	0111-16			
12†		0116-24 *		
12.5	0121-16			
13		0126-24 *		
13.5	0131-16			
14†		0136-24 *		
14.5	0141-16			
15		0146-24 *		
15.5	0151-16			
16†		0156-24 *		
16.5	0161-16			
17		0166-24 *		
17.5	0171-16			
18†		0176-24 *		
18.5	0181-16			
19		0186-24		
19.5	0191-16			
20†		0196-24	0195-30 *	
21		0206-24		
22†		0216-24	0215-30 *	
22.5	0221-16			
23			0225-30 *	
25†		0226-24	0245-30 *	
25.5	0251-16			
26			0255-30 *	
27			0265-30 *	
27.5	0271-16			
28†		0276-24	0275-30 *	
29.5	0291-16			
30		0296-24	0295-30 *	
32†		0316-24	0315-30 *	
32.5	0321-16			
33			0325-30 *	
35		0346-24	0345-30 *	
35.5	0351-16			
36†		0356-24	0355-30 *	
37			0365-30 *	
37.5	0371-16			
38		0376-24	0375-30 *	
40†		0396-24	0395-30 *	
42		0416-24	0415-30 *	
43			0425-30 *	
45†		0446-24	0445-30	0443-57 *
46		0456-24		0453-57 *
48		0476-24		
50†		0496-24	0495-30	0493-57 *
52		0516-24		

Nominal shaft diameter	Section diameter			
	2.4 mm	3.0 mm	5.7 mm	8.4 mm
mm				
53			0523-57 *	
55	0546-24	0545-30	0543-57 *	
56†	0556-24	0555-30	0553-57 *	
58	0576-24	0575-30		
59	0586-24			
60	0596-24	0595-30	0593-57 *	
62	0616-24			
63†	0626-24	0625-30	0623-57 *	
65	0646-24	0645-30	0643-57 *	
68	0676-24			
70†	0696-24	0695-30	0693-57 *	
75		0745-30	0743-57 *	
80†		0795-30	0793-57 *	
85		0845-30	0843-57 *	
90†		0895-30	0893-57 *	
95		0945-30	0943-57 *	
100†		0995-30	0993-57 *	
105		1045-30	1043-57 *	
110†		1095-30	1093-57 *	
115		1145-30	1143-57 *	
120		1195-30	1193-57 *	
125†		1245-30	1243-57 *	
130		1295-30	1293-57 *	
135		1345-30	1343-57 *	
140†		1395-30	1393-57 *	
145		1445-30	1443-57 *	1441-84 *
150		1495-30	1493-57	1491-84 *
155		1545-30	1543-57	1541-84 *
160†		1595-30	1593-57	1591-84 *
165		1645-30	1643-57	1641-84 *
170		1695-30	1693-57	1691-84 *
175		1745-30	1743-57	1741-84 *
180†		1795-30	1793-57	1791-84 *
185		1845-30	1843-57	1841-84 *
190		1895-30	1893-57	1891-84 *
195		1945-30	1943-57	1941-84 *
200†		1995-30	1993-57	1991-84 *
205				2041-84 *
210		2095-30	2093-57	2091-84 *
220†		2195-30	2193-57	2191-84 *
230		2295-30	2293-57	2291-84 *
235				2341-84 *
240		2395-30	2393-57	2391-84 *
245		2445-30		
250†		2495-30	2493-57	2491-84 *
260			2593-57	
270			2693-57	
280†			2793-57	
290			2893-57	
300			2993-57	
310			3093-57	
320†			3193-57	
340			3393-57	
360†			3593-57	
380			3793-57	
390			3893-57	
400			3993-57	
420			4193-57	
440			4393-57	
460			4593-57	
480			4793-57	
490			4893-57	
500			4993-57	

* Recommended for dynamic sealing.

† Preferred size in accordance with BS 5755.

SEALS 9.1.8

'O'-rings for nominal cylinder sizes: Sizes

'O'-RING REFERENCE NUMBERS FOR NOMINAL CYLINDER DIAMETERS

Nominal cylinder diameter	Section diameter			
	1.6 mm	2.4 mm	3.0 mm	5.7 mm
mm				
6	0031-16			
7	0041-16			
8†	0051-16	0036-24 *		
9	0061-16	0046-24 *		
10†	0071-16	0056-24 *		
11	0081-16	0066-24 *		
12†	0091-16	0076-24 *		
13	0101-16	0086-24 *		
14	0111-16	0096-24 *		
15	0121-16	0106-24 *		
16†	0131-16	0116-24 *		
17	0141-16	0126-24 *		
18	0151-16	0136-24 *		
19	0161-16	0146-24 *		
20†	0171-16	0156-24 *		
21	0181-16	0166-24 *		
22	0191-16	0176-24 *		
23		0186-24		
24		0196-24		
25†	0221-16	0206-24	0195-30 *	
26		0216-24		
27			0215-30 *	
28	0251-16		0225-30 *	
29		0246-24		
30	0271-16		0245-30 *	
31			0255-30 *	
32†	0291-16	0276-24	0265-30 *	
33			0275-30 *	
34		0296-24		
35	0321-16		0295-30 *	
36		0316-24		
37			0315-30 *	
38	0351-16		0325-30 *	
39		0346-24		
40†	0371-16	0356-24	0345-30 *	
41			0355-30 *	
42		0376-24	0365-30 *	
43			0375-30 *	
44		0396-24		
45			0395-30 *	
46		0416-24		
47			0415-30 *	
48			0425-30 *	
49		0446-24		
50†		0456-24	0445-30 *	
52		0476-24		
54		0496-24		
55			0495-30	0443-57 *
56		0516-24		0453-57 *
59		0546-24		
60		0556-24	0545-30	0493-57 *
61			0555-30	
62		0576-24		
63†		0586-24	0575-30	0523-57 *

Nominal cylinder diameter	Section diameter			
	2.4 mm	3.0 mm	5.7 mm	8.4 mm
mm				
64	0596-24			
65		0595-30	0543-57 *	
66	0616-24		0553-57 *	
67	0626-24			
68		0625-30		
69	0646-24			
70		0645-30	0593-57 *	
72	0676-24			
73			0623-57 *	
74	0696-24			
75		0695-30	0643-57 *	
80†		0745-30	0693-57 *	
85		0795-30	0743-57 *	
90		0845-30	0793-57 *	
95		0895-30	0843-57 *	
100†		0945-30	0893-57 *	
105		0995-30	0943-57 *	
110		1045-30	0993-57 *	
115		1095-30	1043-57 *	
120		1145-30	1093-57 *	
125†		1195-30	1143-57 *	
130		1245-30	1193-57 *	
135		1295-30	1243-57 *	
140		1345-30	1293-57 *	
145		1395-30	1343-57 *	
150		1445-30	1393-57 *	
155		1495-30	1443-57 *	
160†		1545-30	1493-57	1441-84 *
165		1595-30	1543-57	1491-84 *
170		1645-30	1593-57	1541-84 *
175		1695-30	1643-57	1591-84 *
180		1745-30	1693-57	1641-84 *
185		1795-30	1743-57	1691-84 *
190		1845-30	1793-57	1741-84 *
195		1895-30	1843-57	1791-84
200†		1945-30	1893-57	1841-84 *
205		1995-30	1943-57	1891-84 *
210			1993-57	1941-84 *
215		2095-30		1991-84 *
220			2093-57	2041-84 *
225		2195-30		2091-84 *
230			2193-57	
235		2295-30		2191-84 *
240			2293-57	
245		2395-30		2291-84 *
250†		2445-30	2393-57	2341-84 *
255		2495-30		2391-84 *
260			2493-57	
265				2491-84 *
270			2593-57	
280			2693-57	
290			2793-57	
300			2893-57	
310			2993-57	
320†			3093-57	
330			3193-57	
350			3393-57	
370			3593-57	
390			3793-57	
400†			3893-57	
410			3993-57	
430			4193-57	
450			4393-57	
470			4593-57	
490			4793-57	
500			4893-57	
510			4993-57	

* Recommended for dynamic sealing.
† Preferred size in accordance with BS 5755.

SUPPLIERS

SEALS: 'O'-rings

COMPANY	ADDRESS	TELEPHONE	FAX
Avon Group Manufacturing Ltd	Aiken Street Barton Hill BRISTOL Avon BS5 9TG	0272 557874	0272 541596
Beldam Crossley Ltd	PO Box 7 Hill Mill Temple Road Astley Bridge BOLTON Gt Manchester BL1 6PB	0204 494711	0204 40550
DORS Ltd	8 Brickfield Ind Est New Road GILLINGHAM Dorset SP8 5JL	0747 824670	0747 825466
Dowty Seals Ltd	Ashchurch TEWKESBURY Glos GL20 8JS	0684 299111	0684 852210
Greene Tweed & Co Ltd	Finch Close NOTTINGHAM Notts NG7 2NN	0602 866555	0602 866235
Hallite Seals International Ltd	Oldfield Road HAMPTON Middlesex TW12 2HT	081-941 2244	081-783 1669
Rubber Engineering Services Ltd	Windmill Lane Ind Est Denton MANCHESTER M34 3RB	061 320 9900	
Technical Rubber Products Ltd	Netherwood Road Rotherwas Ind Est HEREFORD HR2 6JZ	0432 279366	
James Walker & Co Ltd	Lion Works WOKING Surrey GU22 8AP	0483 757575	0483 755711

USEFUL ADDRESSES

SEALS

ADDRESS	TELEPHONE
High Pressure Technology Association Holly Cottage Clay Lane Beenham READING RG7 5PA	0734 713722
Plastics and Rubber Institute 11 Hobart Place LONDON SW1W 0HL	071 245 9555
RAPRA Technology Ltd Shawbury SHREWSBURY SY4 4NR	0939 250383

COIL SPRINGS 9.2.1

Helical compression, extension and torsion springs: Construction, selection and use

TYPICAL APPLICATIONS: Engineering assemblies ranging from precision instruments to mechanical handling devices. High usage in materials handling and packaging machinery, jigs, tools, counterbalances for shutters and doors, locking and security devices, timers, automatic valves, vehicle transmissions.

DEFINITION: A mechanical component which behaves elastically when under load.

CONSTRUCTION: Springs are made by either hot or cold working processes from a range of materials including steels, copper alloys and composites. The most popular material is coiled circular section, high carbon steel wire. This may then be pre-stressed, stress relieved or shot-peened (a cold working process) depending on user requirements. A variety of end coil formations are available to suit fixing method and material and a range of protective coatings from plastic to chrome may be specified. With hot operating conditions, materials such as silicon chrome steel are used which can withstand temperatures up to 250°C.

NOTES ON SELECTION AND USE:
Mechanical springs may be used to apply force, store or absorb energy or provide elastic movement. They are frequently key elements in the operation of safety devices and their failure can often have damaging results. Selection criteria should include : space available, magnitude and direction of loads and deflections, accuracy and reliablility, environmental conditions, tolerances and costs. Spring dimensions may be simply specified by : wire diameter (or cross-sectional area), coil diameter, free length and number of coils. For a full specification however, it is important to follow guidelines and complete spring data sheets as laid out in the relevant standard. Loading conditions are usually the first design priority since at one end of the scale performance under load may be unimportant, whereas at the other, detailed spring rate data may be needed. The two most common types are helical compression and extension springs, the former having flat end coils and the latter either hooks or eyes for load transfer (which are an additional cost factor). Compression springs should close 'solid' without damage and extension springs need either large safety factors or mechanical stops to prevent overstressing. Springs must normally be constrained at one or both ends so that the risk of lift or slide is minimised although some transverse or eccentric loading may be desirable to suit a particular application. End fixing for compression springs may require a pad to evenly distribute loading and prevent damage to the base structure especially if it is thin sheet or plastic. Where springs are fitted over a rod or inside a hole or tube, care must be taken with tolerances, (especially if temperature rises are expected), to prevent jamming or scuffing. Where very close fitting is needed springs can be supplied with the outside and ends pre-ground (barrelled and faced). One of the most important long-term considerations is corrosion and as a general rule springs at risk should be located within a protective surround and, if made of ferrous metal, be lightly coated with oil or grease. Electroplating may be specified as an alternative to lubrication but note that its effect may be to cause an increase in spring rate. If blind holes are used for end fixings in wet environments, these may become moisture traps and should be avoided. The same applies to situations where electrolytic corrosion may occur between the spring and the material to which it is fixed. High temperatures can cause tempering of the spring material and undesirable expansion may also effect physical performance.

REFERENCES:

BS 970 :	Specification for wrought steels for mechanical and allied engineering purposes
BS 1726 :	Coil springs
	Part 1 : 1987 Guide for the design of helical compression springs
	Part 2 : 1988 . . . . helical extension springs Part 3: 1988 . . . . helical torsion springs
BS 2056 : 1991	Specification for stainless steel wire for mechanical springs
BS 4637 : 1970 (1990)	Specification for carbon steel wire for coiled springs (bedding and seating)
BS 4638 : 1970 (1990)	Specification for carbon steel wire for zigzag and square-form springs
BS 2803 : 1980 (1986)	Pre-hardened and tempered steel wire for general engineering springs (etc)
BS 2786 : 1963	Brass wire for springs (etc)
BS 1429 : 1980 (1986)	Annealed round steel wire for general engineering springs
BS 4638 : 1970 (1990)	Carbon steel wire for zigzag and square form springs
BS 7612 : 1993	Non-circular steel wire for mechanical springs

For Aero applications see : Aero S201 to 205

COIL SPRINGS 9.2.2

Helical compression, extension and torsion springs: Types

TYPES COMMONLY AVAILABLE

a. Cylindrical helical compression spring of wire of circular cross section.

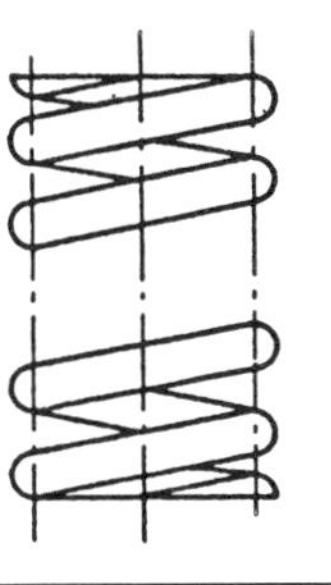

b. Cylindrical helical compression spring of wire of rectangular cross section.

c. Conical helical compression spring of wire of circular cross section.

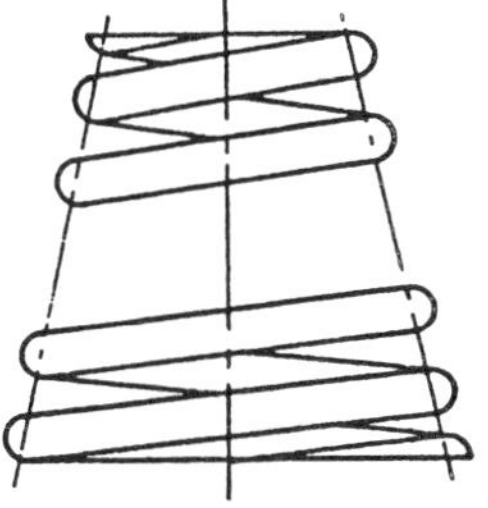

d. Conical helical compression spring of wire of rectangular cross section (volute spring).

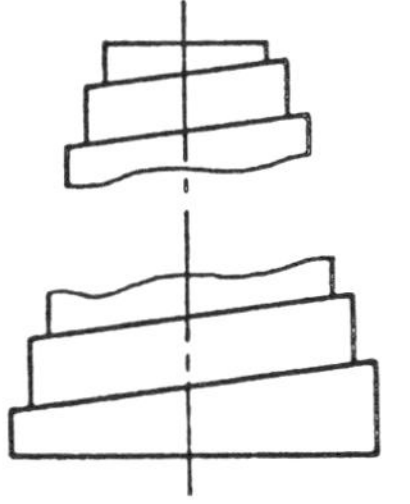

i. Spiral spring

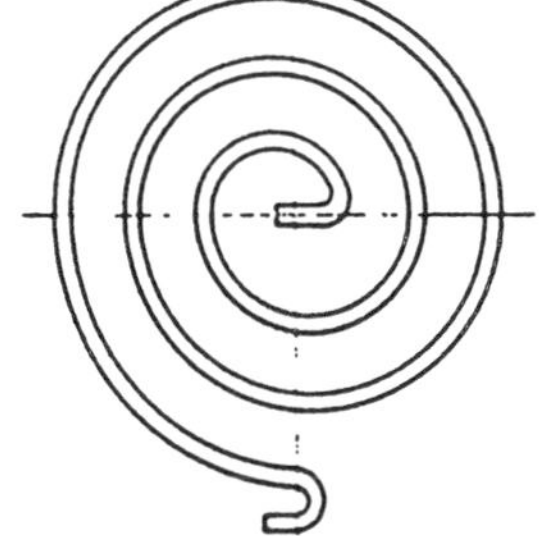

ii. Semi-elliptic leaf spring with eyes

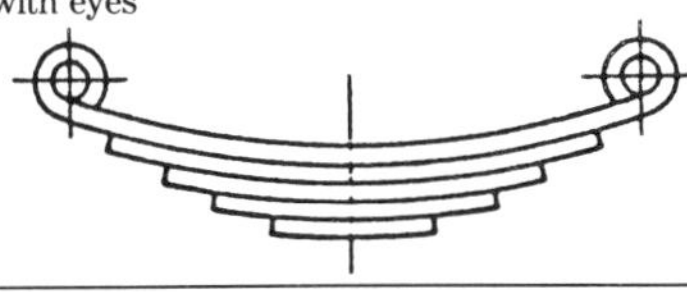

A. Cylindrical helical tension spring of wire of circular cross section.

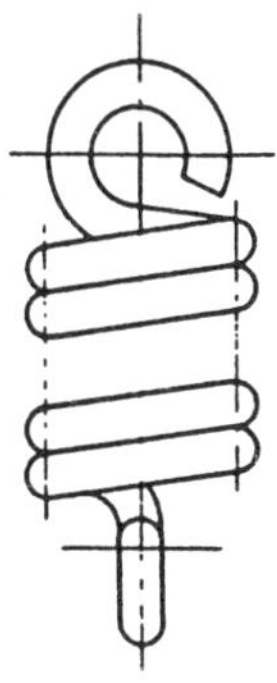

B. Double-conical helical tension spring of circular cross section.

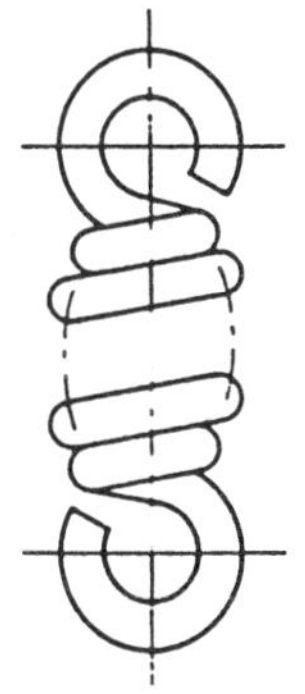

C. Cylindrical helical torsion spring of wire of circular cross section (wound right hand).

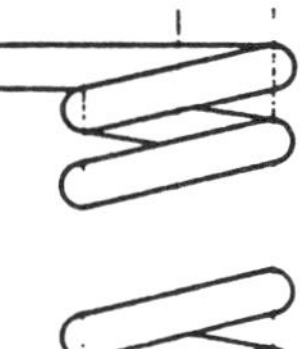

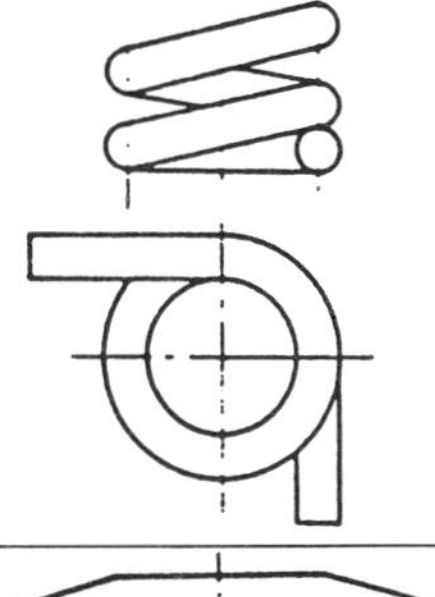

I. Cup spring.

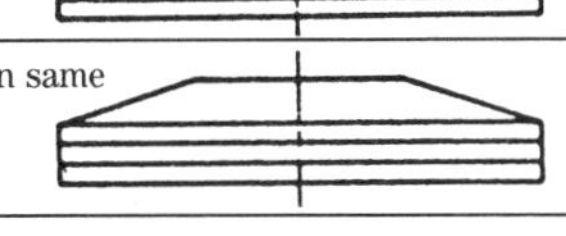

II. Multi-cup spring (cups placed in same direction).

III. Multi-cup spring (successive cups alternating in direction).

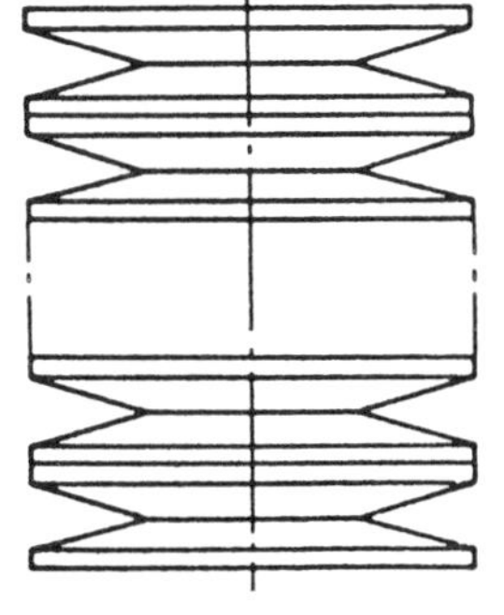

COIL SPRINGS 9.2.3

Helical compression, extension and torsion springs: Types of end coils and legs

NOTE: Other standard end types may be available or new designs agreed between purchaser and supplier. Where non-standard thin wire loops or legs are required, special care must be taken to avoid fatigue or bending failure at the point of fixing. Exposed ends of compression and torsion springs may present safety risks and covers or guards should be specified in these cases.

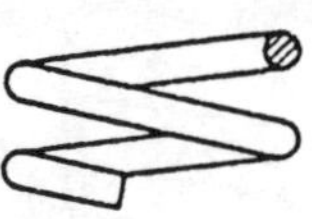

(a) Open end

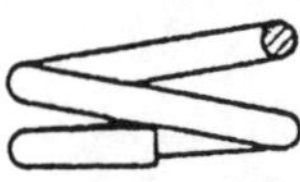

(b) Closed end

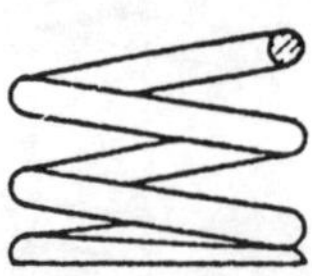

(c) Closed and ground end

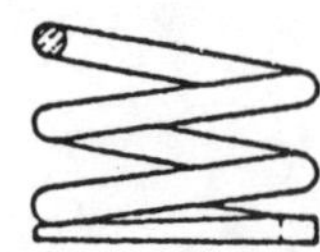

(d) Coil end formed from tapered bar

COMPRESSION SPRINGS

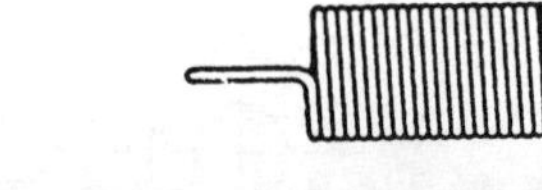

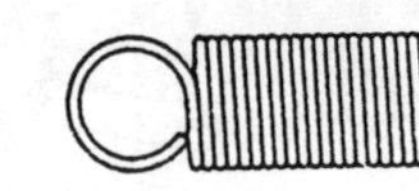

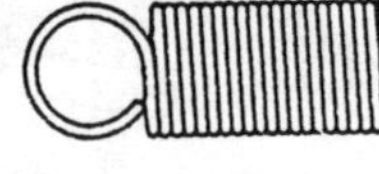

(a) Machine loop

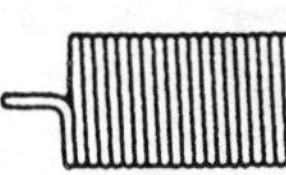

(b) D-loop

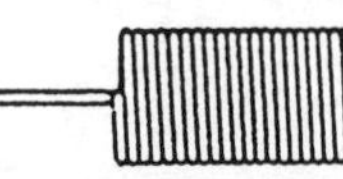

(c) Crossover loop

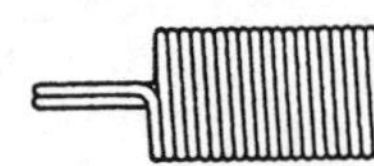

(d) Double machine loop

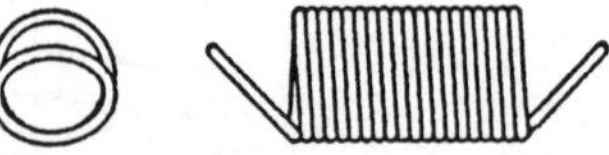

(e) Angled loop
NOTE: The loading is axial

EXTENSION SPRINGS Group 1 end loops
(See BS 1726 : Part 2 for details of other groups)

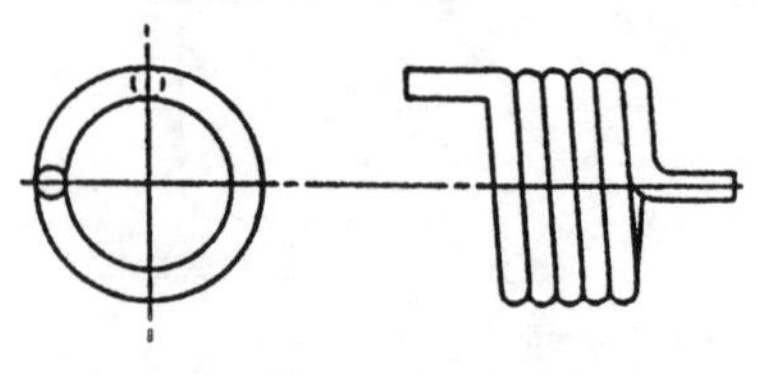

(a) Axial legs

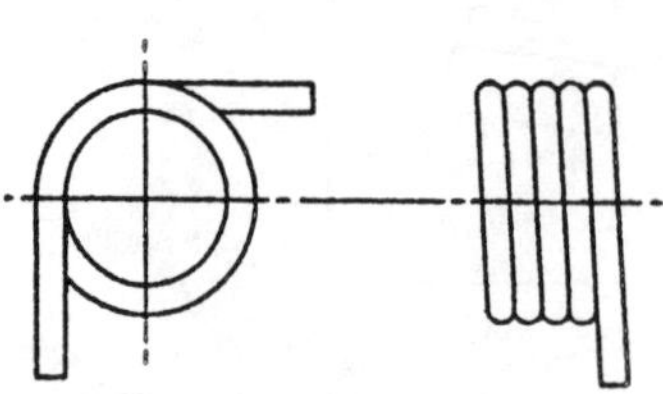

(b) Tangential legs

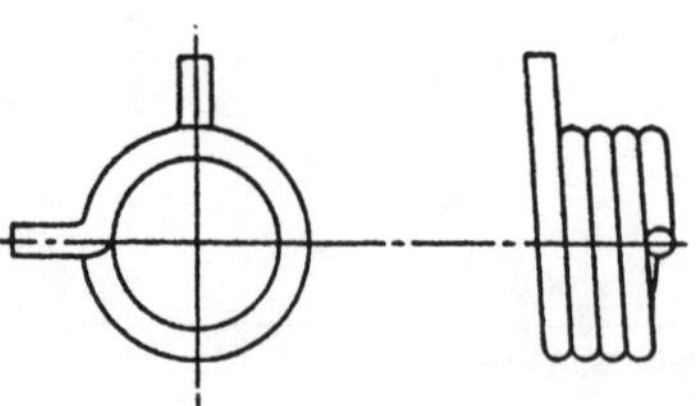

(c) Radial external legs

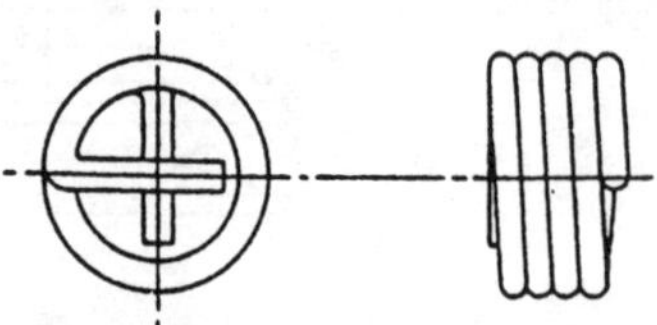

(d) Radial over-centre legs

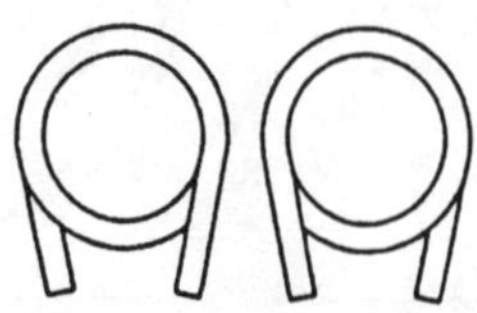

Left hand   Right hand
DIRECTION OF COILING

TORSION SPRINGS
(See BS 1726 : Part 3 for special drawing conventions for these springs)

COIL SPRINGS 9.2.4

Helical compression, extension and torsion springs: Calculations for compression and extension springs

BASIC FORMULAE FOR SIMPLE CALCULATIONS

These formulae are for compression and extension springs made from *circular section* material only. Effects of : heat and surface treatments and coatings, tolerances, stability and end coil types (see 9.2.3) are not taken into account here. The comprehensive standard BS 1726 (Parts 1, 2 and 3) should be referred to when specifying springs for manufacture. It is recommended that specification pro-formas shown in this standard are used both as a formal document for the supplier and as an 'aide memoire' and record for the designer.

MODULUS OF RIGIDITY VALUES

Material	Modulus of rigidity kN / mm²
All carbon, low alloy and martensitic stainless steels	79
Austenitic stainless steel	70
Phosphor bronze	43
Hard drawn brass wire	36
Copper beryllium	41
Titanium alloy	38

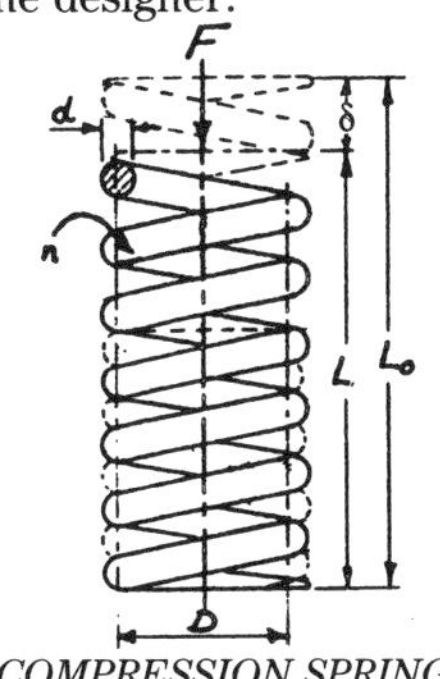

COMPRESSION SPRING

SYMBOLS

Symbol	Term	Unit
c	spring index	–
D	mean coil diameter	mm
d	material diameter	mm
F	spring force	N
Δ F	change in spring force	N
f	natural frequency of unloaded spring	Hz
G	modulus of rigidity (see table above)	N / mm²
K	stress correction factor	–
L	spring length	mm
L_0	free length of spring	mm
Δ L	change in spring length	mm
n	number of active coils in spring	–
S	spring rate	N / mm
τ	shear stress in spring	N / mm²
ρ	density of material	kg / mm³
δ	deflection from nominal free length to loaded length	mm
F_0	nominal initial tension	N

FORMULAE FOR COMPRESSION AND EXTENSION SPRINGS

(See BS 1726 for detailed calculations including torsion springs)

SPRING RATE:

The spring rate, S is given by the equation:

$$S = \frac{\Delta F}{\Delta L} = \frac{G\,d^4}{8\,n\,D^3}$$

NATURAL FREQUENCY OF UNLOADED SPRING

The natural frequency of the unloaded spring, f, is given by the equation:

$$f = \frac{d}{2\,p\,n\,D^2}\sqrt{\frac{G}{2\,r}}$$

STRESS CORRECTION FACTOR

The stress correction factor, K, is given by the equation:

$$K = \frac{c + 0.2}{c - 1} \quad \text{where} \quad c = \frac{D}{d}$$

NOTE : In the case of springs with an index less than 5 this correction factor will lead to conservative results and when such springs are subject only to static operating conditions the spring designer may make allowance for this fact.

SHEAR STRESS

The shear stress, τ, is given by the equation:

$$\tau = \frac{8\,F\,D\,K}{\pi\,d^3}$$

HELICAL EXTENSION SPRINGS

The calculation below only predicts the stress in the body of the spring. The point of maximum stress might occur elsewhere in the spring, e.g. in the end loops. If this is important, further analysis should be carried out. It should be noted that, when considering stresses in the end loops, a curvature correction factor for bending will have to be used.

SPRING FORCE

The spring force, F, is given by the equation:

$$F = S\,\delta + F_0$$

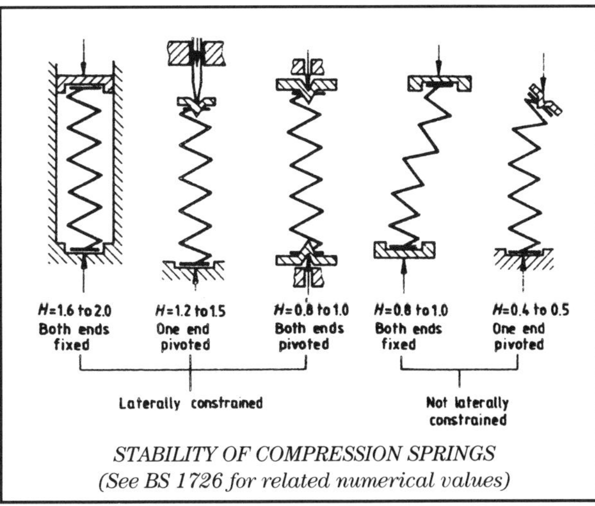

STABILITY OF COMPRESSION SPRINGS
(See BS 1726 for related numerical values)

SUPPLIERS

MECHANICAL COMPONENTS: Springs

COMPANY	ADDRESS	TELEPHONE	FAX
Airedale Springs Ltd	Ebor Works Haworth KEIGHLEY W Yorks BD22 8HT	0535 43456	
A-P Springs Ltd	Reddings Lane Tyseley BIRMINGHAM B11 3HA	021 706 2236	021 708 1253
Baumann Springs & Pressings (UK) Ltd	East Mill Lane SHERBORNE Dorset DT9 3DR	0935 812333	0935 814141
Dixons of Halifax	Raglan Street HALIFAX W Yorks HX1 5QY	0422 53339	0422 64532
Harris Springs Ltd	Clifford House Ind Est Ruscombe Lane Ruscombe READING Berks RG10 9LR	0734 340024	0734 341365
Heath Springs Ltd	Heath House Hewell Road REDDITCH Worcs B97 6AY	0527 61952	0527 591660
Lewis Spring Products Ltd	Studley Road REDDITCH Worcs B98 7HJ	0527 510535	0527 500868
Quality Springs & Productions Ltd	St Georges Rd REDDITCH Worcs B98 8EF	0527 63617	0527 584536
Salter Springs & Pressings Ltd	Spring Road Smethwick WARLEY W Midlands B66 1PF	021-553 2929	021-553 7096
Vernier Spring Co Ltd	Vernier Works Edward Street REDDITCH Worcs B97 6HA	0527 61001	0527 584614

USEFUL ADDRESSES

SPRINGS

ADDRESS	TELEPHONE
SRAMA Spring Research and Manufacturers Association Henry Street SHEFFIELD S3 7EQ	0742 760771
Wire Goods Manufacturer's Association 136 Suffolk Street Queensway BIRMINGHAM B1 1LL	021 631 2288
Wire Products Association 23 St Aubyns Road LONDON SE19 3AA	081 771 6444

Notes

SECTION 10 – GRAPHIC REPRESENTATION

ENGINEERING DRAWING 10.1.1

Forms of drawing, Computer-aided drawing/design

DEFINITION:

An engineering drawing is a graphical representation, on one or more sheets, of the position and/or form of an object. Graphical production is by manual or computer-aided instruments.

FORMS OF DRAWING :

Layout and **scheme** drawings present the broad principles and feasibility for a design. **Detail** drawings depict single objects and include all necessary information for them to be fully defined. **Assembly** drawings show two or more parts, or sub-assemblies, in their finished form but with only limited information such as general dimensions. **General Arrangement** drawings show the complete finished product or installation made up from its various assemblies. A **parts list** is a detailed record of all the items which go together to form the assembly or arrangement, and will usually include: an identifying number, a description, material(s) of construction and source of supply. It is often drawn on the same sheet as the general arrangement, although it can form part of the general paperwork associated with the drawings. **Change** from the original drawing is indicated on the sheet by an **issue** number followed by a note about the change. Where a drawn item is already in manufacture, then some form of **change note** needs to be sent, followed by an update of all drawings affected.

COMPUTER-AIDED DRAWING AND DESIGN :

In principle, the CAD system serves the same function as the drawing board for straightforward draughting, but operates more like an electronic storage and retrieval device when used for design work. It permits the engineer to file away and recover large amounts of data associated with any particular design including: sketches, calculations, parts lists, components and materials. One major advantage over the traditional drawing board is the speed and accuracy with which changes can be made, and with a 'redraw' taking only seconds, a large number of drawings can be done very quickly, each one being slightly different from the other. Symbols and shapes which are in constant use may be saved and easily recovered at any scale, given a code number, then automatically listed on a bill of parts and materials. If there are calculations associated with a part, then these can be done on the screen by just interrupting the drawing process. In many instances, the CAD system is used to provide a complete record of 'work in progress' including process times and product costs.

Computer-aided manufacture (CAM) is now commonly linked to CAD so that the Design and Manufacturing functions in many organisations are now integrated rather than operating as separate departments. The basic rules of engineering drawing and communication in BS 308 still apply however, despite the rapid progress in CAD/CAM. The engineer still needs to learn the skills of careful planning and attention to detail using the universal language of graphical presentation, even though it is no longer necessary to acquire a high level of ability in manual draughting techniques.

REFERENCES :

BS 308 :	Engineering drawing practice
	Part 1: 1984 Recommendations for general principles
	Part 2: 1985 (1992) Recommendations for dimensioning and tolerancing of size
	Part 3: 1990 Recommendations for geometrical tolerancing
BS 5070:	Engineering diagram drawing practice
PP 7308: 1986	Engineering drawing practice for schools and colleges
	(An abridgement of BS 308 : Parts 1 & 2 for teachers and students)
ISO 2692: 1988	Technical drawings - Geometrical tolerancing - Maximum material principle
ISO 6413: 1988	Technical drawings - Representation of splines and serrations
ISO 7000: 1984	Graphic symbols for use on equipment, index and synopsis
PD 7304	(PP 7304) Geometrical tolerancing : an introduction
BS 3934:	Mechanical strandardization of semiconductor devices (drawings)
BS 1192:	Construction (industry) drawing practice
BS 5536: 1988	Recommendations for preparation of technical drawing for microfilming

ENGINEERING DRAWING 10.1.2

Basic data, sheet sizes, projections and abbreviations

DRAWING SHEETS

Basic information. It is recommended that provision be made for basic information such as the following.

(a) Name of company or organization
(b) Drawing number
(c) Descriptive title of depicted part or assembly
(d) Date of drawing
(e) Signature(s), e.g. drawn by, authorized by
(f) Original scale
(g) Copyright clause
(h) Projection symbol
(i) Unit of measurement
(j) Reference to standards and/or related specifications
(k) Sheet number
(l) Number of sheets
(m) Issue information

RECOMMENDED DRAWING SHEET SIZES (TRIMMED)

Designation	Size	Minimum border width from drawing frame to edge of sheet
	mm	mm
A0	841 x 1189	20
A1	594 x 841	20
A2	420 x 594	10
A3	297 x 420	10
A4	210 x 297	10

CHARACTER HEIGHT

Application	Drawing sheet size	Minimum character height
		mm
Drawing numbers etc.	A0, A1, A2 and A3	7
	A4	5
Dimensions and notes	A0	3.5
	A1, A2, A3 and A4	2.5

SYMBOLS INDICATING METHOD OF PROJECTION

Projection	Symbol
First angle	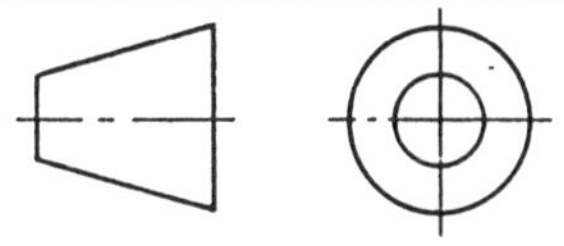
Third angle	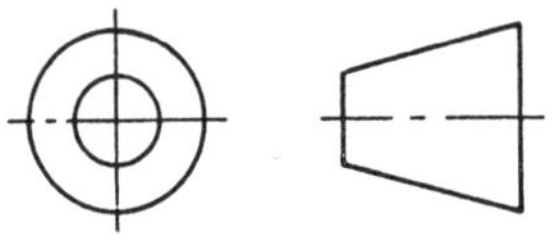

COMMONLY ACCEPTED SYMBOLS AND ABBREVIATIONS

Term	Abbreviation or symbol
Across flats	AF
Assembly	ASSY
British Standard	BS
Centres	CRS
Centre line	
on a view	℄
in a note	CL
Centre of gravity	CG
Chamfered, chamfer (in a note)	CHAM
Cheese head	CH HD
Countersunk	CSK
Countersunk head	CSK HD
Counterbore	CBORE
Cylinder or cylindrical	CYL
Diameter (in a note)	DIA
Diameter (preceding a dimension)	Ø
Dimension	DIM
Drawing	DRG
Equally spaced	EQUI SP
External	EXT
Figure	FIG.
Full indicated movement	FIM
Hexagon	HEX
Hexagon head	HEX HD
Insulated or insulation	INSUL
Internal	INT
Left hand	LH
Long	LG
Machine	MC
Material	MATL
Maximum	MAX
Maximum material condition	MMC
Minimum	MIN
Not to scale	NTS
Number	NO.
Pattern Number	PATT NO.
Pitch circle diameter	PCD
Radius (in a note)	RAD
Radius (preceding a dimension)	R
Reference	REF
Required	REQD
Right hand	RH
Round head	RD HD
Screw (or screwed)	SCR
Sheet	SH
Sketch	SK
Specification	SPEC
Spherical	SPHERE
Spherical diameter (only preceding a dimension)	SØ
Spherical radius (only preceding a dimension)	SR
Spotface	SFACE
Square (in a note)	SQ
Square (preceding a dimension)	□ or ⊠
Standard	STD
Taper, on diameter or width (orientated to direction of taper)	→
Thread	THD
Thick	THK
Tolerance	TOL
Typical or typically	TYP
Undercut	UCUT
Volume	VOL
Weight	WT

ENGINEERING DRAWING 10.1.3

Linework conventions : Example drawing

This illustration shows the application of various types of line defined in the adjacent table.
See BS 308 for additional details.

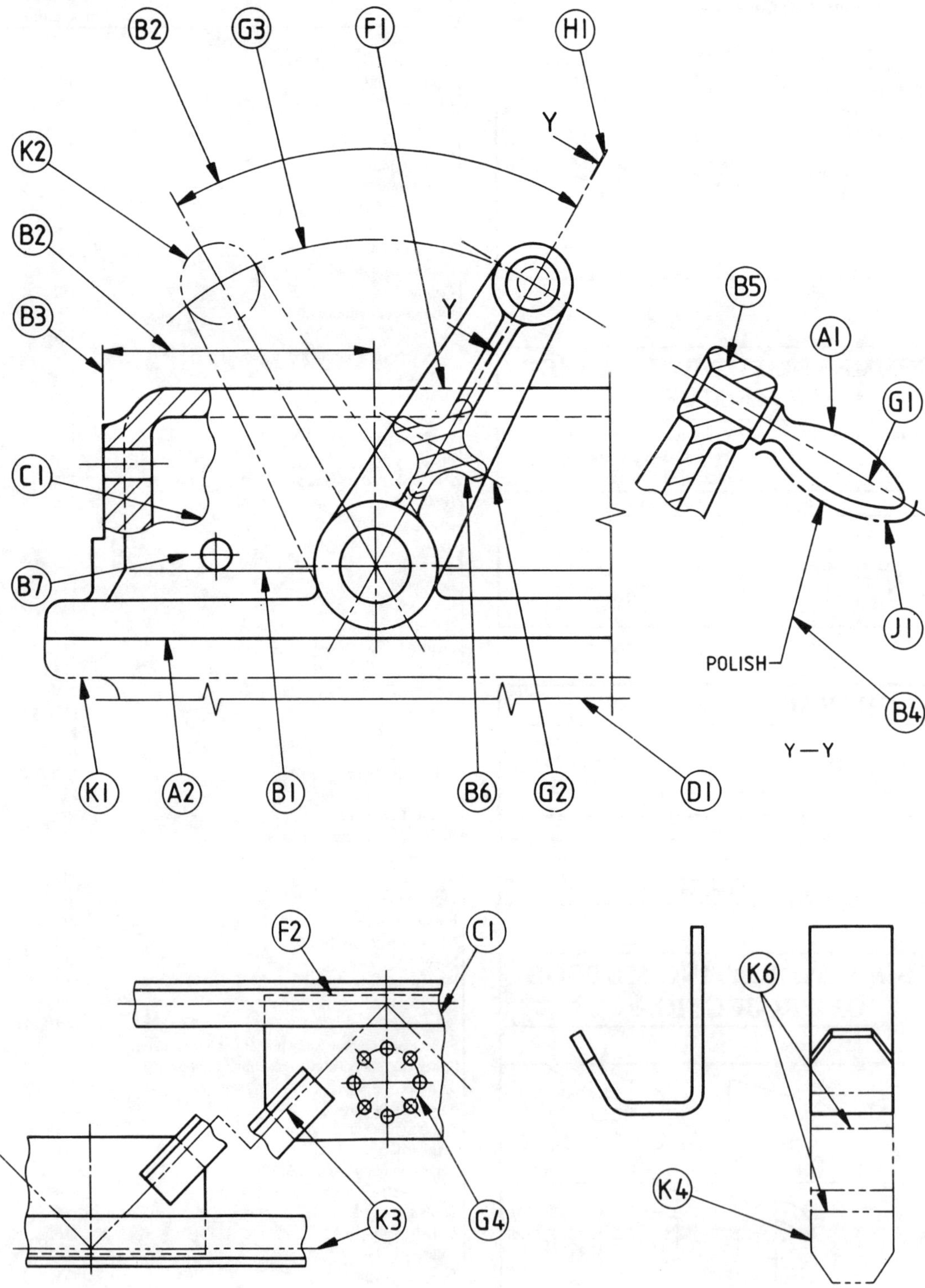

Applications of the various types of line.

ENGINEERING DRAWING 10.1.4

Linework conventions : Line types

PRESENTATION

All lines should be black and dense. It is important that all the lines on a drawing, including those added in any revision, should be of consistent density and reflectance. The lines on any one drawing sheet should preferably be entirely in pencil or entirely in ink. If a mixture of pencil and ink is used, every effort should be made to ensure that uniform density and reflectance are maintained.
The clear space between lines should be not less than 1mm. It is accepted that in some cases the scale of the drawing will be violated.

THICKNESS

Two thicknesses of line are recommended: thick and thin, which should be in the ration of 2:1. Thickness should be selected from the range 0.25, 0.35, 0.5, 0.7, 1.0, 1.4, 2.0 mm.

TYPES OF LINE

Line	Description	Application
A	Continuous thick	A1 Visible outlines A2 Visible edges
B	Continuous thin	B1 Imaginary lines of intersection B2 Dimension lines B3 Projection lines B4 Leader lines B5 Hatching B6 Outlines of revolved sections B7 Short centre lines
C	Continuous thin irregular	C1 Limits of partial or interrupted views and sections, if the limit is not an axis
D	Continuous thin straight †	D1 Limits of partial or interrupted views and sections, if the limit with zigzags is not an axis
E	Dashed thick	E1 Hidden outlines E2 Hidden edges
F	Dashed thin ‡	F1 Hidden outlines F2 Hidden edges
G	Chain thin	G1 Centre lines G2 Lines of symmetry G3 Trajectories and loci G4 Pitch lines and pitch circles
H	Chain thin, thick at ends and changes of direction	H1 Cutting planes
J	Chain thick	J1 Indication of lines or surfaces to which a special requirement applies (drawn adjacent to surface)
K	Chain thin double dashed	K1 Outlines and edges of adjacent parts K2 Outlines and edges of alternative and extreme positions of movable parts K3 Centroidal lines K4 Initial outlines prior to forming § K5 Parts situated in front of a cutting plane K6 Bend lines on developed blanks or patterns

Note The lengths of the long dashes shown for lines G, H, J and K are not necessarily typical due to the confines of the space available.

† This type of line is suited for production of drawings by machines

‡ The thin F type line is more common in the UK, but on any one drawing or set of drawings only one type of dashed line should be used.

§ Included in ISO 128-1982 and used mainly in the building industry.

ENGINEERING DRAWING 10.1.5

Threads and shafts : Drawing conventions (1 - 9)

TITLE		SUBJECT	CONVENTION
External Screwthread (Detail)	1	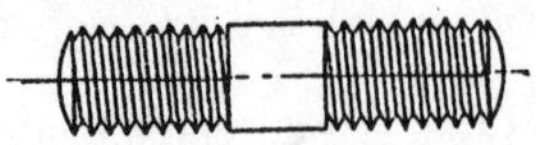	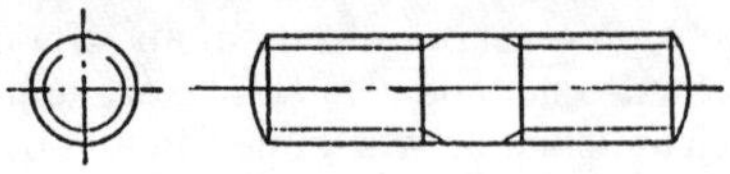
Internal Screwthread (Detail)	2	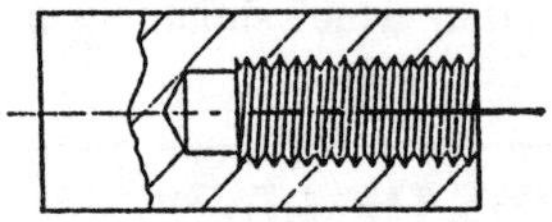	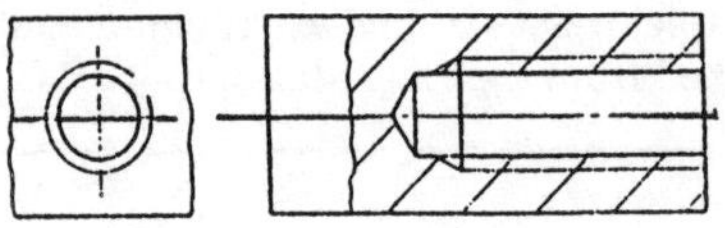
Screwthread (Assembly)	3	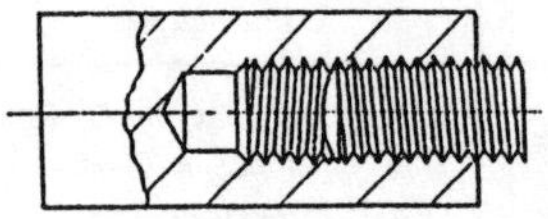	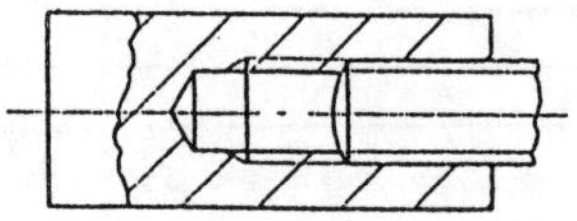
Thread Inserts	4	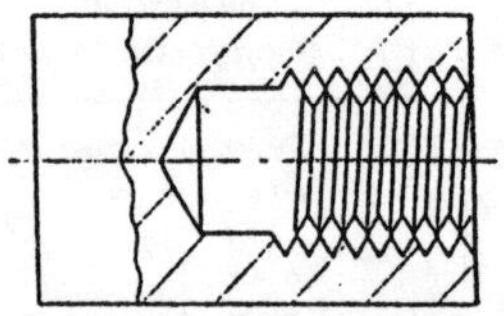	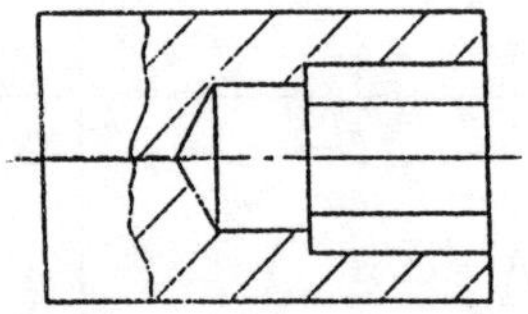
Splined Shafts	5	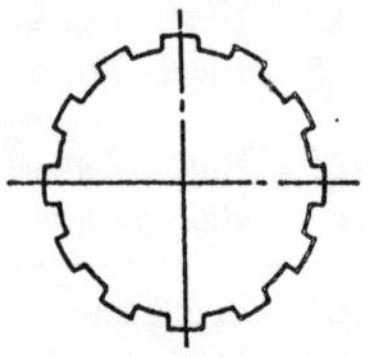	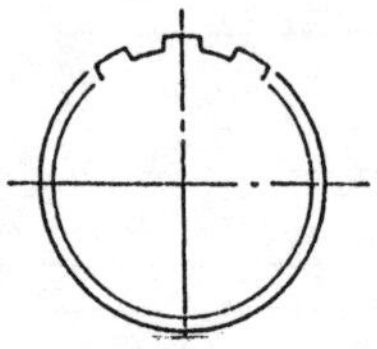
Serrated Shafts	6	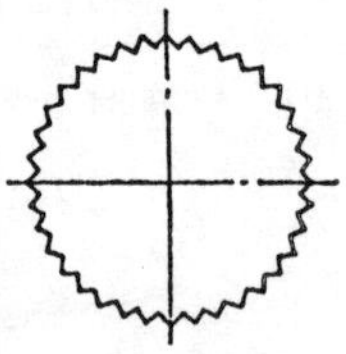	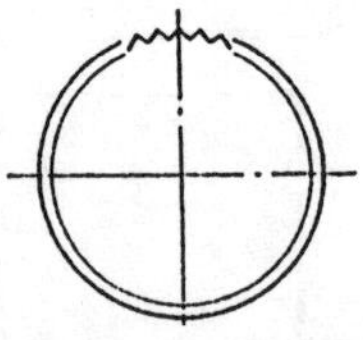
	7		
Interrupted Views	8		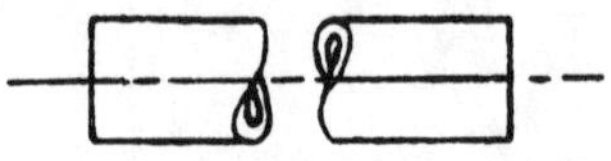
	9		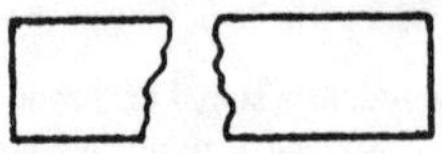

ENGINEERING DRAWING 10.1.6

Drilling, knurling, repeated parts: Drawing conventions (10 - 16)

TITLE	SUBJECT	CONVENTION
Straight Knurling	10 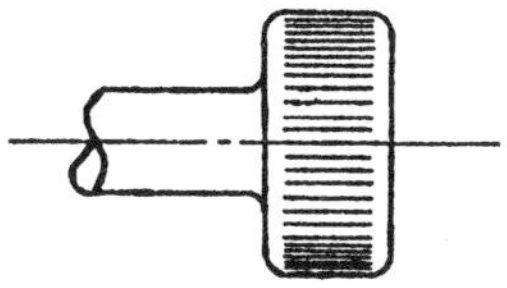	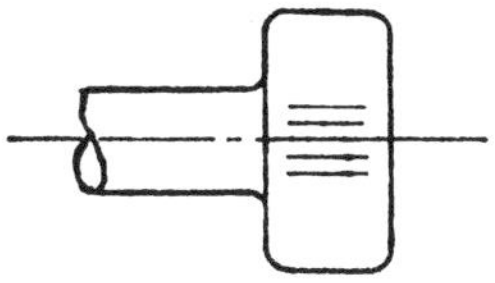
Diamond Knurling	11 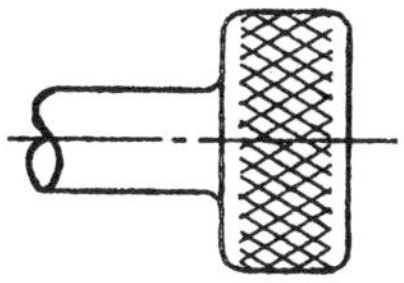	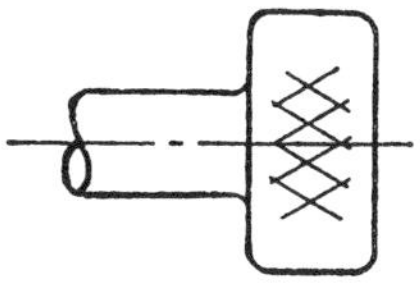
Square on Shaft	12 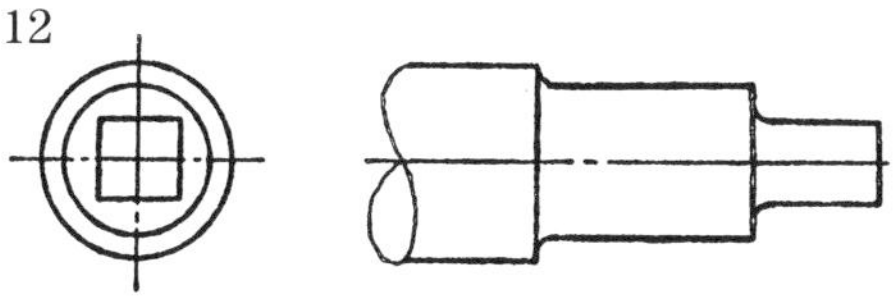	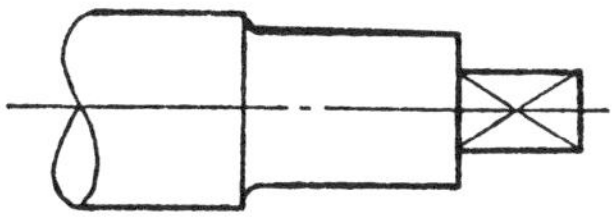
Holes on Circular Pitch	13 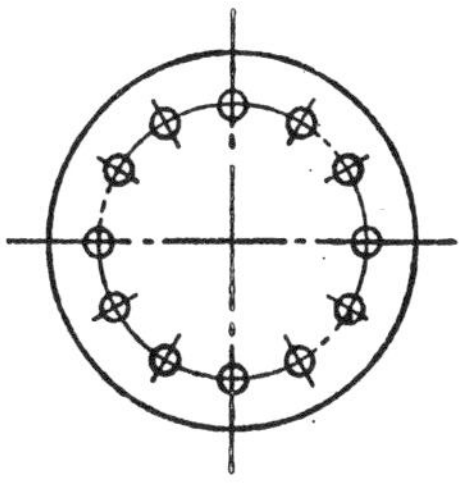	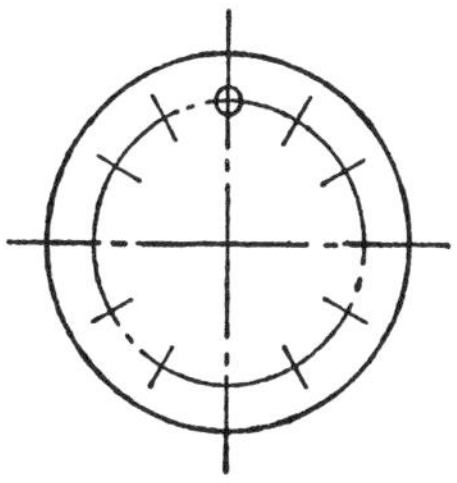
Holes on Linear Pitch	14 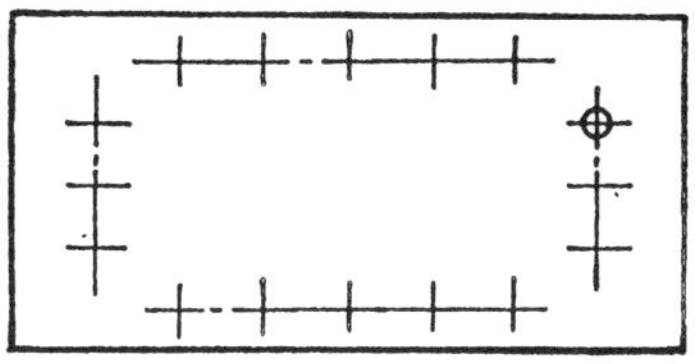	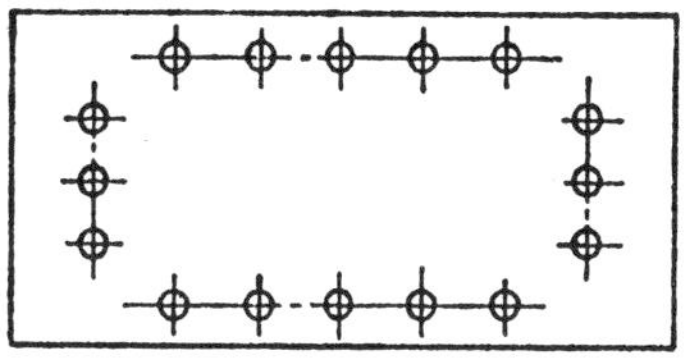
Bearings	15 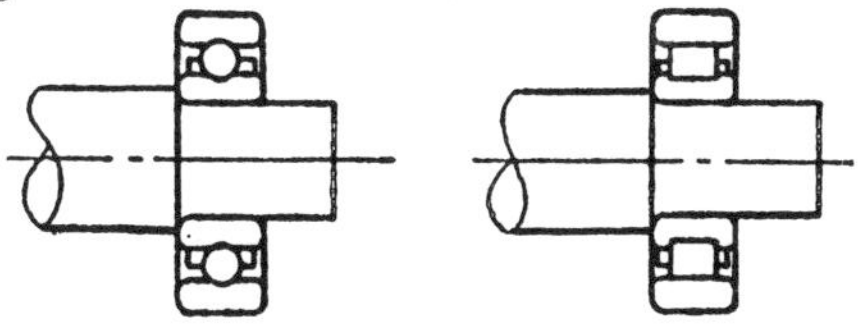	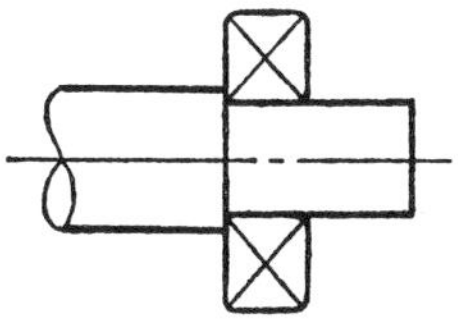
Repeated Parts	16 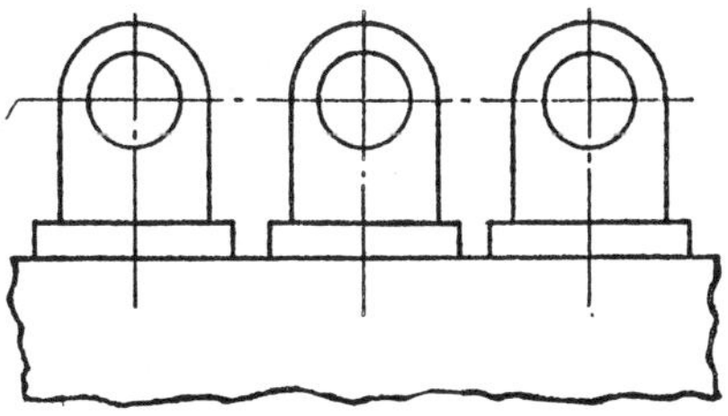	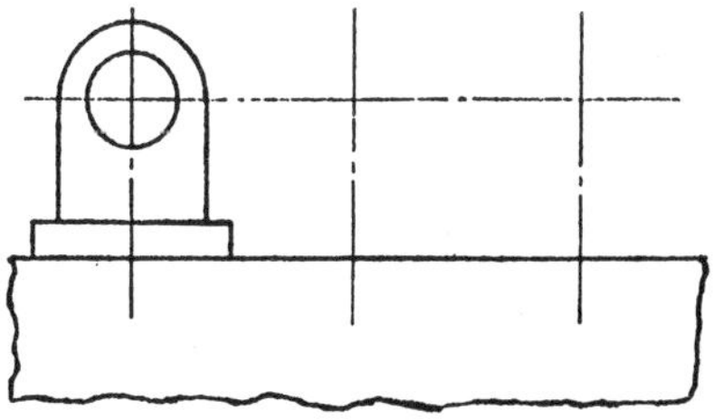

ENGINEERING DRAWING 10.1.7

Gears : Drawing conventions (17 - 23)

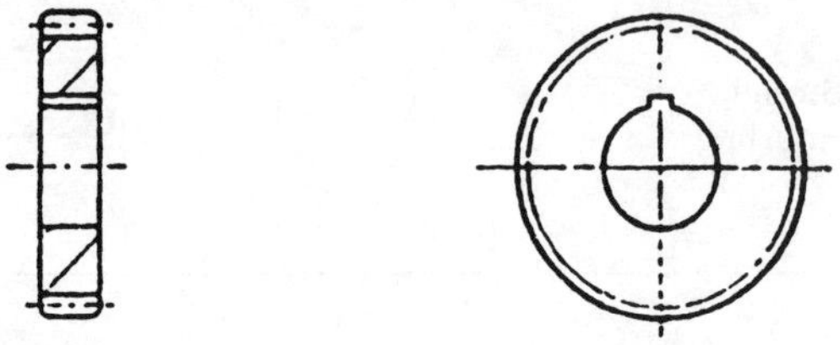

	TITLE	CONVENTION
17	Spur Gear	
18	Bevel Gear	
19	Assembly	
20	Wormwheel	
21	Worm	
22	Teeth Rack Form	
23	Teeth Indication of Direction	

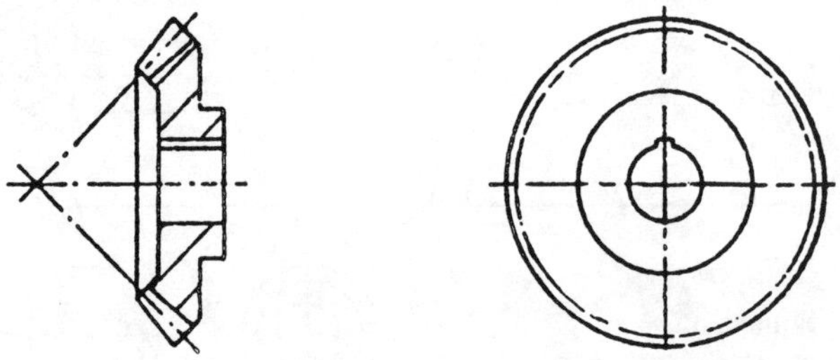

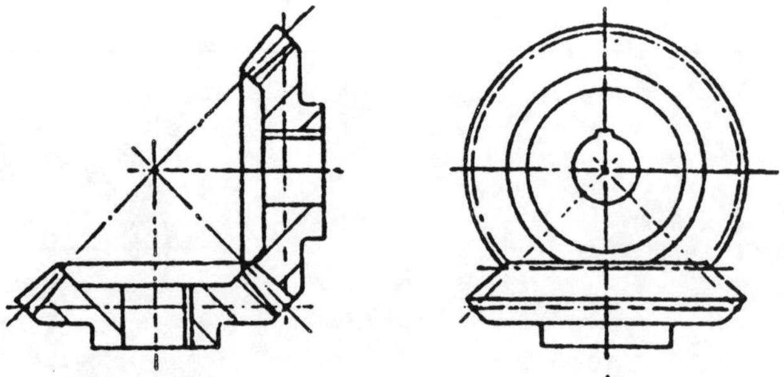

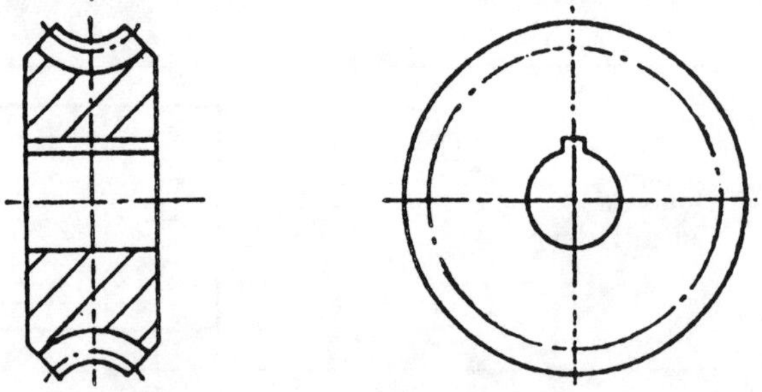

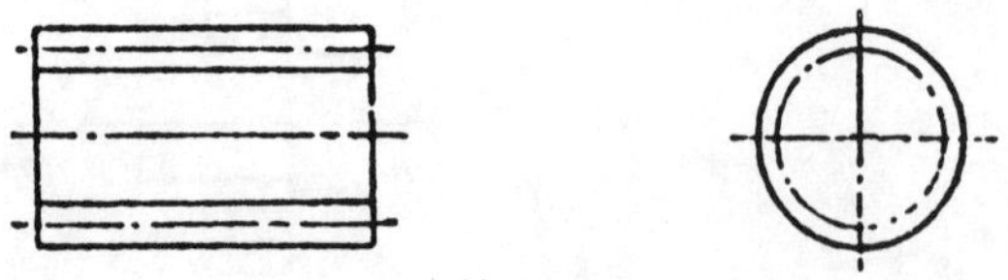

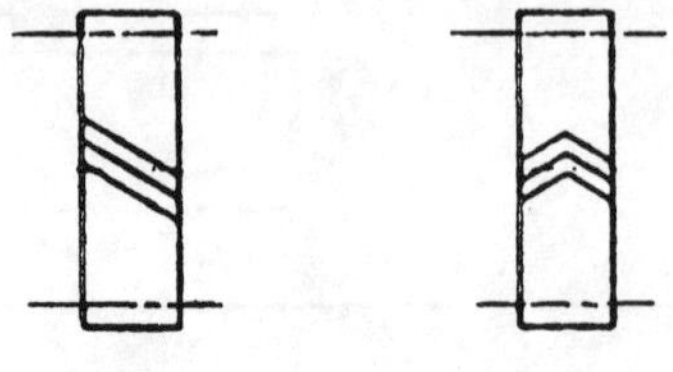

Springs : Drawing conventions (24 - 28)

COMPRESSION SPRINGS

DESCRIPTION	REPRESENTATION		
	View	Section	Simplified *
Cylindrical helical compression spring of wire of circular cross section	24 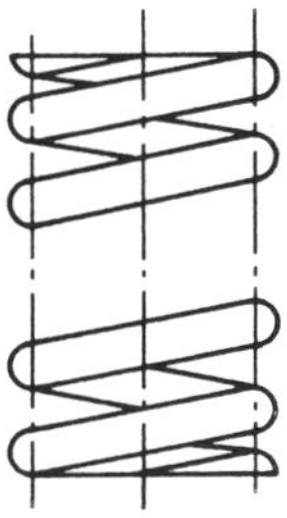	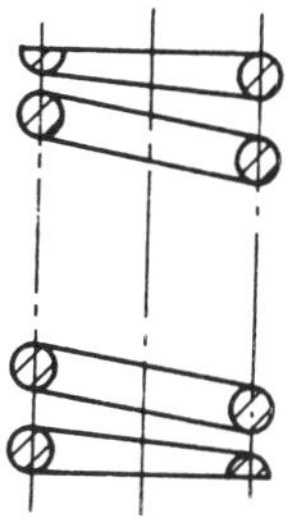	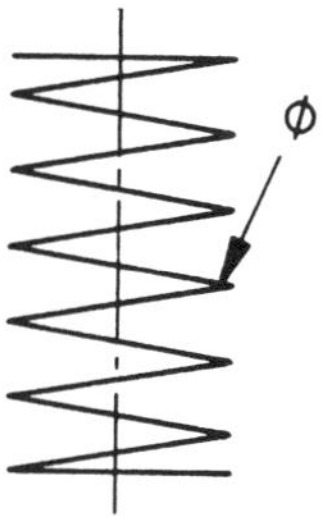 ∅
Cylindrical helical compression spring of wire of rectangular cross section	25 	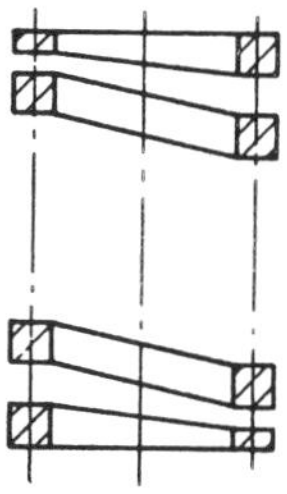	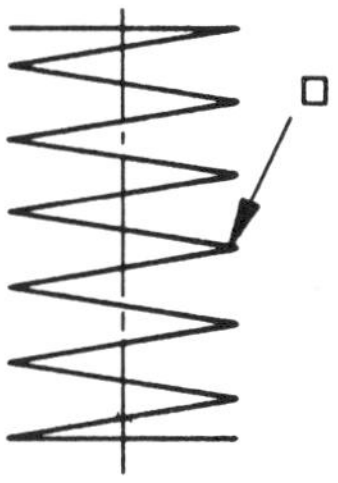 □
Conical helical compression spring of wire of circular cross section	26 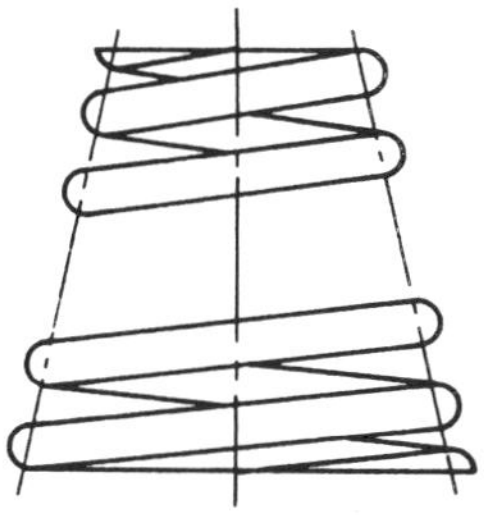	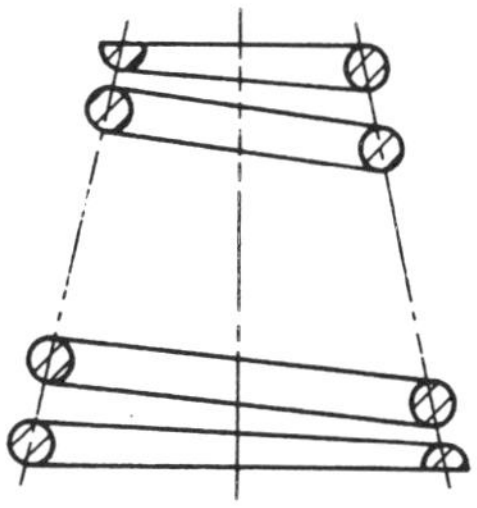	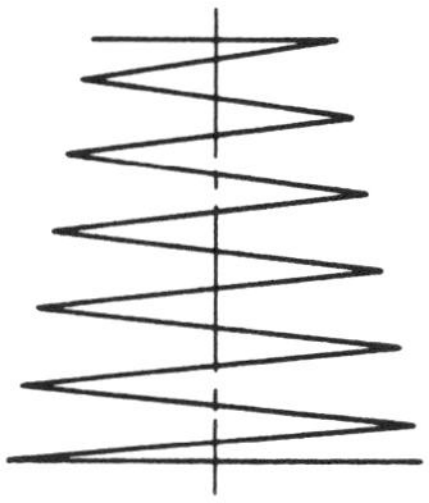
Conical helical compression spring of wire of rectangular cross section (volute spring)	27 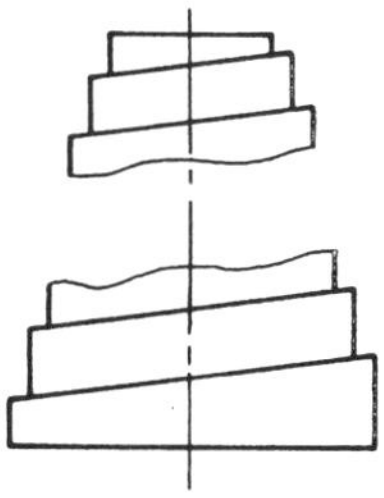	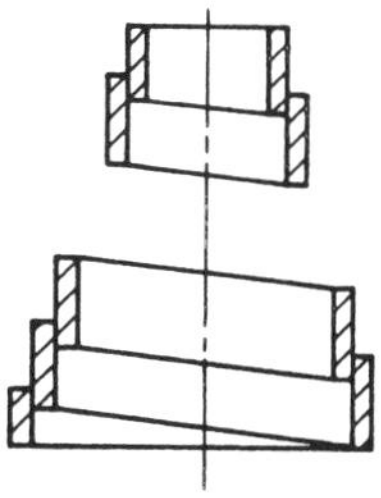	

* If necessary, indicate 'wound left- (or right-) hand'.
If necessary, the cross section of the spring material may be indicated in words or by a symbol, see 24 and 25.

LEAF SPRINGS

DESCRIPTION	REPRESENTATION	
	View	Simplified
Semi-elliptic leaf spring with eyes	28 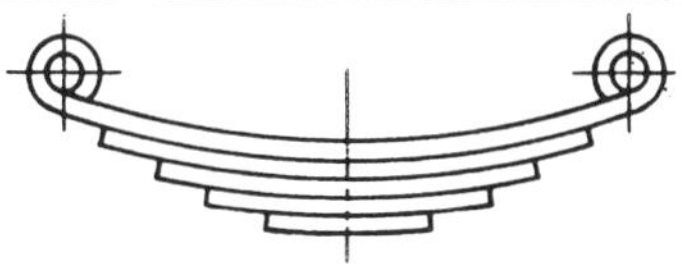	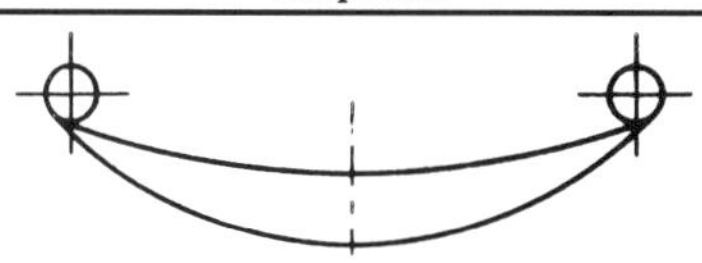

ENGINEERING DRAWING 10.1.8

Springs: Drawing conventions (29 - 31)

TENSION SPRINGS

DESCRIPTION	REPRESENTATION		
	View	Section	Simplified *
Cylindrical helical tension spring of wire of circular cross section	29		
Double - conical helical tension spring of circular cross section	30		

* If necessary, indicate 'wound left- (or right-) hand'.
If necessary, the cross section of the spring material may be indicated in words or by a symbol, see 24 and 25.

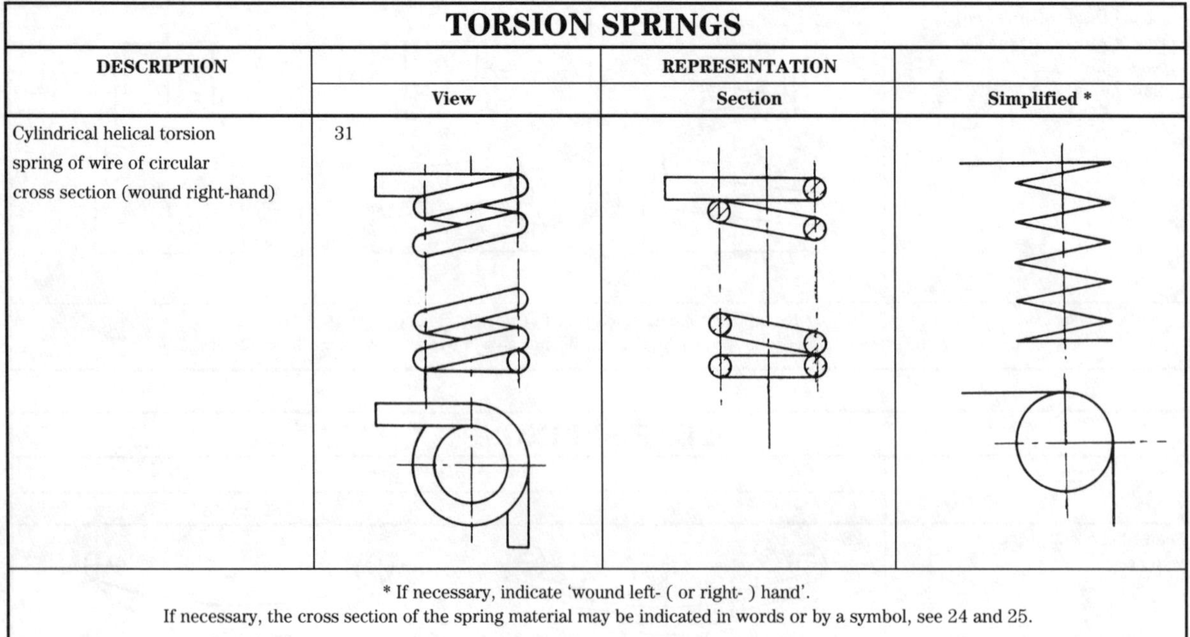

TORSION SPRINGS

DESCRIPTION	REPRESENTATION		
	View	Section	Simplified *
Cylindrical helical torsion spring of wire of circular cross section (wound right-hand)	31		

* If necessary, indicate 'wound left- (or right-) hand'.
If necessary, the cross section of the spring material may be indicated in words or by a symbol, see 24 and 25.

SPIRAL SPRINGS

DESCRIPTION	REPRESENTATION	
	View	Simplified
Spiral spring	32 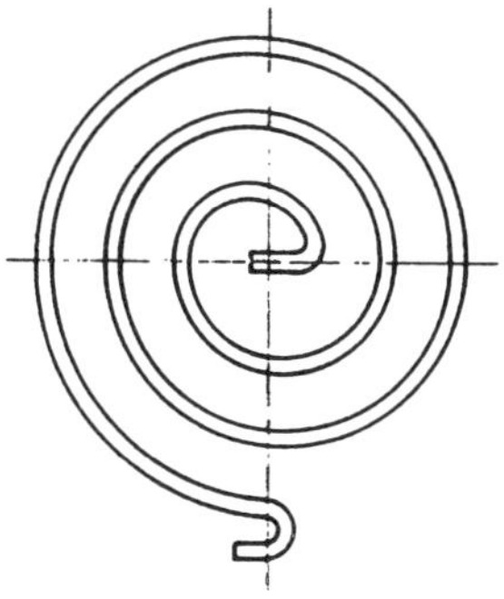	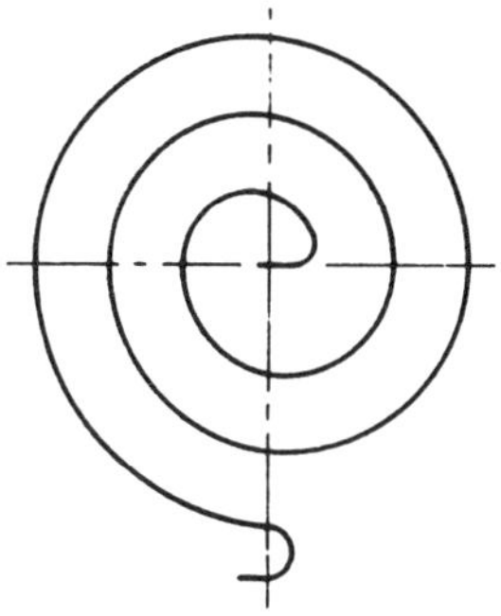
Spiral spring (close wound in housing)	33 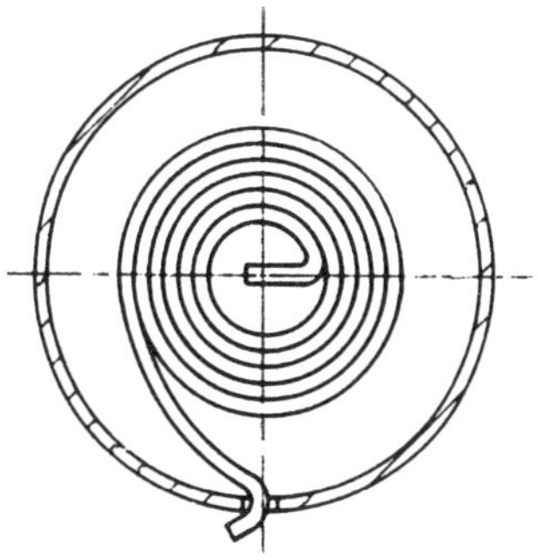	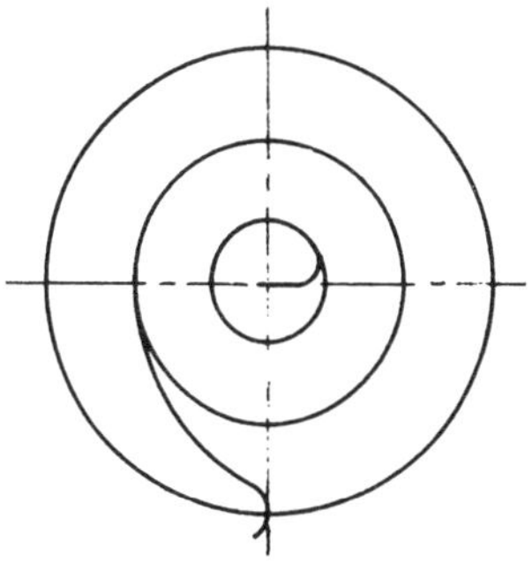

CUP SPRINGS (disc springs)

DESCRIPTION	REPRESENTATION		
	View	Section	Simplified
Cup spring	34 		
Multi-cup spring (cups placed in the same direction)	35 	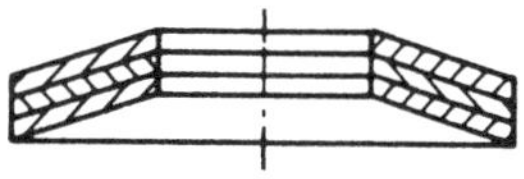	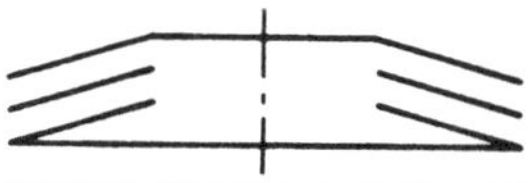
Multi-cup spring (successive cups alternating in direction)	36 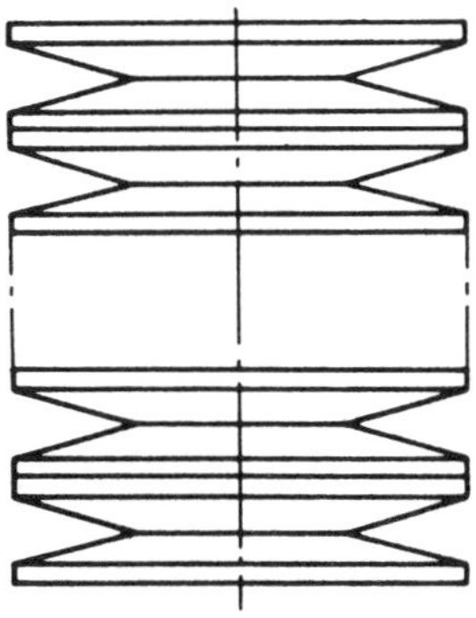	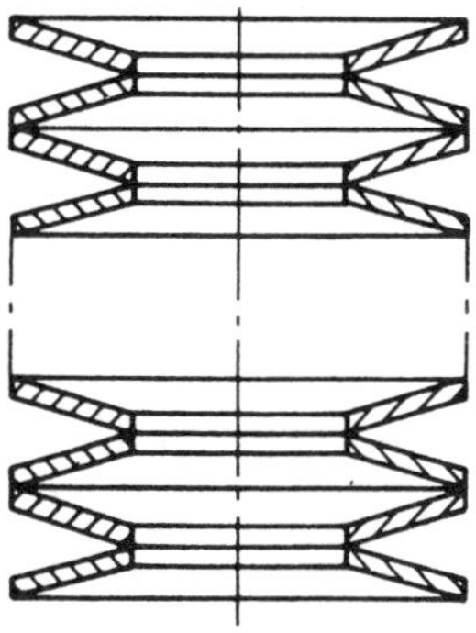	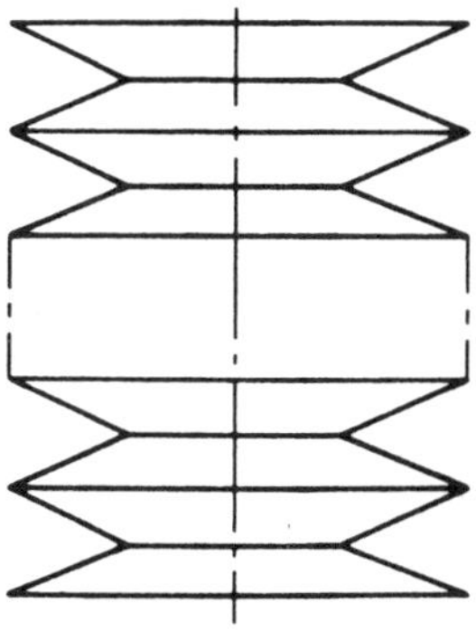

SYMBOLS 10.2.1

Welding: Symbols used on drawings
(see also PP 7307)

POSITION OF THE SYMBOL

	Projection 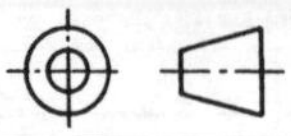		
Illustration	**Graphic representation**	**Symbolic representation**	**Description of position**
	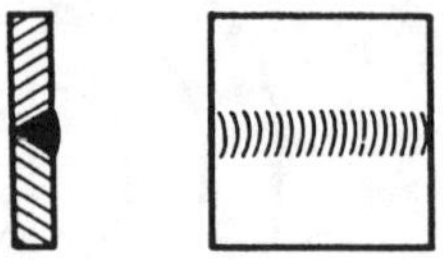	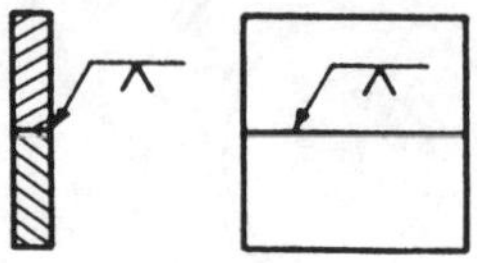	Below the reference line if the external surface of the weld (weld face) is on the arrow side of the joint.
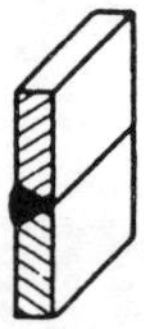	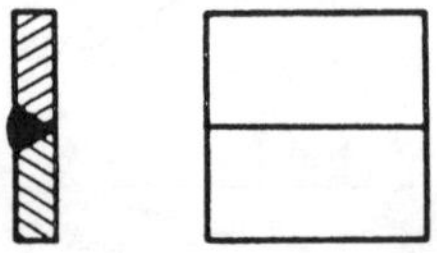	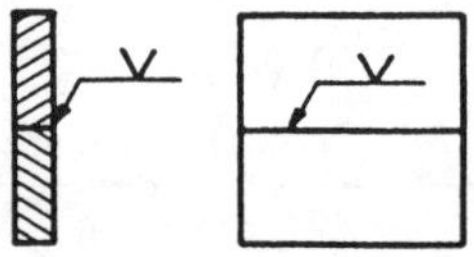	Above the reference line if the external surface of the weld (weld face) is on the other side of the joint.
	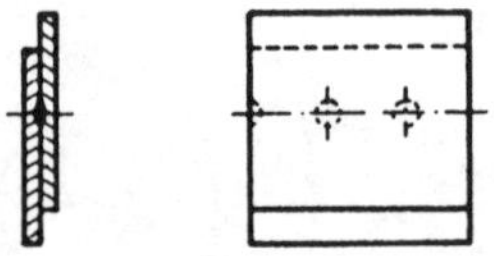	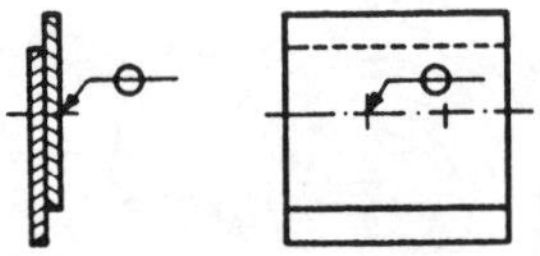	Across the reference line in the case of welds made within the plane of the joint.

EXAMPLES OF THE USE OF ELEMENTARY SYMBOLS

Designation symbol	**Illustration**	Projection 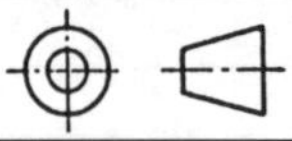	
		Graphic representation	**Symbolic representation**
Butt weld between flanged plates 	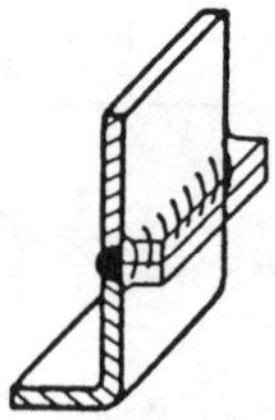	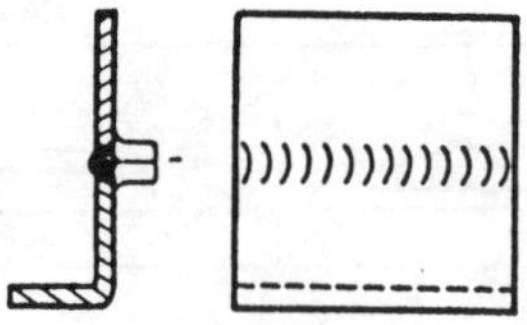	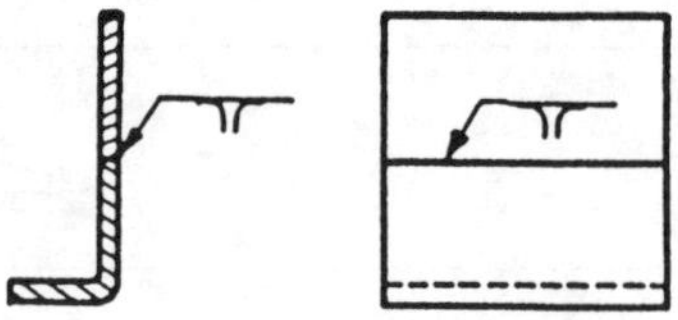
Single-V butt weld 	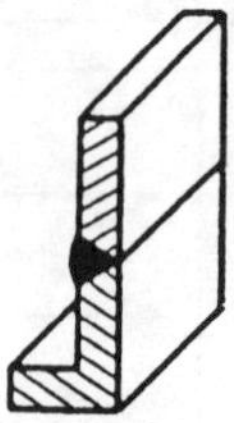	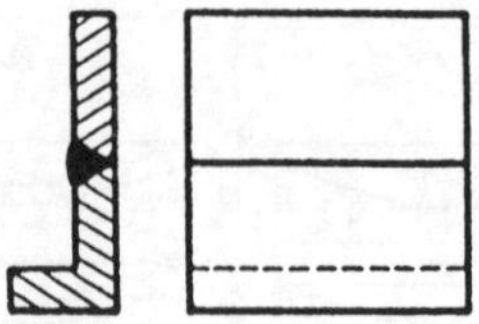	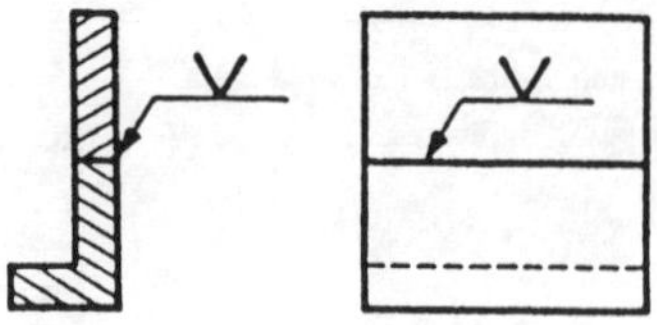
Fillet weld 	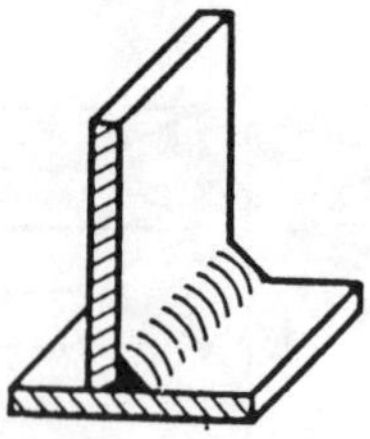	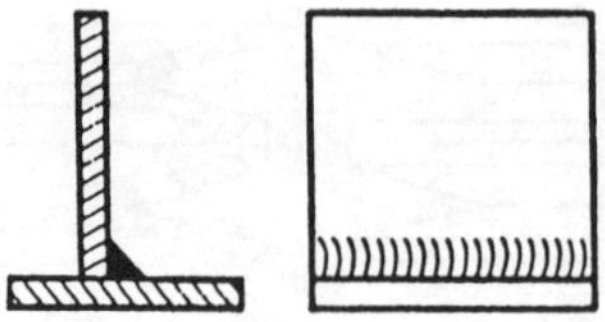	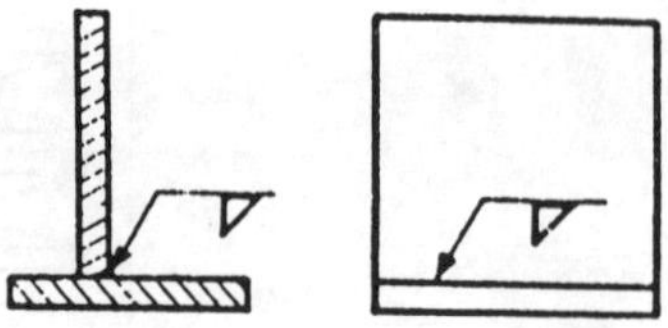

ENGINEERING DRAWING 10.2.1

Welding: Symbols used on drawings continued

Designation	Illustration	Symbol
Butt weld between flanged plates (the flanges being melted down completely)		
Square butt weld		
Single-V butt weld		
Single-bevel butt weld		
Single-V butt weld with broad root face		
Single-bevel butt weld with broad root face		
Single-U butt weld		
Single-J butt weld		
Backing or sealing run		
Fillet weld		
Plug weld (circular or elongated hole completely filled)		
Spot weld (resistance or arc welding) or projection weld	(a) resistance (b) Arc	
Seam weld		

SUPPLEMENTARY SYMBOLS FOR WELDING

Shape of weld surface	Symbol
(a) flat (usually finished flush)	
(b) convex	
(c) concave	

USE OF SYMBOL FOR PERIPHERAL WELDS

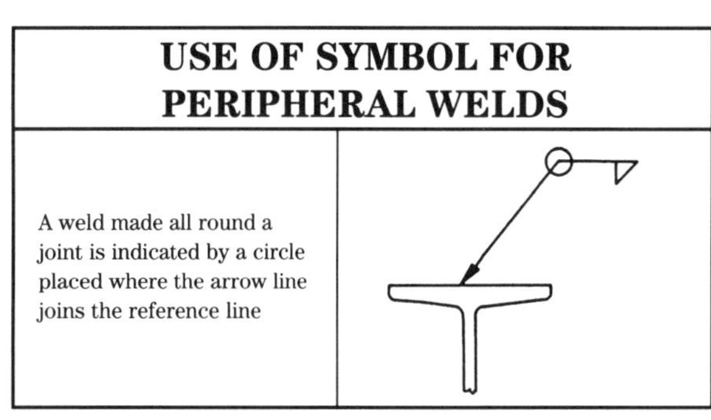

A weld made all round a joint is indicated by a circle placed where the arrow line joins the reference line

EXAMPLES OF SUPPLEMENTARY SYMBOLS FOR WELDING

Designation	Illustration	Symbol
Flat (flush) single-V butt weld		
Convex double-V butt weld		
Concave fillet weld		
Flat (flush) single-V butt weld with flat (flush) backing run		

SELECTED ELECTRICAL AND ELECTRONIC GRAPHICAL SYMBOLS FROM BS 3939 (SEE ALSO PP 7307 AND PP 7311)

For symbols to be marked on electrical equipment see BS 6217
See also BS 4727: Glossary of electrotechnical, power, telecommunication, electronics, lighting and colour terms.

Description	Symbol
Direct current	
Alternating current	
Positive polarity	+
Negative	−
Variability	
Pre-set adjustment	
Primary or secondary cell	
Battery of primary or secondary cells	
Alternative symbol	
Earth or ground	
Signal lamp, general symbol	
Electric bell	
Electric buzzer	
Crossing of conductors with no electrical connection	
Junction of conductors	
Double junction of conductors	
Plug (male)	
Socket (female)	

Description	Symbol
Fuse	
Resistor, general symbol	
Variable resistor	
Resistor with sliding contact	
Potentiometer with moving contact	
Heating element	
Capacitor, general symbol	
Polarized capacitor	+
Voltage-dependent polarized	+ V
Capacitor with pre-set adjustment	
Inductor, winding, coil, choke	
Inductor with magnetic core	
Transformer with magnetic core	
Ammeter	A
Voltmeter	V
Wattmeter	W
Watt-hour meter	Wh

SYMBOLS 10.2.2

Electrical and electronic circuits: Symbols used on drawings (continued)

Description	Symbol
Galvanometer	
Oscilloscope	
Motor	M
Generator	G
Microphone	
Earphone (receiver)	
Transducer head, general symbol	
Loudspeaker	
Electric clock	
Make contact, normally open	
Break contact, normally closed	
Make contact with spring return	
Break contact with spring return	
Relay (for relay contact units use those already given)	
Semiconductor diode, general symbol	

Description		Symbol
Photodiode		
Light-emitting diode, LED		
Tunnel diode		
PNP transistor		
NPN transistor with collector connected to envelope		
Amplifier, simplified form		
Laser		
Binary logic elements	AND	&
	OR	≥ 1
	Logic identity	=
	Exclusive OR	=1
	NOT (negator)	1
	NAND	&
	NOR	≥ 1

Heating, piping and electrical systems: Symbols used on drawings

SYMBOLS FOR HEATING INSTALLATIONS AND PIPING SYSTEMS (SEE ALSO PP 7307 AND PP 7311)

Description	Symbol
Crossing (unconnected) of pipelines	
Junction (connected) of pipelines	
Pipe in front of (or above) section	
View of pipe perpendicular to the plane of the drawing	
Indication of fall (or rise)	FALL 1:60
In-line (any type or pattern) valve	plain servo
3-way valve	
Trap drain, e.g. condensate release	
Trapped vent, e.g. automatic air valve	
Meter (any type) NOTE. Letter F indicates flow measurement	F
Open tank (basic symbol)	
Rotary pump, fan or simple compressor (basic symbol)	
Centrifugal pump or centrifugal fan	

Description	Symbol
Positive displacement pump (reciprodating electric motor driven)	
Compressor : reciprocating (basic symbol) with mechanical linkage	
Fired heater/boiler (basic symbol)	
Tank heater	
Electrical heater (basic symbol)	
Oil burner	
Gas burner	
Radiator	
Towel rail	
Heater/cooler unit, downward type Example: heater unit NOTE. Annotate to indicate function, as follows. Heater: H or + Cooler: C or –	

SYMBOLS 10.2.3

Heating, piping and electrical systems: Symbols used on drawings (continued)

Description	Symbol
Lighting outlet position	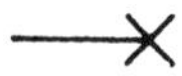
Lighting outlet on wall	
Lamp, general symbol	
Emergency lighting luminaire	
Self-contained emergency lighting luminaire	
Lighting point with built in switch	
Projector or lamp with reflector	
Spotlight	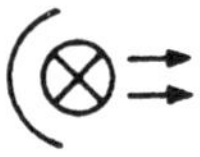
Floodlight	
Luminaire, fluorescent lamp	
Luminaire with three fluoresent tubes	
Alternative symbol, with five tubes	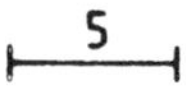 5
Switch, general symbol	
Switch with pilot light	
Switch, two-pole	
Pull-cord switch, single pole	

Description	Symbol
Two-way switch, single pole	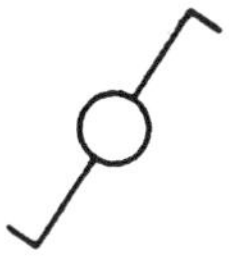
Intermediate switch	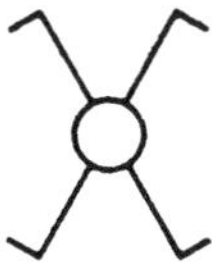
Dimmer	
Time switch	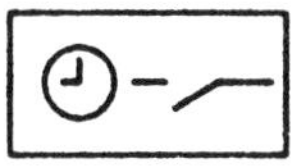
Push button	
Push button with indicator lamp	
Push button with restricted access (glass cover etc.)	
Socket outlet (power), general symbol	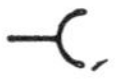
Socket outlet (power) with single-pole switch	
Multiple socket outlet	 3
Socket outlet with isolating transformer, for example, shaver socket	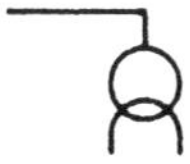
Socket outlet (telecommunications)	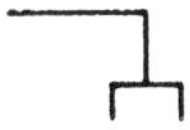
Distribution centre, shown with five conduits	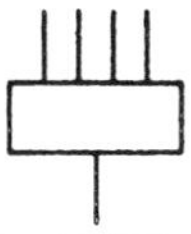
Fan, shown with wiring	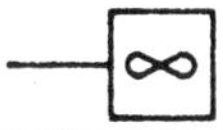
Water heater shown with wiring	
Antenna	

SYMBOLS 10.2.4

Fluid power systems: Symbols used on drawings

SELECTED SYMBOLS FOR FLUID POWER SYSTEMS (FROM BS 2917) (SEE ALSO PP 7307)

NOTE 1. The symbols for hydraulic and pneumatic equipment and accessories are functional and consist of one or more basic symbols and in general of one or more functional symbols. The symbols are neither to scale nor in general orientated in any particular direction.

NOTE 2. In circuit diagrams, hydraulic and pneumatic units are normally shown in the unoperated position.

NOTE 3. The symbols show connections, flow paths and the functions of the components, but do not include constructional details. The physical location of control elements on actual components is not illustrated.

NOTE 4. Asterisked symbols (with the exception of the unlocking symbol in the locking device control mechanism) may be used in conjunction with ↗ to indicate variability or adjustment.

Description	Symbol
General symbols	
Basic symbols	
Restriction: affected by viscosity	
unaffected by viscosity	
Functional symbols	
hydraulic flow	
pneumatic flow or exhaust to atmosphere	
Energy conversion	
Pumps and compressors	
Fixed capacity hydraulic pump: with one direction of flow	* 
with two directions of flow	* 
Motors	
Fixed capacity hydraulic motor: with one direction or flow	* 
Oscillating motor: hydraulic	
Cylinders	
Single acting returned by an unspecified force	Detailed: 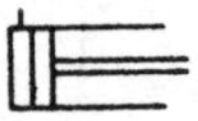 Simplified: 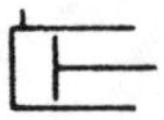
Double acting: with single piston rod	Detailed: 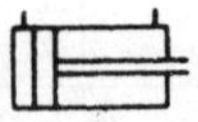 Simplified: 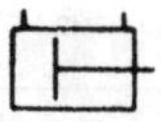
Cylinder with cushion: single fixed	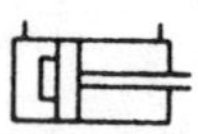
Air-oil actuator (transforms pneumatic pressure into a substantially equal hydraulic pressure or vice versa)	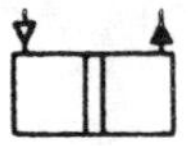
Directional control valves	
Flow paths:	
one flow path	
two closed ports	
two flow paths	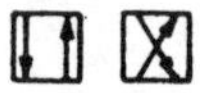
two flow paths and one closed port	
two flow paths with cross connection	
one flow path in a by-pass position, two closed ports	
Directional control valve 2/2: with manual control	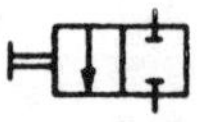
controlled by pressure against a return spring	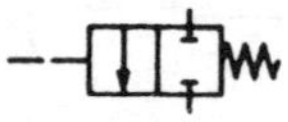
Direction control valve 5/2: controlled by pressure in both directions	
NOTE. in the above designations the first figure indicates the number of ports (excluding pilot ports) and the second figure the number od distinct positions	
Non-return valves, shuttle valve, rapid exhaust valve	
Non-return valve: free (opens if the inlet pressure is higher than the outlet pressure	
spring loaded (opens if the inlet pressure is greater than the outlet pressure and the spring pressure)	
pilot controlled (opens if the inlet pressure is higher than the outlet pressure but by pilot control it is possible to prevent:	
closing of the valve	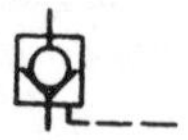
opening of the valve)	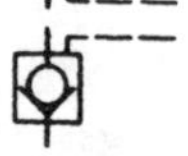
with restriction (allows free flow in one direction but restricted flow in the other)	* 
Shuttle vale (the inlet port connected to the higher pressure is automatically connected to the outlet port while the other inlet port is closed)	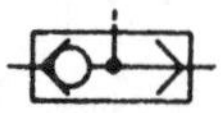
Pressure control valves	
Pressure control valve:	
one thottling orifice normally closed	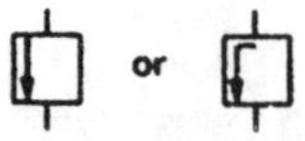
one throttling orifice normally open	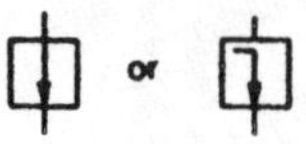
two throttling orifices, normally closed	
Sequence valve (when the inlet pressure overcomes the spring, the valve opens, permitting flow from the outlet port)	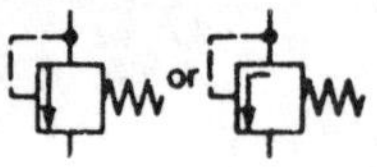

SYMBOLS 10.2.4

Fluid power systems: Symbols used on drawings (continued)

Description	Symbol
Flow control valves	
Throttle valve: simplified symbol	
Example braking valve	
Flow control valve (variations in inlet pressure do not affect the rate of flow): with fixed output	• Simplified
Flow dividing valve (divided into a fixed rato substantially independent of pressure variations)	
Energy transmission and conditioning	
Sources of energy	
Pressure source	
Electric motor	
Heat engine	
Flow lines and connections	
Flow line:	
working line, return line and feed line	
pilot control line	
drain or bleed line	
flexible pipe	
Pipeline junction	
Crossed pipelines (not connected)	
Air bleed	
Power take-off	
plugged	
with take-off line	
connected, with mechanically opened non-return valves	
uncoupled, with opened end	
uncoupled, closed by free non-return valve	

Description	Symbol
Rotary connection	
one way	
three way	
Reservoirs	
Reservoir open to atmosphere:	
with inlet pipe above fluid level	
with inlet pipe below fluid level	
with a header line	
pressurized reservoir	
Accumulators	
The fluid is maintained under pressure by a spring, weight or compressed gas	
Filters, water traps, lubricators and miscellaneous apparatus	
Filter or strainer	
Heat exchangers	
Temperature controller (arrows indicate that heat may be either introduced or dissipated)	
Cooler (arrows indicate the extraction of heat) with representation of the flow lines of the coolant	
Heater (arrows indicate the introduction of heat)	
Control mechanisms	
Mechanical components	
Rotating shaft:	
in one direction	
in either direction	
Detent (device for maintaining a given position)	
Locking device (symbol for unlocking control)*	

Description	Symbol
Over-centre device (prevents stopping in a dead centre position)	
Pivoting devices:	
Simple	
with traversing lever	
with fixed fulcrum	
Control methods	
Muscular control:	
general symbol	
by push-button	
by lever	
by pedal	
Mechanical control:	
by plunger or tracer	
by spring	
by roller	
by roller, operating in one direction only	
Electrical control: by solenoid (one winding)	
by electric motor	
Control by application or release of pressure	
Direct acting control:	
by application of pressure	
by release of pressure	
Combined control: by solenoid and pilot directional valve (pilot direction valve is actuated by the solenoid)	
Measuring instruments	
Pressure measurement: pressure gauge	
Other apparatus	
Pressure electric switch	

Notes

APPENDICES

APPENDIX A

Quality systems Specification for design/ development, production, installation and servicing

Extract from BS 5750: Quality systems: Part 1: 1987 NOTE: The following is a small part of a comprehensive standard covering all aspects of quality systems. If a product or service is required to meet BS 5750 then the full standard must be used. BS 5750 is a direct equivalent of ISO 9000 and EN 2900.

DESIGN CONTROL

General

The supplier shall establish and maintain procedures to control and verify the design of the product in order to ensure that the specified requirements are met.

Design and development planning

The supplier shall draw up plans that identify the responsibility for each design and development activity. The plans shall describe or reference these activities and shall be updated as the design evolves.

Activity assignment:
The design and verification activities shall be planned and assigned to qualified personnel equipped with adequate resources.

Organizational and technical interfaces:
Organizational and technical interfaces between different groups shall be identified and the necessary information documented, transmitted and requlariy reviewed.

Design input

Design input requirements relating to the product shall be identified, documented and their selection reviewed by the supplier for adequacy.

Incomplete, ambiguous or conflicting requirements shall be resolved with those responsible for drawing up these requirements.

Design output

Design output shall be documented and expressed in terms of requirements, calculations and analyses.

Design output shall

a) meet the design input requirements;

b) contain or reference acceptance criteria;

c) conform to appropriate regulatory requirements whether or not these have been stated in the input information;

d) identify those characteristics of the design that are crucial to the safe and proper functioning of the product.

Design verification

The supplier shall plan, establish, document and assign to competent personnel functions for verifying the design.

Design verification shall establish that design output meets the design input requirement (see *'Design output'* above) by means of design control measures such as:

a) holding and recording design reviews (see *'Quality records'* below);

b) undertaking qualification tests and demonstrations;

c) carrying out alternative calculations;

d) comparing the new design with a similar proven design, if available.

Design changes

The supplier shall establish and maintain procedures for the identification, documentation and appropriate review and approval of all changes and modifications.

DOCUMENT CONTROL

Document approval and issue

The supplier shall establish and maintain procedures to control all documents and data that relate to the requirements of BS 5750. These documents shall be reviewed and approved for adequacy by authorized personnel prior to issue. This control shall ensure that

a) the pertinent issues of appropriate documents are available at all locations where operations essential to the effective functioning of the quality system are performed;

b) obsolete documents are promptly removed from all points of issue or use.

Document changes / modifications

Changes to documents shall be reviewed and approved by the same functions / organizations that performed the original review and approval unless specifically designated otherwise. The designated organizations shall have access to pertinent background information upon which to base their review and approval.

Where practicable, the nature of the change shall be identified in the document or the appropriate attachments.

A master list or equivalent document control procedure shall be established to identify the current revision of documents in order to preclude the use of non-applicable documents.

Documents shall be re-issued after a practical number of changes have been made.

QUALITY RECORDS

The supplier shall establish and maintain procedures for identification, collection, indexing, filing, storage, maintenance and disposition of quality records.

Quality records shall be maintained to demonstrate achievement of the required quality and the effective operation of the quality system. Pertinent sub-contractor quality records shall be an element of these data.

All quality records shall be legible and identifiable to the product involved. Quality records shall be stored and maintained in such a way that they are readily retrievable in facilities that provide a suitable environment to minimize deterioration or damage and to prevent loss. Retention times of quality records shall be established and recorded. Where agreed contractually, quality records shall be made available for evaluation by the purchaser or his representative for an agreed period.

APPENDIX A

Quality systems Specification for design/ development, production, installation and servicing

REFERENCES:

British Standard		**Identical to International Standard:**
BS 4778	Quality vocabulary :	
	Part 1: 1987 International terms	ISO 8402 – 1966
BS 5750:	Quality systems :	
	Part 0: Principal concepts and applications	
	Section 0.1: 1987 Guide to selection and use	ISO 9000 – 1987 = EN 29000
	Section 0.2: 1987 Guide to quality management and quality system elements	
	Part 1: 1987 Specification for design/development, production, installation & servicing	ISO 9001 – 1987 = EN 29001
	Part 2: 1987 Specification for production and installation	ISO 9002 – 1987 = EN 29002
	Part 3: 1987 Specification for final inspection and test	ISO 9003 – 1987 = EN 29003
	Part 4: 1990 Guide to the use of BS 5750 Pts 1, 2, 3	EN 29004
	Part 8: 1991 Guide to quality management	EN 29008
	Part 13: 1991 Guide to the use of BS 5750 for software	EN 29013

APPENDIX B NOISE REDUCTION – Charts and tables

APPLICATION of NOISE-REDUCTION PRINCIPLES

Exciting forces

In order to minimize exciting forces the following rules should be observed:

1) Avoid impacts by fitting resilient stops to moving members or otherwise minimizing the relative velocity at impact; if impacts must occur, minimize running clearances.
2) Run at the slowest possible speed.
3) Make gears accurately; fit plastics gears whenever possible.
4) Avoid obstructions close to fan blades.
5) Ensure that fastenings such as bolts and rivets do not work loose and allow rattles to occur.
6) Avoid rapid acceleration of moving members.
7) Minimize the weight of moving parts.
8) Balance rotating machinery.
9) Consider if possible using a process involving the application of a steady rather than an oscillating force.
10) Use only the minimum force required for the operation.

MATERIAL DAMPING

Material	Approximate specific damping capacity (per cent)
brass	1
mild steel	3
hiduminium *	10
cast iron	13
55 / 45 nickel titanium	55
70 / 30 magnesium copper	84

* Al. alloy 2.5 % Cu, 1.5 % Ni, 1.2 % Mg.

Relationship between force-time history, force spectrum, and noise; LF = force level, f = frequency, and n = rotational speed (Friede 1968)

	Force-time history	Spectrum of force	Increase in noise with speed
Diesel engine combustion	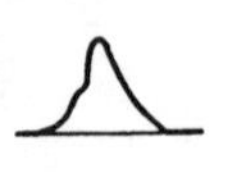	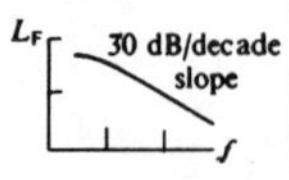 L_F 30 dB/decade slope f	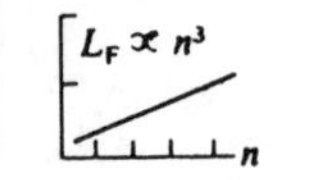 $L_F \propto n^3$ n
Petrol engine combustion		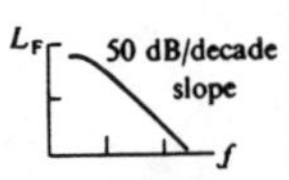 L_F 50 dB/decade slope f	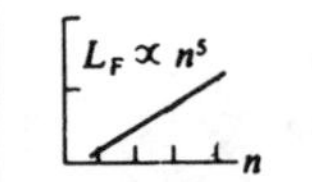 $L_F \propto n^5$ n
Hydraulic pump	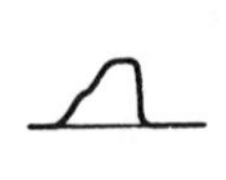	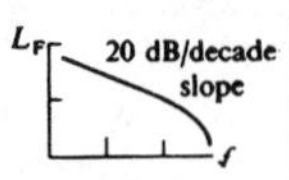 L_F 20 dB/decade slope f	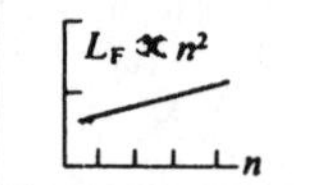 $L_F \propto n^2$ n
Spring operated valve	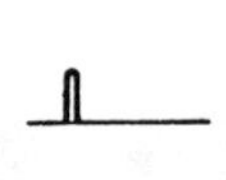	 L_F f	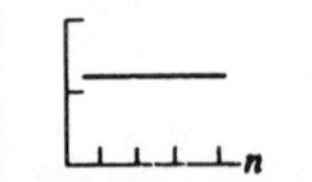 n
Ball bearing		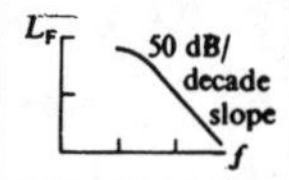 L_F 50 dB/ decade slope f	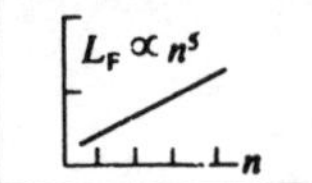 $L_F \propto n^5$ n

Absorption Coefficients of some Common Constructional Materials

Material	Frequency (Hz) 63	125	200	500	1000	2000	4000
Brickwork	0.05	0.05	0.04	0.02	0.05	0.05	
Concrete	0.05	0.02	0.02	0.04	0.05	0.05	
4 mm glass sheet		0.30		0.10		0.05	
6 mm glass sheet		0.10		0.04		0.02	
Plaster on solid backing	0.05	0.03	0.03	0.02	0.03	0.04	0.05
Wood boards on joists	0.10	0.15	0.20	0.10	0.10	0.10	0.10
Wood block floor	0.05	0.02	0.04	0.05	0.05	0.10	0.05
Asbestos sheet	0.15	0.10	0.60	0.05	0.04	0.02	0.02
Steel sheet	0.02 approx. but depends on method of support						
Glass fibre mat 50 mm thick		0.15	0.40	0.75	0.85	0.80	0.85
Glass fibre mat 25 mm thick		0.10	0.25	0.45	0.60	0.70	0.70

Approximate Sound Reduction index R of Single Leaf Panels in dB

Material	Octave - band centre frequency (Hz) 63	125	250	500	1000	2000	4000	8000
18 mm chipboard	—	17	22	27	30	32	30	—
6 mm glass	—	20	24	29	33	25	30	—
9 mm glass	—	20	26	30	30	32	39	—
9 mm plywood	—	12	17	22	25	26	20	—
112 mm brick	—	36	38	40	46	54	58	—
3 mm steel	16	22	28	34	40	45	32	41
6 mm steel	22	28	34	40	45	37	42	51
12 mm steel	28	34	40	45	37	41	51	60
3 mm aluminium	8	14	19	25	31	36	29	32
8 mm aluminium	13	19	25	30	36	30	32	42

British Standards - Noise Measurement

BS 2750:	Measurement of sound insulation in buildings and of building elements Parts 1 - 9
BS 3425: 1966	Method for the measurement of noise emitted by motor vehicles
BS 4813: 1972	Method of measuring noise from machine tools excluding testing in anechoic chambers
BS 6840:	Sound system equipment
BS 5944:	Measurement of airborne noise from hydraulic fluid power systems and components Parts 1 - 5
BS 6086: 1981	(1992) Method of measurement of noise inside motor vehicles
BS 8233: 1987	Code of practice for sound insulation and noise reduction for buildings Replaces CP 3: Chapter III: 1972
CP 153	Windows and rooflights
BS EN 20140	Acoustics in buildings (etc)
BS EN 21680	Acoustics: rotating machinery (etc)
BS EN 27574	Statistical methods (etc)

APPENDIX C

METAL CORROSION – Charts and tables

PERFORMANCE of VARIOUS METALLIC COMBINATIONS in 1 % SALT SPRAY

Completely satisfactory combinations:
copper — nickel-plated copper
copper — gold-plated copper
tin-plated copper — aluminium
tin-plated copper — nickel-plated copper
tin-plated copper — solder-dipped copper
tin-plated brass — aluminium
solder-dipped copper — nickel-plated copper
nickel-plated copper — gold-plated copper
nickel-plated copper — silver-plated copper
gold-plated copper — silver-plated copper
aluminium — tin-plated aluminium (no copper undercoat)

Satisfactory : slight galvanic corrosion:
copper — silver-plated copper
solder-dipped copper — tin-plated aluminium
copper — tin-plated copper
copper — solder-dipped copper
copper — reflowed tinned copper
silver-plated copper — tin-plated copper
silver-plated copper — solder-dipped copper
gold-plated copper — tin-plated copper
aluminium — tin-plated aluminium (zincate process)

Border line : moderate galvanic corrosion:
gold-plated copper — solder-dipped copper
tin-plated aluminium — nickel-plated copper
aluminium — solder-dipped aluminium

Unsatisfactory : severe galvanic corrosion:
aluminium — brass
aluminium — copper
tin-plated aluminium — copper
aluminium — nickel-plated copper
aluminium — nickel-plated brass
aluminium — silver-plated copper
tin-plated aluminium — silver-plated copper
aluminium — gold-plated copper
tin-plated aluminium — gold-plated copper

AVOIDANCE OF CORROSION BY REARRANGEMENT OF SHAPE

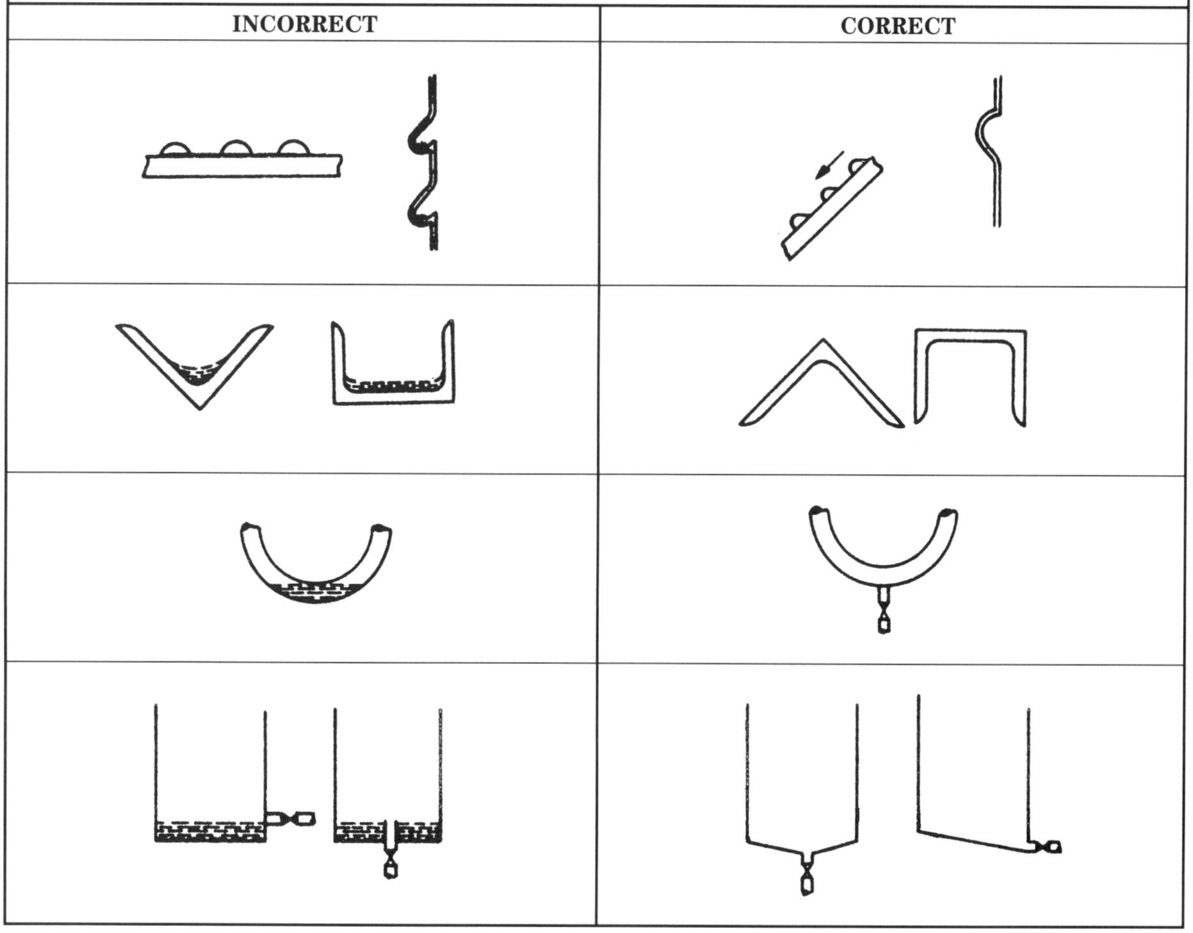

INCORRECT	CORRECT

APPENDIX C

METAL CORROSION
– Charts and tables

GALVANIC SERIES OF METALS IN WATER

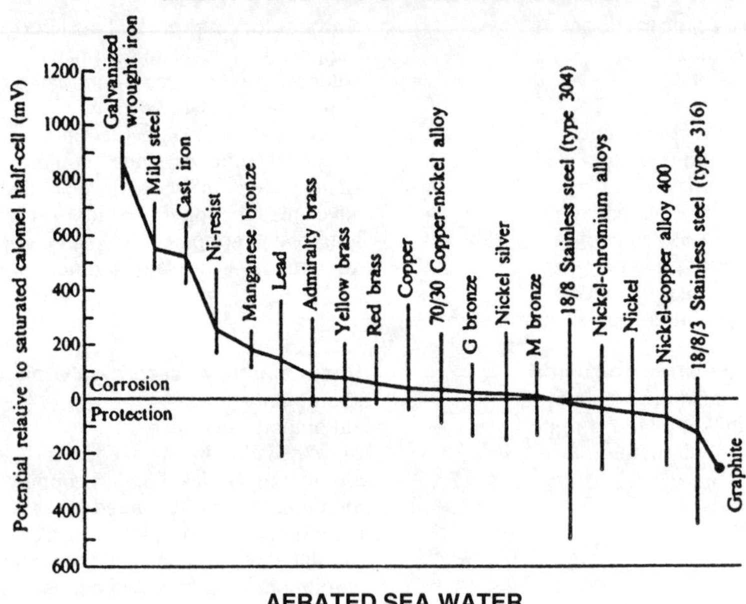

AERATED SEA WATER

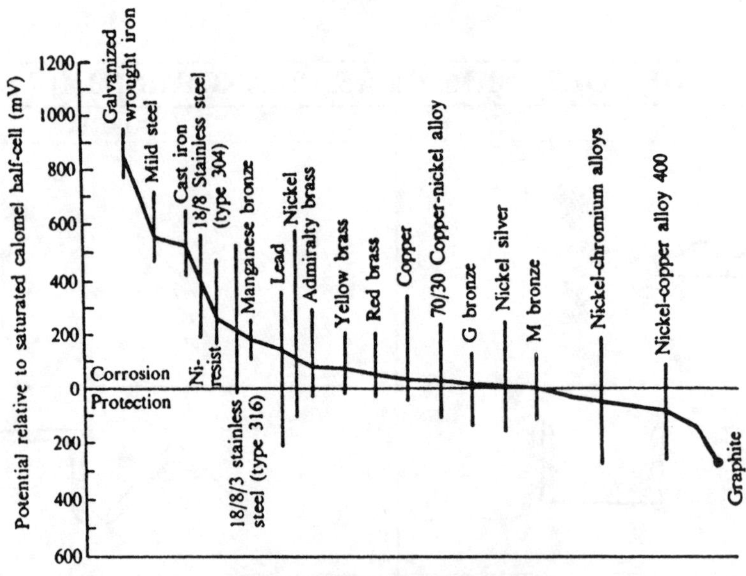

DE-AERATED FRESH WATER

BRITISH STANDARDS

BS 443: 1982 (1990)	Specification for testing zinc coatings on steel wire and for quality requirements
BS 558 & 564: 1970	Specifications for nickel anodes, anode nickel and nickel salts for electroplating
BS 622: 1967	Specification for potassium and sodium cyanides for electroplating
BS 729: 1971 (1986)	Specification for hot dip galvanized coatings on iron and steel articles
BS 1224: 1970	Specification for electroplated coatings of nickel and chromium
BS 1468: 1967 (1990)	Specification for tin anodes and tin salts for electroplating
BS 3745: 1970 (1988)	Method for the evaluation of results of accelerated corrosion tests on metallic coatings
BS 5493: 1977	Code of practice for protective coating of iron and steel structures against corrosion
BS 5735: 1979	Test methods for determining electrolytic corrosion with electrical insulating materials
BS 5903: 1980 (1987)	Method for determination of resistance to intergranular corrosion of austenitic stainless steels: copper sulphate - sulphuric acid method (Moneypenny Strauss test)

PAGES 218 & 219 REPRODUCED FROM 'DESIGN GUIDE NO. 21' OXFORD UNIVERSITY PRESS

APPENDIX D

FITS AND TOLERANCES FOR HOLES – Introduction

SELECTED ISO FITS – HOLE BASIS

Extracted from BS 4500.
(See next page for table of sizes.)

The ISO system provides a great many hole and shaft tolerances so as to cater for a very wide range of conditions. However, experience shows that the majority of fit conditions required for normal engineering products can be provided by a quite limited selection of tolerances.

The following selected hole and shaft tolerances have been found to be commonly applied :
Selected hole tolerances : H7; H8; H9; H11
Selected shaft tolerances : c11; d10; e9; f7; g6; h6; k6; n6; p6; s6

The table on the next page shows a range of fits derived from these selected hole and shaft tolerances. As will be seen, it covers fits from loose clearance to heavy interference and it may therefore be found to be suitable for most normal requirements. Many users may in fact find that their needs are met by a further selection within this selected range.

It should be noted, however, that this table is offered only as an example of how a restricted selection of fits can be made. It is clearly impossible to recommend selections of fits which are appropriate to all sections of industry, but it must be emphasized that a user who decides upon a selected range will always enjoy the economic advantages this conveys. Once he has installed the necessary tooling and gauging facilities, he can combine his selected hole and shaft tolerances in different ways without any additional investment in tools and equipment.

For example, if it is assumed that the range of fits shown in the table has been adopted but that, for a particular application the fit H8 - f7 is appropriate but provides rather too much variation, the hole tolerance H7 could equally well be associated with the shaft f7 and may provide exactly what is required without necessitating any additional tooling.

For most general applications it is usual to recommend hole basis fits as, except in the realm of very large sizes where the effects of temperature play a large part, it is usually considered easier to manufacture and measure the male member of a fit and it is thus desirable to be able to allocate the larger part of the tolerance available to the hole and adjust the shaft to suit.

In some circumstances, however, it may in fact be preferable to employ a shaft-basis. For example, in the case of driving shafts where a single shaft may have to accommodate a variety of accessories such as couplings, bearings, collars, etc., it is preferable to maintain a constant diameter for the permanent member, which is the shaft, and vary the bore of the accessories. For use in applications of this kind, a selection of shaft basis fits is shown in Appendix E : Fits and Tolerances for Shafts (See also BS 4500B : 1970 (1985) Data sheet: selected ISO fits - shaft basis).

REFERENCES

BS 4500 : 1990	Pt 1 General Tolerances and Deviations
BS 969 (1982)	Limits and tolerances on plain limit gauges (Replaces BS 4500 Pt 2)
BS 4500 : 1973 (1985)	Pt 3 Working limits on untoleranced dimensions
BS 4500 : 1985 (1991)	Pt 4 Cone (atper) fits (etc) to ISO 3040
BS 4500 : 1988	Pt 5 Cone Tolerances for rigid workpieces (etc)

See also BS 4500A : 1970 (1985) Data sheet: selected ISO fits - hole basis.

APPENDIX D

FITS AND TOLERANCES FOR HOLES – Table of selected sizes

HOLE BASIS – Diagrams to scale for 25 mm diameter

Holes + 0 − Shafts

Clearance fits: H11 c11, H9 d10, H9 e9, H8 f7, H7 g6, H7 h6

Transition fits: H7 k6, H7 n6

Interference fits: H7 p6, H7 s6

Nominal sizes		Tolerance		Tolerance		Tolerance		Tolerance		Tolerance		Tolerance		Tolerance		Tolerance		Tolerance		Tolerance	
Over	**To**	**H11**	**c11**	**H9**	**d10**	**H9**	**e9**	**H8**	**f7**	**H7**	**g6**	**H7**	**h6**	**H7**	**k6**	**H7**	**n6**	**H7**	**p6**	**H7**	**s6**
mm	mm	0.001mm	0.001mm	0.001mm	0.001mm	0.001mm	0.001mm	0.001mm	0.001mm	0.001mm	0.001mm	0.001mm	0.001mm	0.001mm	0.001mm	0.001mm	0.001mm	0.001mm	0.001mm	0.001mm	0.001mm
–	3	+60 0	−60 −120	+25 0	−20 −60	+25 0	−14 −39	+14 0	−6 −16	+10 0	−2 −8	+10 0	−6 0	+10 0	+6 +0	+10 0	+10 +4	+10 0	+12 +6	+10 0	+20 +14
3	6	+75 0	−70 −145	+30 0	−30 −78	+30 0	−20 −50	+18 0	−10 −22	+12 0	−4 −12	+12 0	−8 0	+12 0	+9 +1	+12 0	+16 +8	+12 0	+20 +12	+12 0	+27 +19
6	10	+90 0	−80 −170	+36 0	−40 −98	+36 0	−25 −61	+22 0	−13 −28	+15 0	−5 −14	+15 0	−9 0	+15 0	+10 +1	+15 0	+19 +10	+15 0	+24 +15	+15 0	+32 +23
10	18	+110 0	−95 −205	+43 0	−50 −120	+43 0	−32 −75	+27 0	−16 −34	+18 0	−6 −17	+18 0	−11 0	+18 0	+12 +1	+18 0	+23 +12	+18 0	+29 +18	+18 0	+39 +28
18	30	+130 0	−110 −240	+52 0	−65 −149	+52 0	−40 −92	+33 0	−20 −41	+21 0	−7 −20	+21 0	−13 0	+21 0	+15 +2	+21 0	+28 +15	+21 0	+35 +22	+21 0	+48 +35
30	40	+160 0	−120 −280	+62 0	−80 −180	+62 0	−50 −112	+39 0	−25 −50	+25 0	−9 −25	+25 0	−16 0	+25 0	+18 +2	+25 0	+33 +17	+25 0	+42 +26	+25 0	+59 +43
40	50	+160 0	−130 −290																		
50	65	+190 0	−140 −330	+74 0	−100 −220	+74 0	−60 −134	+46 0	−30 −60	+30 0	−10 −29	+30 0	−19 0	+30 0	+21 +2	+30 0	+39 +20	+30 0	+51 +32	+30 0	+72 +53
65	80	+190 0	−150 −340																	+30 0	+78 +59
80	100	+220 0	−170 −390	+87 0	−120 −260	+87 0	−72 −159	+54 0	−36 −71	+35 0	−12 −34	+35 0	−22 0	+35 0	+25 +3	+35 0	+45 +23	+35 0	+59 +37	+35 0	+93 +71
100	120	+220 0	−180 −400																	+35 0	+101 +79
120	140	+250 0	−200 −450	+100 0	−145 −305	+100 0	−84 −185	+63 0	−43 −83	+40 0	−14 −39	+40 0	−25 0	+40 0	+28 +3	+40 0	+52 +27	+40 0	+68 +43	+40 0	+117 +92
140	160	+250 0	−210 −460																	+40 0	+125 +100
160	180	+250 0	−230 −480																	+40 0	+133 +108
180	200	+290 0	−240 −530	+115 0	−170 −355	+115 0	−100 −215	+72 0	−50 −96	+46 0	−15 −44	+46 0	−29 0	+46 0	+33 +4	+46 0	+60 +31	+46 0	+79 +50	+46 0	+151 +122
200	225	+290 0	−260 −550																	+46 0	+159 +130
225	250	+290 0	−280 −570																	+46 0	+169 +140
250	280	+320 0	−300 −620	+130 0	−190 −400	+130 0	−110 −240	+81 0	−56 −108	+52 0	−17 −49	+52 0	−32 0	+52 0	+36 +4	+52 0	+66 +34	+52 0	+88 +56	+52 0	+190 +158
280	315	+320 0	−330 −650																	+52 0	+202 +170
315	355	+360 0	−360 −720	+140 0	−210 −440	+140 0	−125 −265	+89 0	−62 −119	+57 0	−18 −54	+57 0	−36 0	+57 0	+40 +4	+57 0	+73 +37	+57 0	+96 +62	+57 0	+226 +190
355	400	+360 0	−400 −760																	+57 0	+244 +208
400	450	+400 0	−440 −840	+155 0	−230 −480	+155 0	−135 −290	+97 0	−68 −131	+63 0	−20 −60	+63 0	−40 0	+63 0	+45 +5	+63 0	+80 +40	+63 0	+106 +68	+63 0	+272 +232
450	500	+400 0	−480 −880																	+63 0	+292 +252

APPENDIX E

FITS AND TOLERANCES FOR SHAFTS – Introduction

SELECTED ISO FITS – SHAFT BASIS

Extracted from BS 4500.
(See next page for table of sizes.)

The ISO system provides a great many hole and shaft tolerances so as to cater for a very wide range of conditions. However, experience shows that the majority of fit conditions required for normal engineering products can be provided by a quite limited selection of tolerances.

The following selected hole and shaft tolerances have been found to be commonly applied :

Selected hole tolerances :	H7; H8; H9; H11
Selected shaft tolerances :	c11; d10; e9; f7; g6; h6; k6; n6; p6; s6

For most general applications it is usual to recommend hole basis fits, i.e. fits in which the design size for the hole is the basic size and variations in the grade of fit for any particular hole are obtained by varying the clearance and the tolerance on the shaft. Appendix D: Fits and Tolerances for Holes gives a range of hole basis fits derived from the selected hole and shaft tolerances above. (See also BS 4500A : 1970 (1985) Data sheet: selected ISO fits - hole basis).

In some circumstances, however, it may in fact be preferable to employ a shaft-basis. For example, in the case of driving shafts where a single shaft may have to accommodate a variety of accessories such as couplings, bearings, collars, etc., it is preferable to maintain a constant diameter for the permanent member, which is the shaft, and vary the bore of the accessories. Shaft basis fits also provide a useful economy where bar stock material is available to standard shaft tolerances of the ISO System.

For the benefit of those wishing to use shaft basis fits, the table on the next page shows the shaft basis equivalents of the hole basis fits in Appendix D. They are all direct conversions except that the fit H9 - d10, instead of being converted to D9 - h10, is adjusted to D10 - h9 to avoid introducing the additional shaft tolerance h10.

As will be seen, the table covers fits from loose clearance to heavy interference and it may therefore be found suitable for most normal requirements. Many users may in fact find that their needs are met by a further selection within this selected range.

It should be noted, however, that this table is offered only as an example of how a restricted selection of fits can be made. It is clearly impossible to recommend selections of fits which are appropriate to all sections of industry, but it must be emphasized that a user who decides upon a selected range will always enjoy the economic advantages this conveys. Once he has installed the necessary tooling and gauging facilities, he can combine his selected hole and shaft tolerances in different ways without any additional investment in tools and equipment.

For example, if it is assumed that the range of fits shown in the table has been adopted but that, for a particular application the fit F8 - h7 is appropriate but provides rather too much variation, the shaft tolerance h6 could equally well be associated with the hole F8 and may provide exactly what is required without necessitating any additional tooling.

REFERENCES

BS 4500 : 1990	Pt 1 General Tolerances and Deviations
BS 969 (1982)	Limits and tolerances on plain limit gauges (Replaces BS 4500 Pt 2)
BS 4500 : 1973 (1985)	Pt 3 Working limits on untoleranced dimensions
BS 4500 : 1985 (1991)	Pt 4 Cone (atper) fits (etc) to ISO 3040
BS 4500 : 1988	Pt 5 Cone Tolerances for rigid workpieces (etc)

See also BS 4500B : 1970 (1985) Data sheet: selected ISO fits - shaft basis

APPENDIX E

FITS AND TOLERANCES FOR SHAFTS – Table of selected sizes

SHAFT BASIS – Diagrams to scale for 25 mm diameter

Holes + 0 − Shafts

Clearance fits: c11 h11 · D10 h9 · E9 h9 · F8 h7 · G7 h6 · H7 h6

Transition fits: h6 K7 · h6 N7

Interference fits: h6 P7 · h6 S7

Nominal sizes		Tolerance		Tolerance		Tolerance		Tolerance		Tolerance		Tolerance		Tolerance		Tolerance		Tolerance		Tolerance	
Over	To	h11	C11	h9	D10	h9	E9	h7	F8	h6	G7	h6	H7	h6	K7	h6	N7	h6	P7	h6	S7
mm	mm	0.001mm	0.001mm	0.001mm	0.001mm	0.001mm	0.001mm	0.001mm	0.001mm	0.001mm	0.001mm	0.001mm	0.001mm	0.001mm	0.001mm	0.001mm	0.001mm	0.001mm	0.001mm	0.001mm	0.001mm
–	3	0 –60	+120 +60	0 –25	+60 +20	0 –25	+39 +14	0 –10	+20 +6	0 –6	+12 +2	0 –6	+10 0	0 –6	0 –10	0 –6	–4 –14	0 –6	–6 –16	0 –6	–14 –24
3	6	0 –75	+145 +70	0 –30	+78 +30	0 –30	+50 +20	0 –12	+28 +10	0 –8	+16 +4	0 –8	+12 0	0 –8	+3 –9	0 –8	–4 –16	0 –8	–8 –20	0 –8	–15 –27
6	10	0 –90	+170 +80	0 –36	+98 +40	0 –36	+61 +25	0 –15	+35 +13	0 –9	+20 +5	0 –9	+15 +0	0 –9	+5 –10	0 –9	–4 –19	0 –9	–9 –24	0 –9	–17 –32
10	18	0 –110	+205 +95	0 –43	+120 +50	0 –43	+75 +32	0 –18	+43 +16	0 –11	+24 +6	0 –11	+18 0	0 –11	+6 –12	0 –11	–5 –23	0 –11	–11 –29	0 –11	–21 –39
18	30	0 –130	+240 +110	0 –52	+149 +65	0 –52	+92 +40	0 –21	+53 +20	0 –13	+28 +7	0 –13	+21 0	0 –13	+6 –15	0 –13	–7 –28	0 –13	–14 –35	0 –13	–27 –48
30	40	0 –160	+280 +120	0 –62	+180 +80	0 –62	+112 +50	0 –25	+64 +25	0 –16	+34 +9	0 –16	+25 0	0 –16	+7 –18	0 –16	–8 –33	0 –16	–17 –42	0 –16	–34 –59
40	50	0 –160	+290 +130																		
50	65	0 –190	+330 +140	0 –74	+220 +100	0 –74	+134 +60	0 –30	+76 +30	0 –19	+40 +10	0 –19	+30 0	0 –19	+9 –21	0 –19	–9 –39	0 –19	–21 –51	0 –19	–42 –72
65	80	0 –190	+340 +150																	0 –19	–48 –78
80	100	0 –220	+390 +170	0 –87	+260 +120	0 –87	+159 +72	0 –35	+90 +36	0 –22	+47 +12	0 –22	+35 0	0 –22	+10 –25	0 –22	–10 –45	0 –22	–24 –59	0 –22	–58 –93
100	120	0 –220	+400 +180																	0 –22	–66 –101
120	140	0 –250	+450 +200	0 –100	+305 +145	0 –100	+185 +85	0 –40	+106 +43	0 –25	+54 +14	0 –25	+40 0	0 –25	+12 –28	0 –25	–12 –52	0 –25	–28 –68	0 –25	–77 –117
140	160	0 –250	+460 +210																	0 –25	–85 –125
160	180	0 –250	+480 +230																	0 –25	–93 –133
180	200	0 –290	+530 +240	0 –115	+355 +170	0 –115	+215 +100	0 –46	+122 +50	0 –29	+61 +15	0 –29	+46 0	0 –29	+13 –33	0 –29	–14 –60	0 –29	–33 –79	0 –29	–105 –151
200	225	0 –290	+550 +260																	0 –29	–113 –159
225	250	0 –290	+570 +280																	0 –29	–123 –169
250	280	0 –320	+620 +300	0 –130	+400 +190	0 –130	+240 +110	0 –52	+137 +56	0 –32	+62 +17	0 –32	+52 0	0 –32	+16 –36	0 –32	–14 –66	0 –32	–36 –88	0 –32	–138 –190
280	315	0 –320	+650 +330																	0 –32	–150 –202
315	355	0 –360	+720 +360	0 –140	+440 +210	0 –140	+265 +125	0 –57	+151 +62	0 –36	+75 +18	0 –36	+57 0	0 –36	+17 –40	0 –36	–16 –73	0 –36	–41 –98	0 –36	–169 –226
355	400	0 –360	+760 +400																	0 –36	–187 –244
400	450	0 –400	+840 +440	0 –155	+480 +230	0 155	+290 +135	0 63	+165 +68	0 40	+83 +20	0 –40	+63 0	0 –40	+18 –45	0 –40	–17 –80	0 –40	–45 –108	0 –40	–209 –272
450	500	0 –400	+880 +480																	0 –40	–229 –292

APPENDIX F

INDEX TO BRITISH STANDARDS REFERRED TO IN THIS BOOK

For further details of contents and scope of these and other standards, refer directly to the current BSI Catalogue and BSI News.
Note: Standards marked * have a corresponding current international standard

STANDARD:	TITLE:	PAGE NO. where BS is referred to in this book
BS 4 :	Structural steel sections Part 1 : 1980 Specification for hot-rolled section Part 2 : 1989 (withdrawn) Hot-rolled hollow sections (replaced by BS 4848 : Part 2)	12, 13
BS 10 : 1962	(Obsolescent) Specification for flanges and bolting for pipes, valves, and fittings	170
BS 12 : 1978	Specification for ordinary and rapid-hardening Portland cement	27
BS 21 : 1985 *	Specification for pipe threads for tubes and fittings where pressure-tight joints are made on the threads (metric dimensions)	126, 130 132, 138
BS 131 : *	Methods for notched bar tests (Parts 1–5)	7
BS 240 : 1986 *	Method for Brinell hardness test and for verification of Brinell hardness testing machines	7
BS 292 :	Rolling bearings: ball bearings, cylindrical and spherical roller bearings Part 1 : 1982 Specification for dimensions of ball bearings, cylindrical and spherical roller bearings (metric series) Part 2 : 1982 Specification for dimensions of ball bearings and cylindrical roller bearings (inch series)	70, 72
BS 308 : *	Engineering drawing practice Part 1 : 1984 Recommendations for general principles Part 2 : 1985 Recommendations for dimensioning and tolerancing of size Part 3 : 1972 Geometrical tolerancing see also PD 7304	62, 64, 66, 68, 168 196, 198
(BS 310 : 1972	(withdrawn) Specification for blackheart malleable iron castings (Replaced by BS 6681 : 1986)	135, 139)
BS 350 :	Conversion factors and tables Part 1 : 1974 (1983) Basis of tables. Conversion factors Part 2 : 1982 (withdrawn) Detailed conversion tables Supplement No. 1 (1987) to BS 350 : Part 2 : 1962 (1982) Additional tables for SI conversions	3
BS 427 : *	Method for Vickers hardness test (Parts 1, 2)	7
BS 436 : *	Spur and helical gears Part 1 : 1967 (1987) Basic rack form, pitches and accuracy (diametral pitch series) Part 2 : 1970 (1984) Basic rack form, modules and accuracy (1 to 50 metric module) Part 3 : 1986 Method for calculation of contact & root bending stress limitations for metallic involute gears	96, 98
BS 443 : 1982	Specification for testing zinc coatings on steel wire and for quality requirements	219
BS 449 :	Specification for the use of structural steel in building (see also BS 5950) Part 1 (withdrawn), Supplement No. 1 (withdrawn), Addendum No. 1 to BS 449 : Part 1 (withdrawn) Part 2 : 1969 Metric units Addendum No. 1 (1975) to BS 449 : Part 2 (withdrawn)	12, 13
BS 499 : *	Welding terms and symbols Parts 1, 2, 2C	42, 44, 46-9
BS 545 : 1982 (1987) *	Specification for bevel gears (machine cut)	98
BS 558 & 564 : 1970	Specifications for nickel anodes, anode nickel and nickel salts for electroplating	219
BS 622 : 1967	Specification for potassium and sodium cyanides for electroplating	219
BS 638 : *	Arc welding power sources, equipment and accessories Parts 1–8	42
BS 709 : 1983	Methods of destructive testing fusion welded joints and weld metal in steel	42
BS 729 : 1971 (1986) *	Specification for hot dip galvanized coatings on iron and steel articles	219
BS 745 :	Specification for animal glue for wood (joiner's glue) (dry glue; jelly or liquid glue)	52

APPENDIX F INDEX TO BRITISH STANDARDS REFERRED TO IN THIS BOOK

STANDARD	TITLE	PAGE NO.
BS 856 : 1969	Specification for wing nuts	32
BS 864 : *	Capillary and compression tube fittings of copper and copper alloy Part 2 and Part 3 (obsolescent)	160
BS 903 : *	Methods of testing vulcanised rubber Parts A1-A6, A8-A19, A21, A24-A40, A42-A44, A46-A56, B1-B17, B19, C1-C5, D1-D7, E1-39, F1-F9, G1-G9, H1-H11	27
BS 952 :	Glass for glazing Parts 1 and 2	27
BS 969 : 1982	Specification for limits and tolerances on plain limit gauges	220
BS 970 : *	Specification for wrought steels for mechanical and allied engineering purposes Part 1 : 1983 General inspection and testing procedures and specific requirements for carbon, carbon manganese, alloy and stainless steels Part 2 : 1988 Requirements for steels for the manufacture of hot formed springs Part 4 : 1970 (1988) Valve steels Part 5 : 1972 Carbon and alloy spring steels for the manufacture of hot formed springs Part 6 : 1973 SI metric values (for use with BS 970 : Parts 4 and 5)	6-10, 96, 126 129-132, 135-138, 188
BS 978 :	Specification for fine pitch gears Part 1 : 1968 (1990) Involute spur and helical gears Part 2 : 1952 (1990) Cycloidal type gears Part 3 : 1952 (1990) Bevel gears Part 5 : 1965 Hobs and cutters	96
BS 1004 : 1972 *	Specification for zinc alloys for die casting & zinc alloy die castings	135, 139
BS 1098 :	Specification for jig bushes Part 1 : 1967 (1992) Inch units Part 2 : 1977 (1992) Metric units	64
BS 1134 : *	Method for the assessment of surface texture Parts 1 and 2	172, 178
BS 1154 : 1986	Specification for natural rubber compounds	27
BS 1178 : 1982	Specification for milled lead sheet for building purposes	27
BS 1192 :	Construction drawing practice Parts 1–5	196
BS 1203 : 1979 (1991)	Specification for synthetic resin adhesives (phenolic and aminoplastic) for plywood	52
BS 1204 : 1993	Specification for type MR phenolic and aminoplastic synthetic resin adhesives for wood	52
BS 1212 :	Float operated valves Parts 1–4	138
BS 1224 : 1970 *	Specification for electroplated coatings for nickel and chromium	219
BS 1306 : 1975 (1990)	Specification for copper and copper alloy pressure piping systems	150
BS 1400 : 1985 *	Specification for copper alloy ingots and copper alloy and high conductivity copper castings	129, 135-7, 139
BS 1407 : 1970	Specification for high carbon bright steel (silver steel)	6
BS 1414 : 1975 (1983)	Specification for steel wedge gate valves (flanged and butt-welding ends) for the petroleum, petrochemical and allied industries	132
BS 1452 : 1977 *	Specification for grey iron castings	6, 96, 129, 131, 135-7, 139
BS 1468 : 1967	Specification for tin anodes and tin salts for electroplating	219
BS 1470 : 1987 *	Specification for wrought aluminium and aluminium alloys for general engineering purposes : plate, sheet and strip	16, 17
BS 1471 : 1972 *	Specification for wrought aluminium and aluminium alloys for general engineering purposes : drawn tube	16, 17
BS 1472 : 1972 *	Specification for wrought aluminium and aluminium alloys for general engineering purposes : forging stock and forgings	16, 17
BS 1473 : 1972 *	Specification for wrought aluminium and aluminium alloys for general engineering purposes : rivet, bolt and screw stock	16, 17

APPENDIX F

INDEX TO BRITISH STANDARDS REFERRED TO IN THIS BOOK

STANDARD	TITLE	PAGE NO.
BS 1474 : 1987 *	Specification for wrought aluminium and aluminium alloys for general engineering purposes : bars, extruded round tube and sections	16, 17
BS 1475 : 1972 *	Specification for wrought aluminium and aluminium alloys for general engineering purposes : wire	17
BS 1490 : 1988 *	Specification for aluminium and aluminium alloy ingots and castings for general engineering purposes	16, 135, 139
BS 1493 : 1987	Method for specifying general purpose polystyrene (PS) moulding and extrusion materials	23
BS 1501 : *	Steels for fired and unfired pressure vessels : plates Pts 1, 2, Addenda, Pt 3	6, 131
BS 1502 : 1982	Specification for steels for fired and unfired pressure vessels : sections and bars	135
BS 1503 : 1980 *	Specification for steel forgings (including semi-finished forged products) for pressure purposes	8, 131, 135
BS 1504 : 1976 (1984)	Specification for steel castings for pressure purposes	131, 135 139
BS 1506 : 1986	Specification for carbon, low alloy and stainless steel bars and billets for bolting material to be used in pressure retaining applications	135
BS 1524 : 1993	Specification for cellulose acetate moulding materials	23
BS 1560 : *	Specification for steel pipe flanges (nominal sizes ½in to 24in) for the petroleum industry Part 2 : 1970 Metric dimensions Superseded – see below	170
BS 1560 : *	Circular flanges for pipes, valves and fittings (Class designated) Part 3 : Steel, cast iron and copper alloy flanges Section 3.1 : 1989 Supersedes BS 1560 : Part 2 : 1970 Section 3.3 : 1989	
BS 1625-6 and 4830 : 1972 (1992)	Specifications for woven cotton tapes, light, medium and heavy qualities	124
(BS 1631 : 1957	(withdrawn) Austenitic chromium-nickel steel castings for resistance to corrosion (replaced by BS 3100 : 1967)	139)
(BS 1632 : 1957	(withdrawn) Austenitic chromium-nickel-molybdenum steel castings for resistance to corrosion (replaced by BS 3100 : 1987)	139)
BS 1706 : 1960 *	Specification for electroplated coatings of cadmium and zinc on iron and steel	161
BS 1723 :	Brazing Parts 1–4 :	42
BS 1726 :	Guide to the design and specification of coil springs Part 1 : 1987 Guide for the design of helical compression springs Part 2: 1988 Guide for the design of helical extension springs Part 3 : 1988 Guide for the design of helical torsion springs	188, 190 191
BS 1740 : *	Specification for wrought steel pipe fittings (screwed BS 21 R-series thread) Part 1 : 1971 (1983)	160
BS 1755 : *	Glossary of terms used in the plastics industry Parts 1 & 2	22
BS 1763 : 1975	Specification for thin PVC sheeting (calendered, flexible, unsupported)	23
BS 1806 : 1989	Specification for dimensions of toroidal sealing rings ('O' rings) and their housings (inch series)	178
BS 1873 : 1975 (1983)	Specification for steel globe and globe stop & check valves (flanged and butt-welding ends) for the petroleum, petrochemical and allied industries	126
BS 1902 : *	Methods of testing refractory materials Parts 1A, 1B, 2, 2A, 2B, 2D, 3-7, 9	27
BS 1936 : *	Specification for undercuts and runouts for screw thread Part 1 & 2	32, 168, 169
BS 2045 : 1965 (1982) *	Preferred numbers	113
BS 2048 :	Specification for dimensions of fractional horse-power motors Part 1 : 1961 (1984)	104
BS 2056 : 1983 *	Specification for stainless steel wire for mecanical springs	188
BS 2080 : 1989	Specification for face-to-face, centre-to-face, end-to-end and centre-to-end dimensions of valves	124
BS 2470 : 1973 (1984)	Specification for hexagon socket screws and wrench keys. Inch series.	32
BS 2519 : *	Glossary for gears Parts 1 & 2	96, 98

APPENDIX F INDEX TO BRITISH STANDARDS REFERRED TO IN THIS BOOK

STANDARD	TITLE	PAGE NO.
BS 2571 : 1990	Specification for general-purpose flexible PVC compounds for moulding and extrusion	23
BS 2598 : *	Glass plant, pipeline and fittings Parts 1–4	27
BS 2633 : 1987	Specification for class 1 arc welding of ferritic steel pipework for carrying fluids	42
BS 2739 : 1975	Specification for thick PVC sheeting (calendered, flexible, unsupported)	23
BS 2750 : *	Measurement of sound insulation in buildings and of building elements Parts 1–9	217
BS 2751 and 3222 : 1982	Specification for acrylonitrile-butadiene rubber compounds	27
BS 2752 : 1982 (1987)	Specification for chloroprene rubber compounds	27
BS 2779 : 1986 *	Specification for pipe threads for tubes and fittings where pressure-tight joints are not made on the threads (metric dimensions)	145, 146 160, 169
BS 2782 : 1970 *	Methods of testing plastics (Partially replaced by BS 3794 : Part 2 : 1982 & by revision)	22
BS 2782 : *	Methods of testing plastics Parts 0–11	22
BS 2789 : 1985 *	Specification for spheroidal graphite or nodular graphite cast iron	6, 135, 139
BS 2870 : 1980	Specification for rolled copper and copper alloys : sheet, strip and foil	27,135,139
BS 2871 : *	Specification for copper and copper alloys. Tubes Part 1 : 1971 Copper tubes for water, gas and sanitation Part 2 : 1972 Tubes for general purposes Part 3 : 1972 Tubes for heat exchangers	27
BS 2872 : 1989	Specification for copper and copper alloys. Forging stock and forgings	27, 129, 135-7, 139
BS 2873 : 1969	Specification for copper and copper alloys. Wire	27, 135
BS 2874 : 1986	Specification for copper and copper alloy rods and sections (other than forging stock)	27, 129, 135-7, 139
BS 2875 : 1969	Specification for copper and copper alloys. Plate	27, 135
BS 2917 : 1977 *	Specification for graphical symbols used on diagrams for fluid power systems and components	212
BS 3016 : 1989	Specification for pressure regulators and automatic changeover devices for liquefied petroleum gases	138
BS 3063 : 1965	Specification for dimensions of gaskets for pipe flanges	170
BS 3071 : 1986	Specification for nickel-copper alloy castings	135
BS 3076 : 1976 (1983)	Specification for nickel and nickel alloys: bar	135
BS 3100 : 1976 (1984)	Specification for steel castings for general engineering purposes	139
BS 3126 : 1987	Method of specifying toughened polystyrene (SB) moulding and extrusion materials	23
BS 3189 : 1973	Specification for phosphate treatment of iron and steel	161
BS 3222 :	See BS 2751	
BS 3332 : 1987 *	Specification for white metal bearing alloy ingots	27, 64, 66, 68
BS 3382 :	Specification for electroplated coatings on threaded components Parts 1 & 2 : 1961 Cadmium on steel components. Zinc on steel components Parts 3 & 4 : 1965 Nickel or nickel plus chromium on steel components Nickel or nickel plus chromium on copper and copper alloy (including brass) components Parts 5 & 6 : 1967 Tin on copper and copper alloy (including brass) components Silver on copper and copper alloy (including brass) components Part 7 : 1966 Thicker platings for threaded components	32, 161
BS 3412 : 1992	Methods of specifying general purpose polyethylene materials for moulding and extrusion	23
BS 3425 : 1966 *	Method for the measurement of noise emitted by motor vehicles	217

APPENDIX F

INDEX TO BRITISH STANDARDS REFERRED TO IN THIS BOOK

STANDARD	TITLE	PAGE NO.
BS 3496 : 1989	Specification for E glass fibre chopped strand mat for reinforcement of polyester and other liquid laminating systems	27
BS 3532 : 1990	Method of specifying unsaturated polyester resin systems	23
BS 3600 : 1976 (1988)*	Specification for dimensions and masses per unit length of welded and seamless steel pipes and tubes for pressure purposes	150
BS 3601 : 1987 *	Specification for carbon steel pipes and tubes with specified room temperature properties for pressure purposes	150
BS 3602 : *	Specification for steel pipes and tubes for pressure purposes : carbon and carbon manganese steel with specified elevated temperature properties Parts 1 & 2	150, 153
BS 3603 : 1977	Specification for steel pipes and tubes for pressure purposes : carbon and alloy steel with specified low temperature properties	150
BS 3604 : 1978 *	Specification for steel pipes and tubes for pressure purposes : ferritic alloy steel with specified elevated temperature properties	150
BS 3605 : 1973	Specification for seamless and welded austenitic stainless steel pipes and tubes for pressure purposes	150
BS 3643 : *	ISO metric screw threads Parts 1 & 2	32, 33, 115, 145, 146, 169
BS 3691 : 1990	Specification for E glass fibre rovings for reinforcement of polyester and epoxy resin systems	27
BS 3692 : 1967 *	Specification for ISO metric precision hexagon bolts, screws and nuts. Metric units.	32
BS 3696 : *	Specification for master gears Part 1 : 1977 (1984)	96
BS 3733 : 1974 *	Specification for endless V-belt drives for agricultural purposes	80
BS 3745 : 1970 (1979)*	Method for the evaluation of results of accelerated corrosion tests on metallic coatings	219
BS 3749 : 1991	Specification for E glass fibre woven roving fabrics for the reinforcement of polyester and epoxy resins systems	27
BS 3757 : 1978 (1990)	Specification for rigid PVC sheet	23
BS 3779 : 1985	Specification for glass and glass polyester fibre woven tapes for electrical purposes	27
BS 3790 :	Specification for endless wedge belt drives and endless V-belt drives	80, 81, 83, 85
BS 3794 : *	Decorative, high pressure laminates (HPL) based on thermosetting resins Part 1 : 1966 Specification for performance Part 2 : 1966 Methods of determination of properties	22
BS 3832 : 1981 (1986)*	Specification for wire reinforced rubber hoses and hose assemblies for hydraulic installations	150, 165 166
BS 3837 :	Expanded polystyrene boards Part 1 : 1986 Specification for boards manufactured from expandable beads Part 2 : 1990 Specification for extruded boards	23
BS 3869 : 1965	Specification for rigid expanded polyvinyl chloride for thermal insulation purposes and building applications	23
BS 3920 : *	Derivation and verification of elevated temperature properties for steel products for pressure purposes Parts 1 & 2	6
BS 3923 :	Methods for ultrasonic examination of welds Parts 1 & 2	42
BS 3934 :	Mechanical standardization of semiconductor devices Parts 1–6 incl. and 10	196
BS 3939 : *	Guide for graphical symbols for electrical power, telecommunications and electronic diagrams Parts 1–13	208
BS 3990 : 1980 (1988)	Specification for acrylic resin teeth	23
BS 3992 : 1966	(withdrawn) Specification for dimensions of aerial rods and slabs made of ferromagnetic oxides for use in telecommunication and allied electronic equipment	33

APPENDIX F INDEX TO BRITISH STANDARDS REFERRED TO IN THIS BOOK

APPENDIX F

INDEX TO BRITISH STANDARDS REFERRED TO IN THIS BOOK

STANDARD	TITLE	PAGE NO.
BS 4618 : *	Recommendations for the presentation of plastics design data Introduction, Parts 1–5	22
BS 4637 : 1970 (1982)	Specification for carbon steel wire for coiled springs (bedding and seating)	188
BS 4638 : 1970 (1982)	Specification for carbon steel wire for zigzag and square-form springs	188
BS 4659 : 1971	Specification for tool steels	6
BS 4683 :	Specification for electrical apparatus for explosive atmospheres Parts 1, 2, 3 (withdrawn) and 4 (obsolescent)	104
BS 4727 : *	Glossary of electrotechnical, power, telecommunication, electronics, lighting and colour terms Parts 1–5	208
BS 4749 : 1991	Specification for textile reinforced rubber hydraulic hoses and hose assemblies	150
BS 4772 : 1980 *	Specification for ductile iron pipes and fittings	150, 156-7, 170
BS 4778 : *	Quality vocabulary Parts 1 and 2	216
BS 4808 :	Specification for L.F. cables and wires with PVC insulation and PVC sheath for telecommunication Parts 1–5	23
BS 4813 : 1972	Method of measuring noise from machine tools excluding testing in anechoic chambers	217
BS 4848 : *	Specification for hot-rolled structural steel sections (See also BS 4) Parts 2, 4, 5	10, 12
BS 4870 :	Specification for approval testing of welding procedures Parts 1–4	42
BS 4871 :	Specification for approval testing of welders working to approved welding procedures Parts 1–3	42
BS 4872 :	Specification for approval testing of welders when welding procedure approval is not required Parts 1 and 2	42
BS 4881 : 1993	Specification for polypropylene film cords, lines and twines	23
BS 4882 : 1990	Specification for bolting for flanges and pressure containing purposes	128
BS 4928 : 1985	Specification for man-made fibre ropes	23
BS 4935 : 1989	Method for specifying acrylonitrile-butadiene-styrene (ABS) moulding and extrusion materials	23
BS 4983 : 1992	Specification for textile reinforced thermoplastics hydraulic hoses and hose assemblies	150
BS 4991 : 1974 (1982)	Specification for propylene copolymer pressure pipe	23
BS 4994 : 1987	Specification for design and construction of vessels and tanks in reinforced plastics	23
BS 4999 : *	General requirements for rotating electrical machines Index, Parts 101–109, Part 111–112, Part 140–145, Part 147	104-5, 107, 109, 112-7
BS 5000 : *	Specification for rotating electrical machines of particular types or for particular applications Index, Parts 2–3, 10–11, 15–17, 25, 40, 50, 60, 99	104, 107, 109-111
BS 5041 :	Fire hydrant systems equipment Parts 1–5	126, 132, 138
BS 5070 :	Engineering diagram drawing practice Parts 1–3	196
BS 5106 : 1982	Specification for dimensions of spiral anti-extrusion back-up rings and their housings	23, 178
BS 5135 : 1984	Specification for arc welding of carbon and carbon manganese steels	10, 42
BS 5139 : 1991	Method of specifying general purpose polypropylene and propylene copolymer materials for moulding and extrusion	23
BS 5150 : 1974	Specification for cast iron wedge and double disk gate valves for general purposes	132
BS 5151 : 1974 (1983)	Specification for cast iron gate (parallel slide) valves for general purposes	132
BS 5152 : 1974 (1983)	Specification for cast iron globe and globe stop and check valves for general purposes	126, 129
BS 5154 : 1989	Specification for copper alloy globe, globe stop and check, check and gate valves	126, 135

APPENDIX F INDEX TO BRITISH STANDARDS REFERRED TO IN THIS BOOK

APPENDIX F

INDEX TO BRITISH STANDARDS REFERRED TO IN THIS BOOK

STANDARD	TITLE	PAGE NO.
BS 5903 : 1980 (1987)*	Method for determination of resistance to intergranular corrosion of austenitic stainless steels: copper sulphate – sulphuric acid method (Moneypenny Strauss test)	219
BS 5944 : *	Measurement of airborne noise from hydraulic fluid power systems and components Parts 15	217
BS 5950 :	Structural use of steelwork in building (see also BS 449) Parts 1, 2, 4, 5	12
BS 5983 : *	Metric spherical plain bearings Parts 1–6	64
BS 6005 : 1993	Specification for moulded transparent polycarbonate bowls used in compressed air filters and lubricators	23
BS 6086 : 1981 (1985)*	Method of measurement of noise inside motor vehicles	217
BS 6104 : *	Mechanical properties of fasteners Parts 1–3	32
BS 6105 : 1981 *	Specification for corrosion-resistant stainless steel fasteners	32
BS 6107 : *	Rolling bearings : tolerances Parts 1–3	70, 72
BS 6138 : 1989	Glossary of terms used in the adhesives industry	52
BS 6168 : 1987	Specification for non-metallic spur gears	96
BS 6203 : 1991	Guide to fire characteristics and fire performance of expanded polystyrene materials used in building applications	23
BS 6217 : 1981 *	Guide to graphical symbols for use on electrical equipment	208
BS 6234 : 1987	Specification for polyethylene insulation and sheath of electric cables	23
BS 6258 : 1988 *	Specification for hollow steel bars for machining	6
BS 6267 : 1982 *	Specification for rolling bearings: boundary dimensions for radial bearings	70, 72
BS 6276 : 1987 *	Specification for dimensions and identification code for mounting flanges and shaft ends for hydraulic fluid power pumps and motors	142
BS 6322 : *	Tolerance for fasteners	
	Part 1 : 1962 Specification for tolerances of bolts, screws and nuts with thread diameters ≥ 1.6 mm and ≤ 150 mm and product grades A, B and C	
	Part 2 : 1962 Specification for tolerances of bolts, screws and nuts with thread diameters from 1 mm up to 3 mm and product grade F, for the mechanics	
	Part 3 : 1962 Specification for tolerances of washers for metric bolts, screws and nuts with thread diameters from 1 mm up to and including 150 mm. Product grades A and C	
BS 6323 : *	Specification for seamless and welded steel tubes for automobile, mechanical and general engineering purposes Parts 1–6	6, 10
BS 6331 : *	Mounting dimensions of single rod double acting hydraulic cylinders	142, 145-7
	Part 1 : 1983 Specification for 160 bar medium series	
	Part 2 : 1983 Specification for 160 bar compact series	
	Part 3 : 1983 Specification for 250 bar series	
	Part 4 : 1985 Specification for 63 bar series, including associated components	
BS 6340 :	Shower units Parts 1–8	23
BS 6346 : 1989	Specification for PVC-insulated cables for electricity supply	23
BS 6363 : 1983	Specification for welded cold formed steel structural hollow sections	10
BS 6374 :	Lining of equipment with polymeric materials for the process industries Parts 1–5	27
BS 6442 : 1984 *	Specification for limits of surface imperfections on elastomeric toroidal sealing rings ('O'-rings)	178
BS 6467 :	Electrical apparatus with protection by enclosure for use in the presence of combustible dusts Part 1 : 1985	104
BS 6494 :	Hydraulic fluid power valve mounting surfaces Parts 1–6	124
BS 6501 :	Flexible metallic hose assemblies Parts 1 & 2	150
BS 6564 :	Polytetrafluoroethylene (PTFE) materials and products Parts 1–3	23
BS 6681 : 1986 *	Specification for malleable cast iron (Replaces BS 309 : 1972, BS 310 : 1972 & BS 3333 : 1972)	139

APPENDIX F INDEX TO BRITISH STANDARDS REFERRED TO IN THIS BOOK

STANDARD	TITLE	PAGE NO.
BS 6683 : 1985 (1991)	Guide to installation and use of valves	124
BS 6747 : 1987 (1993)	Specification for orthodontic resins	23
BS 6840 :	Sound system equipment Parts 1–17	217
BS 6889 : 1987	Specification for generating racks for synchronous belt drive pulleys (partially supersedes BS 4548 : 1970)	88
BS 6931 : 1988	Glossary of terms for copper and copper alloys	24
BS 6944 : 1988	Specification for flash welding of butt joints in ferrous metals (excluding pressure piping applications)	42
BS 6974 : 1991	Specification for unsintered PTFE tape for thread sealing applications (coarse threads)	23
BS 6984 : 1988	Specification for dimensions of housings for elastomer-energized plastic-faced hydraulic seals in reciprocating applications	142, 176
BS 6990 : 1989	Code of practice for welding on steel pipes containing process fluids or their residuals	42
BS 6997 : 1990	Specification for elastomeric toroidal sealing rings ('O'-rings) manufactured from acrylonitrile-butadiene rubbers complying with BS 6996	170
BS 7008 :	Aquisition and presentation of comparable data for basic properties of plastics Parts 1 & 2	22
BS 7009 : 1988	Application of real-time radiography to weld inspection	42
BS 7010 : 1988	Code of practice for a system of tolerances for the dimensions of plastics mouldings (Supersedes BS 2026 : 1953)	22
BS 7015 : 1989	Specification for cast acrylic sheet for baths and shower trays for domestic purposes	23
BS 7198 :	Hydraulic fluid power quick-action couplings Part 1 : 1989 Specification for dimensions and performance Part 2 : 1989 Methods of test	160
BS 7253 :	Non-metallic materials for surgical implants Parts 1–5	23
BS 7296 :	Cavities for hydraulic fluid power cartridge valves Part 1	124
BS 7303 :	Sacks for the transport of food aid Part 1	23
BS 7344 : 1990	Specification for reeled low density polyethylene film for general purpose application	23
BS 7350 : 1990	Specification for double regulating globe valves and flow measurement devices for heating and chilled water systems	124
BS 7389 :	Pneumatic fluid power valve mounting surfaces Part 1 : 1990 Specification for five-port directional control valves (without electrical connector)	124
BS 7620 : 1993	Specification for industrial belt drives. Dimensions of pulleys and V-ribbed belts of PH, PJ, PK, PL and PM profiles	80, 81, 83, 85
BS 8010 :	Code of practice for pipelines Parts 1–3	170
BS 8233 : 1987	Code of practice for sound insulation and noise reduction for buildings Replaces CP 3 : Chapter III : 1972	217

EUROPEAN STANDARDS:

STANDARD	TITLE	PAGE NO.
BS EN 19 : 1992	Marking of general purpose industrial valves	124
BS EN 196 :	Methods of testing cement Parts 1–3, 5–7 and 21	27
BS EN 204 : 1991	Classification of non-structural adhesives for joining of wood and derived timber products	52
BS EN 279 : 1991	Specification for homogenous rubber materials for dynamic seals in domestic appliances using combustible gases up to 200 mbar	178
BS EN 287 :	Approval testing of welders for fusion welding Parts 1 and 2	42
BS EN 288 :	Specification and approval of welding procedures for metallic materials Parts 1–4	42

APPENDIX F

INDEX TO BRITISH STANDARDS REFERRED TO IN THIS BOOK

STANDARD	TITLE	PAGE NO.
BS EN 301 : 1992	Adhesives, phenolic and aminoplastic, for load-bearing timber structures: classification and performance requirements	52
BS EN 313 :	Plywood. Classification and terminology Part 1	27
BS EN 438 :	Decorative high-pressure laminates (HPL) sheets based on thermosetting resins Parts 1 and 2	23
BS EN 2243 :	Structural adhesives. Test Methods Parts 2–5	52
BS EN 2285 : 1990	Specification for bushes plain, aluminium alloy with self-lubricating liner. Dimensions and loads	64
BS EN 2377 : 1989	Specification for glass fibre reinforced plastics. Test Method. Determination of apparent interlaminar shear strength	23
BS EN 10020 : 1991	Definition and classification of grade of steel	6
BS EN 10025 : 1990	Specification for hot-rolled products of non-alloy structural steels and their technical delivery conditions	10
BS EN 10027 :	Designation systems for steel Part 1 : 1992 Steel names, principal symbols Part 2 : 1992 Steel numbers	6
BS EN 10131 : 1991	Cold-rolled uncoated low carbon and high yield strength steel flat products for cold forming. Tolerances on dimensions and shape	6
BS EN 20140 :	Acoustics. Measurement of sound insulation in buildings and of building elements Parts 2 and 10	217
BS EN 20225 : 1992	Fasteners. Bolts, screws, studs and nuts. Symbols and designations of dimensions	32
BS EN 20273 : 1992	Fasteners. Clearance holes for bolts and screws	32, 112, 113
BS EN 20898 :	Mechanical properties of fasteners Parts 1, 2 and 6	32
BS EN 21680 :	Acoustics. Test code for the measurement of airborne noise emitted by rotating electrical machinery Parts 1 and 2	217
BS EN 24014 : 1992	Hexagon head bolts. Product grades A and B	32
BS EN 24015 : 1992	Hexagon head bolts. Product grade B. Reduced shank (shank diameter ≈ pitch diameter)	32
BS EN 24016 : 1992	Hexagon head bolts. Product grade C	32
BS EN 24017 : 1992	Hexagon head screws. Product grades A and B	32
BS EN 24018 : 1992	Hexagon head screws. Product grade C	32
BS EN 24032 : 1992	Hexagon nuts, style 1. Product grades A and B	32
BS EN 24033 : 1992	Hexagon nuts, style 2. Product grades A and B	32
BS EN 24034 : 1992	Hexagon nuts. Product grade C	32
BS EN 24035 : 1992	Hexagon thin nuts (chamfered). Product grades A and B	32
BS EN 24036 : 1992	Hexagon thin nuts. Product grade B (unchamfered)	32
BS EN 24063 : 1992	Welding, brazing, soldering and braze welding of metals. Nomenclature of processes and reference numbers for symbolic representation on drawings	42
BS EN 25817 : 1992	Arc welded joints in steel. Guidance on quality levels for imperfections	42
BS EN 27574 :	Acoustics; statistical methods for determining and verifying stated noise emission values of machinery and equipment Parts 1–4	217
BS EN 28167 : 1992	Specification for projections for resistance welding	42
BS EN 28233 : 1992	Thermoplastics valves. Torque. Test method	130
BS EN 29000 :	*See BS 5750 : Part 0 : Section 0.1*	216
BS EN 60947 :	Specification for low-voltage switchgear and control gear Parts 1–7	104

CODES OF PRACTICE :

CP 153 :	Windows and rooflights Part 3 : 1972 Sound insulation	217
CP 3012 : 1972	Codes of practice for cleaning and preparation of metal surfaces	52

APPENDIX F — INDEX TO BRITISH STANDARDS REFERRED TO IN THIS BOOK

STANDARD	TITLE	PAGE NO.
AERO SERIES		
F 131 : 1986	Specification for chlorosulphonated polyethylene rubber coated nylon fabric (300 g/m^2) for aerospace purposes	27
F 136 : 1989	Specification for pigmented chlorosulphonated polyethylene rubber coated nylon fabric (190 g/m^2) for aerospace purposes	27
M 33 : 1970	(Obsolescent) Specification for dimensions of elastomeric toroidal sealing rings (inch series) to Class 1 tolerances for aircraft	178
M 48 : 1975 (1984)	Specification for dimensions of elastomeric toroidal sealing rings for aerospace use – inch series	178
M 57 : 1985	Specification for high temperature convoluted hose assemblies in polytetrafluoroethylene (PTFE) for aerospace applications	23
M 63 : 1987	Specification for dimensions for fluid system port connection, seal and fitting end	178
SP 94 : 1964 (1985)	Specification for bronze oil-retaining bushes and thrust washers for aircraft	64
S 201 : 1967	Specification for patented cold drawn carbon steel wire and springs (high duty unground wire)	188
S 202 : 1967	Specification for patented cold drawn carbon steel wire and springs (high duty ground wire)	188
S 203 : 1967	Specification for carbon steel wire and springs (high duty unground wire – hardened and tempered)	188
S 204 : 1967	Specification for chromium-vanadium steel wire and springs (high duty ground wire – hardened and tempered)	188
S 205 : 1969	Specification for austenitic chromium-nickel steel wire and springs	188
AUTOMOBILE SERIES :		
BS AU 150b : 1984 *	Specification for automotive V-belts and pulleys	80
BS AU 218 : 1987	Specification for automotive synchronous belt drives	88
BS AU 23 : 1964	(withdrawn) General layout of braking connections for articulated vehicles using two-line air pressure system	104
PUBLISHED DOCUMENTS :		
PD 3376 :	*Addendum No. 1 to BS 978 : Part 2*	96
PD 6438 : 1969	A review of present methods for design of bolted flanges for pressure vessels	170
PD 6457 : 1970 (1984)	Guide to the application of addendum modification to involute spur and helical gears	96
PD 6493 : 1980	Guidance on some methods for the derivation of acceptance levels for defects in fusion welded joints	42
PD 7304 : 1982	Introduction to geometrical tolerancing (re-numbered as PP 7304)	196
PD(PP) 7311 : 1984	Modular technology: a teachers' pack	212
EDUCATION PUBLICATIONS :		
PD 7304 : 1982	Introduction to geometrical tolerancing	196
PP 7307 : 1986	Graphical symbols for use in schools and colleges	208, 210, 212
PP 7308 : 1986	Engineering drawing practice for schools and colleges (An abridgement of BS 308 : Part 1 : 1984 and BS 308 : Part 2 : 1985 for teachers and students)	196
PP 7311 : 1984	*See PD(PP) 7311*	212

APPENDIX F

INDEX TO BRITISH STANDARDS REFERRED TO IN THIS BOOK

APPENDIX G

CROSS-REFERENCE OF BRITISH, EUROPEAN AND INTERNATIONAL STANDARDS

Key:
H = Harmonized with
R = Related to
I = Identical to
TE = Technically equivalent to

BSI DOC.	RELATIONSHIP	ISO/EN DOC.
BS 4 : Part 1 : 1980		
BS 10 : 1962		
BS 12 : 1991		
BS 21 : 1985	TE	ISO 7/1 : 1982
	R	ISO 7/2 : 1982
BS 131 : Part 1 : 1961		
BS 131 : Part 4 : 1972	TE	ISO/R 442
BS 131 : Part 5 : 1965		
BS 131 : Part 6 : 1989		
BS 131 : Part 7 : 1990		
BS 240 : 1986	R	ISO 156
		ISO 6506
		EURONORM 3
		EURONORM 125
		EURONORM 128
BS 292 : Part 1 : 1982		
BS 292 : Part 2 : 1982		
BS 308 : Part 1 : 1984	R	ISO 128
		ISO 2162
		ISO 2203
		ISO 3098/1
		ISO 5455
		ISO 5457
		ISO 6410
		ISO 6413
		ISO 6433
		ISO 7200
		ISO 8826-1
BS 308 : Part 2 : 1985	TE	ISO 129 : 1985
		ISO 406 : 1982
		ISO 1302 : 1978
	R	ISO 1660
		ISO 3040 : 1990
		ISO 8015
BS 308 : Part 3 : 1990	TE	ISO 7083
	R	ISO 1101
		ISO 2692
		ISO 5458
		ISO 5459
BS 350 : Part 1 : 1974		
BS 427 : 1990	R	ISO 6507
BS 436 : Part 1 : 1967	R	ISO 53
		ISO 54
		ISO 1328
		ISO 1340
		ISO 1341
BS 436 : Part 2 : 1970	R	ISO 53
		ISO 54
		ISO 1328
		ISO 1340
		ISO 1341
BS 436 : Part 3 : 1986	R	ISO 6336/1
		ISO 6336/2
		ISO 6336/3
BS 443 : 1982		
BS 449 : Part 2 : 1969		
BS 499 : Part 1 : 1991		
BS 499 : Part 1 : Supplement : 1992	I	IEV 50(851) : 1991
BS 499 : Part 2 : 1980	TE	ISO 4063
	R	ISO 2553
BS 499 : Part 2C : 1980	R	ISO 2553
BS 545 : 1982	R	ISO 677
		ISO 678
BS 558 & 564 : 1970		
BS 622 : 1967		
BS 633 : 1970		
BS 638 : Part 1 : 1979	R	ISO 700
		IEC 245

BSI DOC.	RELATIONSHIP	ISO/EN DOC.
BS 638 : Part 2 : 1979	R	ISO 700
		IEC 245
		IEC 974-1
	H	CENELEC HD 24
BS 638 : Part 3 : 1979	R	ISO 700
		IEC 245
		IEC 974-1
	H	CENELEC HD 24
BS 638 : Part 4 : 1979	R	ISO 700
		IEC 246
BS 638 : Part 5 : 1988	R	ISO 700
	H	CENELEC HD 433
BS 638 : Part 6 : 1984	R	ISO 700
		IEC 974-1
	H	CENELEC HD 362
BS 638 : Part 7 : 1984	R	IEC 974-1
	H	CENELEC HD 407
		CENELEC HD 427
BS 638 : Part 8 : 1984	R	ISO 700
BS 638 : Part 9 : 1990	I	EN 50060 : 1989
BS 638 : Part 10 : 1990	I	EN 60974-1 : 1990
BS 709 : 1983	R	ISO 4136
BS 729 : 1971	R	ISO 1459
		ISO 1460
		ISO 1461
BS 745 : 1969		
BS 864 : Part 2 : 1983	R	ISO 2016
BS 864 : Part 3 : 1975		
BS 864 : Part 5 : 1990		
BS 903 : Part 0 : 1990		
BS 903 : Part A1 : 1980	I	ISO 2781
BS 903 : Part A2 : 1989		
BS 903 : Part A3 : 1982	I	ISO 34
BS 903 : Part A4 : 1990	I	ISO 7743
BS 903 : Part A5 : 1993	I	ISO 2285 : 1988
BS 903 : Part A6 : 1992	I	ISO 815 : 1991
BS 903 : Part A8 : 1990	R	ISO 4662 : 1986
BS 903 : Part A9 : 1988	R	ISO 4649
		ISO 5470
BS 903 : Part A10 : 1984	I	ISO 132 : 1993
BS 903 : Part A11 : 1985	I	ISO : 1983
BS 903 : Part A12 : 1975	TE	ISO/R 36
BS 903 : Part A13 : 1990	I	ISO 1432 : 1988
BS 903 : Part A14 : 1992	I	ISO 1827 : 1991
BS 903 : Part A15 : 1990	I	ISO 8013 : 1988
BS 903 : Part A16 : 1987	I	ISO 1817 : 1985
BS 903 : Part A17 : 1973	TE	ISO/R 1399
BS 903 : Part A18 : 1973		
BS 903 : Part A19 : 1986	I	ISO 188 : 1982
	R	ISO 1826
BS 903 : Part A21 : 1989	TE	ISO 813 : 1986
		ISO 814 : 1986
BS 903 : Part A24 : 1992		
BS 903 : Part A25 : 1992	I	ISO 812 : 1991
BS 903 : Part A26 : 1969	TE	ISO 48
		ISO 1400
		ISO 1818
	R	ISO/R 1826
BS 903 : Part A27 : 1986	I	ISO 4637 : 1979
BS 903 : Part A29 : 1984	I	ISO 2921 : 1982
BS 903 : Part A30 : 1975	R	ISO/DIS 2782
BS 903 : Part A31 : 1976	R	ISO 4663
BS 903 : Part A32 : 1988	I	ISO 3383 : 1985
BS 903 : Part A33 : 1985	I	ISO 3865 : 1983
BS 903 : Part A35 : 1985	I	ISO 471 : 1983
BS 903 : Part A36 : 1988	I	ISO 4661/1 : 2986
BS 903 : Part A37 : 1987	TE	ISO 6505
BS 903 : Part A38 : 1991	I	ISO 4648 : 1991
BS 903 : Part A40 : 1988	I	ISO 5600 : 1986

APPENDICES

APPENDIX G

CROSS-REFERENCE OF BRITISH, EUROPEAN AND INTERNATIONAL STANDARDS

BSI DOC.	RELATIONSHIP	ISO/EN DOC.
BS 903 : Part A42 : 1992	I	ISO 3384 : 1991
BS 903 : Part A43 : 1990	I	ISO 1431/1 : 1989
BS 903 : Part A44 : 1983	I	ISO 1431/2 : 1982
BS 903 : Part A46 : 1991	I	ISO 6179 : 1989
BS 903 : Part A47 : 1982	I	ISO 6133 : 1981
BS 903 : Part A48 : 1984	I	ISO 4647 : 1982
BS 903 : Part A49 : 1984	I	ISO 4666/1 : 1982
BS 903 : Part A50 : 1984	I	ISO 4666/3 : 1982
BS 903 : Part A51 : 1986	I	ISO 6943 : 1984
BS 903 : Part A52 : 1986	I	ISO 6914 : 1985
	R	ISO 1826
BS 903 : Part A53 : 1989	I	ISO 4665-2 : 1985
BS 903 : Part A54 : 1989	I	ISO 4665-3 : 1987
BS 903 : Part A55 : 1989	I	ISO 4665-1 : 1985
BS 903 : Part A56 : 1989	I	ISO 5603 : 1986
BS 903 : Part A57 : 1989	I	ISO 7619 : 1986
BS 903 : Part A58 : 1990	R	ISO 289
BS 903 : Part A59 : 1990	R	ISO 289/2
BS 903 : Part A60 :		
Section 60.2 : 1992	I	ISO 3417 : 1991
BS 903 : Part A62 : 1993	I	ISO 9026 : 1991
BS 903 : Parts B6 to B10 : 1958		
BS 903 : Parts B11 &		
B12 : 1960		
BS 903 : Part B19 : 1958		
BS 903 : Part C1 : 1991		
Also numbered as BS 2782 :		
Part 2 : Method 231A : 1991		
BS 903 : Part C2 : 1982		
Also numbered as BS 2782 :		
Part 2 : Method 230A : 1982	R	IEC 93 : 1980
BS 903 : Part C3 : 1982		
Also numbered as BS 2782 :		
Part 2 : Methods 240A and		
240B : 1982	R	IEC 250 : 1969
BS 903 : Part C4 : 1983		
Also numbered as BS 2782 :		
Part 2 : Methods 220 and		
221 : 1983	R	IEC 243 : 1967
BS 903 : Part C5 : 1992		
Also numbered as BS 2782 :		
Part 2 : Method 232 : 1992	I	IEC 167 : 1964
	H	CENELEC HD 568 S1
BS 952 : Part 1 : 1978		
BS 952 : Part 2 : 1980		
BS 969 : 1982		
BS 970 : Part 1 : 1991		
BS 970 : Part 2 : 1988		
BS 970 : Part 3 : 1991		
BS 970 : Part 4 : 1970	R	ISO 683/13
		ISO 683/15
		ISO 683/17
		EURONORM 90
BS 978 : Part 1 : 1968		
BS 978 : Part 2 : 1952		
Addendum No. 1 (1959) to		
BS 978 : Part 2 : 1952		
BS 978 : Part 3 : 1952		
BS 978 : Part 5 : 1965		
BS 1004 : 1972	R	ISO 301
BS 1098 : Part 1 : 1967		
BS 1098 : Part 2 : 1977	R	ISO 4247
BS 1134 : Part 1 : 1988	R	ISO 468
		ISO 4287/1
BS 1134 : Part 2 : 1990		
BS 1154 : 1992		
BS 1178 : 1982		
BS 1192 : Part 1 : 1984	R	ISO 6284
BS 1192 : Part 2 : 1987		

BSI DOC.	RELATIONSHIP	ISO/EN DOC.
BS 1192 : Part 3 : 1987	TE	ISO 4067/2
	R	ISO 4067/1
		ISO 4067/6
		ISO/TR 8545
BS 1192 : Part 4 : 1984		
BS 1192 : Part 5 : 1990	R	ISO/TR 10127
BS 1203 : 1979		
BS 1204 : 1993		
BS 1212 : Part 1 : 1990		
BS 1212 : Part 2 : 1990		
BS 1212 : Part 3 : 1990		
BS 1212 : Part 4 : 1991		
BS 1224 : 1970	R	ISO 1456
		ISO 1458
BS 1306 : 1975		
BS 1400 : 1985		
BS 1407 : 1970		
BS 1414 : 1975		
FR : API Std 600		
BS 1452 : 1990		
BS 1468 : 1967		
BS 1470 : 1987	R	ISO 209-1
		ISO 6361/1
		ISO 6361-2
		ISO 209-2
		ISO 6361/3
		ISO 6361-4
BS 1471 : 1972	R	ISO 209-1
		ISO 209-2
BS 1472 : 1972	R	ISO 209-1
		ISO 209-2
BS 1473 : 1972	R	ISO 209-1
		ISO 209-2
BS 1474 : 1987	R	ISO 6362
		ISO 209-1
		ISO 209-2
BS 1475 : 1972	R	ISO 209-1
		ISO 209-2
BS 1490 : 1988	R	ISO 3522
		ISO 7722
BS 1493 : 1987	R	ISO 1622/1
		ISO 1622/2
BS 1501 : Part 2 : 1988	R	ISO 2604/4
		EURONORM 28
BS 1501 : Part 3 : 1990	R	EURONORM 141
BS 1502 : 1982		
BS 1503 : 1989	R	ISO 2604/1
BS 1504 : 1976		
BS 1506 : 1990		
BS 1524 : 1993		
BS 1560 : Section 3.1 : 1989	R	ISO 7005
FR : ANSI B 16.5		
BS 1560 : Section 3.2 : 1989	R	ISO 7005-2
BS 1560 : Section 3.3 : 1989	R	ISO 7005 : Part 3
FR : ANSI B 16.24		
BS 1625-6 and 4830 : 1972		
BS 1706 : 1990	R	ISO 2081 : 1986
		ISO 2082 : 1986
BS 1723 : Part 1 : 1986		
BS 1723 : Part 2 : 1986		
BS 1723 : Part 3 : 1988		
BS 1723 : Part 4 : 1988		
BS 1726 : Part 1 : 1987		
BS 1726 : Part 2 : 1988		
BS 1726 : Part 3 : 1988		
BS 1740 : Part 1 : 1971	R	ISO 4145
BS 1755 : Part 1 : 1982	TE	ISO 472
BS 1755 : Part 2 : 1974	R	ISO 472
BS 1763 : 1975		

APPENDIX G

CROSS-REFERENCE OF BRITISH, EUROPEAN AND INTERNATIONAL STANDARDS

BSI DOC.	RELATIONSHIP	ISO/EN DOC.
BS 1806 : 1989		
FR : SAE AS 568A		
BS 1873 : 1975		
FR : ANSI B16.5		
ANSI B16.10		
ANSI B16.25		
BS 1902 : Section 2.1 : 1988		
BS 1902 : Section 2.2 : 1974		
BS 1902 : Section 2.3 : 1970		
Addendum No. 1 (1976) to BS 1902 : Section 2.3 : 1970		
BS 1902 : Section 3.0 : 1988		
BS 1902 : Section 3.1 : 1981		
BS 1902 : Section 3.2 : 1981		
BS 1902 : Section 3.3 : 1981		
BS 1902 : Section 3.4 : 1981	R	ISO 5018
BS 1902 : Section 3.5 : 1981		
BS 1902 : Section 3.6 : 1984	R	ISO 8840
BS 1902 : Section 3.7 : 1989	I	ISO 5016 : 1986
BS 1902 : Section 3.8 : 1989	I	ISO 5017 : 1988
BS 1902 : Section 3.9 : 1981		
FR : Recommendation 16 of the Federation Europeenne des Fabricants de Produits Refractaires (PRE)		
BS 1902 : Section 3.10 : 1981		
BS 1902 : Section 3.11 : 1983		
BS 1902 : Section 3.12 : 1989	I	ISO 8890 : 1988
BS 1902 : Section 3.13 : 1985		
BS 1902 : Section 3.14 : 1987		
BS 1902 : Section 3.16 : 1990		
BS 1902 : Section 3.17 : 1990		
BS 1902 : Section 4.0 : 1985		
BS 1902 : Section 4.1 : 1984	TE	ISO 8895
BS 1902 : Section 4.3 : 1985		
BS 1902 : Section 4.4 : 1984	TE	ISO 5014
BS 1902 : Section 4.5 : 1984	R	ISO 5013
BS 1902 : Section 4.6 : 1985		
BS 1902 : Section 4.7 : 1985		
BS 1902 : Section 4.9 : 1985	R	ISO 1893
BS 1902 : Section 4.10 : 1990	I	ISO 3187 : 1989
BS 1902 : Section 5.0 : 1992		
BS 1902 : Section 5.2 : 1983	TE	ISO 528
BS 1902 : Section 5.3 : 1990		
BS 1902 : Section 5.4 : 1989		
BS 1902 : Section 5.5 : 1991		
BS 1902 : Section 5.6 : 1985	TE	ISO 8894/1
BS 1902 : Section 5.8 : 1992		
BS 1902 : Section 5.9 : 1985	TE	ISO 2477
BS 1902 : Section 5.10 : 1986	R	ISO 2478
BS 1902 : Section 5.11 : 1986		
BS 1902 : Section 5.13 : 1984		
BS 1902 : Section 5.14 : 1992		
BS 1902 : Part 6 : 1986		
BS 1902 : Section 7.0 : 1987		
BS 1902 : Section 7.1 : 1987		
BS 1902 : Section 7.2 : 1987		
BS 1902 : Section 7.3 : 1987		
BS 1902 : Section 7.4 : 1987		
BS 1902 : Section 7.5 : 1987		
BS 1902 : Section 7.6 : 1987		
BS 1902 : Part 8 : 1988		
BS 1902 : Section 9.1 : 1987		
BS 1902 : Section 9.2 : 1987		
BS 1902 : Section 10.1 : 1993		
BS 1902 : Part 11 : 1990		
BS 1936 : Part 1 : 1952		
BS 1936 : Part 2 : 1991	R	ISO 3508 : 1976 ISO 4755 : 1983
BS 2045 : 1965	TE	ISO 3 ISO 17 ISO 497
BS 2048 : Part 1 : 1961		
FR : NEMA MG 1		

BSI DOC.	RELATIONSHIP	ISO/EN DOC.
BS 2056 : 1991		
BS 2080 : 1989	TE	ISO 5752
BS 2470 : 1973		
BS 2519 : Part 1 : 1976		ISO/R 1122-1969
BS 2519 : Part 2 : 1976	I	ISO 701 : 1976
BS 2571 : 1990		
BS 2598 : Part 1 : 1991	I	ISO 3585 : 1991
BS 2598 : Part 2 : 1980	I	ISO 3586 : 1976
BS 2598 : Part 3 : 1980	I	ISO 3587 : 1976
BS 2598 : Part 4 : 1980	I	ISO 4704 : 1977
BS 2633 : 1987		
BS 2739 : 1975		
BS 2750 : Part 1 : 1980	I	ISO 140/1 : 1978
BS 2750 : Part 3 : 1980	I	ISO 140/3 : 1978
BS 2750 : Part 4 : 1980	I	ISO 140/4 : 1978
BS 2750 : Part 5 : 1980	I	ISO 140/5 : 1978
BS 2750 : Part 6 : 1980	I	ISO 140/6 : 1978
BS 2750 : Part 7 : 1980	I	ISO 140/7 : 1978
BS 2750 : Part 8 : 1980	I	ISO 140/8 : 1978
BS 2750 : Part 9 : 1987	I	ISO 140/9 : 1985
BS 2751 : 1990		
BS 2752 : 1990		
BS 2779 : 1986	TE	ISO 228/1 ISO 228-2
BS 2782 : Part 0 : 1992	R	ISO 291 : 1977
BS 2782 : Part 1 : Method 115A : 1978		
BS 2782 : Part 1 : Methods 120A, 120B, 120D and 120E : 1990	I	ISO 306 : 1987
BS 2782 : Part 1 : Method 120C : 1990	R	ISO 306 : 1987
BS 2782 : Part 1 : Method 121A and 121B : 1991	I	ISO 75 : 1987
BS 2782 : Part 1 : Method 121C : 1992		
BS 2782 : Part 1 : Method 122A : 1976		
BS 2782 : Part 1 : Method 123A : 1976	TE	ISO 1218
BS 2782 : Part 1 : Method 123B : 1976	TE	ISO 1218
BS 2782 : Part 1 : Method 124A : 1992		
BS 2782 : Part 1 : Methods 125A to 125C2 : 1991	I	ISO 3146 : 1985
BS 2782 : Part 1 : Method 130A : 1991	I	ISO 182-1 : 1990
BS 2782 : Part 1 : Method 130B : 1991	I	ISO 182-2 : 1990
BS 2782 : Part 1 : Method 130C : 1993	I	ISO 182-3 : 1993
BS 2782 : Part 1 : Method 130D : 1993	I	ISO 182-4 : 1993
BS 2782 : Part 1 : Method 131B : 1983		
BS 2782 : Part 1 : Methods 131C and 131D : 1978		
BS 2782 : Part 1 : Method 132B : 1976		
BS 2782 : Part 1 : Methods 134A and 134B : 1992		
BS 2782 : Part 1 : Method 140A : 1992	I	ISO 1210 : 1992
BS 2782 : Part 1 : Method 140B : 1993	I	ISO 9773 : 1990
BS 2782 : Part 1 : Method 140C : 1993	I	ISO 10351 : 1992
BS 2782 : Part 1 : Method 140D : 1980		
BS 2782 : Part 1 : Method 140E : 1982		

APPENDIX G

CROSS-REFERENCE OF BRITISH, EUROPEAN AND INTERNATIONAL STANDARDS

BSI DOC.	RELATIONSHIP	ISO/EN DOC.
BS 2782 : Part 1 : Method 141 : 1986	I	ISO 4589 : 1984
BS 2782 : Part 1 : Methods 143A and 143B : 1989		
BS 2782 : Part 1 : Method 150B : 1976		
BS 2782 : Part 1 : Method 150C : 1983		
BS 2782 : Part 1 : Method 150D : 1976		
BS 2782 : Part 1 : Method 151A : 1984		
BS 2782 : Part 1 : Method 153A : 1991	I	ISO 458/1 : 1985
BS 2782 : Part 1 : Method 153B : 1991	I	ISO 458/2 : 1985
BS 2782 : Part 2 : Method 241A : 1984		
BS 2782 : Part 2 : Method 250A : 1976		
BS 2782 : Part 2 : Method 250B : 1976		
BS 2782 : Part 2 : Method 250C : 1976		
BS 2782 : Part 3 : Methods 320A to 320F : 1976	R	ISO/R 527
BS 2782 : Part 3 : Methods 326A to 326C : 1977	R	ISO 1184
BS 2782 : Part 3 : Method 327A : 1993		
BS 2782 : Part 3 : Method 332A : 1976		
BS 2782 : Part 3 : Method 335A : 1993	I	ISO 178 : 1993
BS 2782 : Part 3 : Methods 340A and 340B : 1978		
BS 2782 : Part 3 : Method 341A : 1977		
BS 2782 : Part 3 : Method 345A : 1979	R	ISO 604
BS 2782 : Part 3 : Method 346A : 1984		
BS 2782 : Part 3 : Method 350 : 1993	I	ISO 180 : 1993
BS 2782 : Part 3 : Method 352D : 1979		
BS 2782 : Part 3 : Method 353A : 1991	I	ISO 6603-1 : 1985
BS 2782 : Part 3 : Method 353B : 1991	I	ISO 6603-2 : 1989
BS 2782 : Part 3 : Methods 354A and 354B : 1991	I	ISO 8256 : 1990
BS 2782 : Part 3 : Method 359 : 1993	I	ISO 179 : 1993
BS 2782 : Part 3 : Method 360A : 1991	I	ISO 6383-2 : 1983
BS 2782 : Part 3 : Method 360B : 1991	I	ISO 6383-1 : 1983
BS 2782 : Part 3 : Method 360C : 1991		
BS 2782 : Part 3 : Method 365A : 1976	R	ISO 48
BS 2782 : Part 3 : Method 365B : 1992	I	ISO 868 : 1985
BS 2782 : Part 3 : Method 365C : 1992	I	ISO 2039-2 : 1987
BS 2782 : Part 3 : Method 365D : 1991	I	ISO 2039-1 : 1987
BS 2782 : Part 3 : Method 370 : 1990	I	ISO 9352 : 1989
BS 2782 : Part 4 : Methods 430A to 430D : 1983	I	ISO 62 : 1980

BSI DOC.	RELATIONSHIP	ISO/EN DOC.
BS 2782 : Part 4 : Method 431C : 1991	I	ISO 585 : 1990
BS 2782 : Part 4 : Method 432A : 1991	I	ISO 4901 : 1985
BS 2782 : Part 4 : Method 432B : 1976	I	ISO 2114 : 1974
BS 2782 : Part 4 : Method 432C : 1978	I	ISO 2554 : 1974
BS 2782 : Part 4 : Method 433A : 1979	I	ISO 4573 : 1978
BS 2782 : Part 4 : Method 433B : 1979	I	ISO 4583 : 1978
BS 2782 : Part 4 : Methods 433C and 433D : 1979	TE	ISO 3001 : 1978
BS 2782 : Part 4 : Method 434A : 1975		
BS 2782 : Part 4 : Method 434B : 1977		
BS 2782 : Part 4 : Method 434C : 1977		
BS 2782 : Part 4 : Method 434D : 1975		
BS 2782 : Part 4 : Method 451A : 1978	I	ISO 59 : 1977
BS 2782 : Part 4 : Method 451B : 1978		
BS 2782 : Part 4 : Method 451C : 1978	I	ISO 308 : 1976
BS 2782 : Part 4 : Method 451D : 1978	I	ISO 120 : 1977
BS 2782 : Part 4 : Method 451E : 1978	I	ISO 119 : 1977
BS 2782 : Part 4 : Methods 451F to 451J : 1978		
BS 2782 : Part 4 : Method 451K : 1978		
BS 2782 : Part 4 : Method 451L : 1980	I	ISO 172 : 1978
BS 2782 : Part 4 : Method 451M : 1991	I	ISO 8618 : 1987
BS 2782 : Part 4 : Method 452B : 1993		
BS 2782 : Part 4 : Method 452C : 1979		
BS 2782 : Part 4 : Methods 452D to 452F : 1978		
BS 2782 : Part 4 : Method 453A : 1978	I	ISO 2561 : 1974
BS 2782 : Part 4 : Method 454C : 1978	I	ISO 1264 : 1975
BS 2782 : Part 4 : Method 454D : 1978	I	ISO 1269 : 1975
BS 2782 : Part 4 : Method 454E : 1992	I	ISO 4608 : 1984
BS 2782 : Part 4 : Method 454F : 1978	I	ISO 4610 : 1977
BS 2782 : Part 4 : Method 455A : 1993	I	ISO 6427 : 1992
BS 2782 : Part 4 : Method 459A : 1991	I	ISO 1061 : 1990
BS 2782 : Part 4 : Method 461A : 1978	I	ISO 3671 : 1976
BS 2782 : Part 4 : Methods 462A and 462B : 1978	I	ISO 4614 : 1977
BS 2782 : Part 4 : Methods 465A and 465B : 1979	I	ISO 176 : 1976
BS 2782 : Part 4 : Method 465C : 1990	I	ISO 177 : 1988
BS 2782 : Part 4 : Method 470A : 1991	I	ISO 3451/1 : 1981
BS 2782 : Part 4 : Method 470B : 1991	I	ISO 3451/2 : 1984

APPENDIX G — CROSS-REFERENCE OF BRITISH, EUROPEAN AND INTERNATIONAL STANDARDS

BSI DOC.	RELATIONSHIP	ISO/EN DOC.
BS 2782 : Part 4 : Method 470C : 1991	I	ISO 3451/3 : 1984
BS 2782 : Part 4 : Method 470D : 1991	I	ISO 3451/4 : 1986
BS 2782 : Part 4 : Method 470E : 1991	I	ISO 3451/5 : 1989
BS 2782 : Part 4 : Method 480A : 1991	I	ISO 1598 : 1990
BS 2782 : Part 5 : Method 520A : 1992		
BS 2782 : Part 5 : Method 521A : 1992		
BS 2782 : Part 5 : Methods 530A and 530B : 1976	R	ISO/DIS 3558
BS 2782 : Part 5 : Method 531A : 1992	I	ISO 489 : 1983
BS 2782 : Part 5 : Method 540A : 1977	I	ISO 877 : 1976
BS 2782 : Part 5 : Method 540B : 1982	I	ISO 4892 : 1981
BS 2782 : Part 5 : Method 540C : 1988		
BS 2782 : Part 5 : Method 541A : 1978		
BS 2782 : Part 5 : Method 542A : 1979	I	ISO 183 : 1976
BS 2782 : Part 5 : Method 550A : 1981	I	ISO 4607 : 1978
BS 2782 : Part 5 : Method 551A : 1988	I	ISO 4611
BS 2782 : Part 5 : Method 552A : 1981	I	ISO 4582 : 1980
BS 2782 : Part 5 : Method 553A : 1991	I	ISO 1600 : 1990
BS 2782 : Part 6 : Methods 620A to 620D : 1991	I	ISO 1183 : 1987
BS 2782 : Part 6 : Method 620E : 1980	I	ISO 1675 : 1975
BS 2782 : Part 6 : Method 621A : 1978	I	ISO 60 : 1977
BS 2782 : Part 6 : Method 621B : 1978	I	ISO 61 : 1976
BS 2782 : Part 6 : Method 621C : 1983	I	ISO 171 : 1980
BS 2782 : Part 6 : Method 621D : 1978	I	ISO 1068 : 1975
BS 2782 : Part 6 : Method 630A : 1982	I	ISO 4593 : 1979
BS 2782 : Part 6 : Method 631A : 1993	I	ISO 4591 : 1992
BS 2782 : Part 6 : Method 632A : 1993	I	ISO 4592 : 1992
BS 2782 : Part 6 : Method 640A : 1979	I	ISO 2577 : 1975
BS 2782 : Part 6 : Method 641A : 1983		
BS 2782 : Part 6 : Method 643A : 1976		
BS 2782 : Part 6 : Method 644A : 1979	I	ISO 3521 : 1976
BS 2782 : Part 7 : Method 720A : 1979	TE	ISO 1133
BS 2782 : Part 7 : Method 720B : 1979		
BS 2782 : Part 7 : Method 721A : 1988	R	IEC 249-3-1
BS 2782 : Part 7 : Method 722A : 1993	I	ISO 7808 : 1992
BS 2782 : Part 7 : Method 730B : 1978	I	ISO 3219 : 1977
BS 2782 : Part 7 : Method 7 30C : 1992	I	ISO 2555 : 1989
BS 2782 : Part 7 : Method 732A : 1991	I	ISO 1628-1 : 1984
BS 2782 : Part 7 : Method 732B : 1991	I	ISO 1628-2 : 1988
BS 2782 : Part 7 : Method 732C : 1991	I	ISO 1628-3 : 1991
BS 2782 : Part 7 : Method 732D : 1991	I	ISO 1628-4 : 1986
BS 2782 : Part 7 : Method 732E : 1991	I	ISO 1628-5 : 1986
BS 2782 : Part 7 : Method 732F : 1991	I	ISO 1628-6 : 1990
BS 2782 : Part 7 : Method 733A : 1991	I	ISO 307 : 1984
BS 2782 : Part 7 : Method 733C : 1991	I	ISO 1157 : 1990
BS 2782 : Part 8 : Method 820A : 1992	I	ISO 2528 : 1974
BS 2782 : Part 8 : Method 821A : 1979	I	ISO 2556 : 1974
BS 2782 : Part 8 : Method 822A : 1992		
BS 2782 : Part 8 : Methods 823A and 823B : 1978		
BS 2782 : Part 8 : Method 824A : 1984		
BS 2782 : Part 8 : Method 826A : 1992		
BS 2782 : Part 8 : Method 830A : 1986	I	ISO 175 : 1981
BS 2782 : Part 8 : Methods 831A to 831B : 1993	I	ISO 4600 : 1992
BS 2782 : Part 8 : Method 832A : 1991	I	ISO 4599 : 1986
BS 2782 : Part 8 : Methods 833A to 833C : 1993	I	ISO 6252 : 1992
BS 2782 : Part 8 : Method 835A : 1980	R	ISO 9396
BS 2782 : Part 8 : Method 835B : 1980		
BS 2782 : Part 8 : Method 835C : 1980	R	ISO 9396
BS 2782 : Part 8 : Method 835D : 1980	R	ISO 8987
BS 2782 : Part 8 : Method 835E : 1980		
BS 2782 : Part 9 : Method 901A : 1988	I	ISO 293 : 1986
BS 2782 : Part 9 : Method 902A : 1992	I	ISO 295 : 1991
BS 2782 : Part 9 : Method 910A : 1977	I	ISO 294 : 1975
BS 2782 : Part 9 : Methods 920A to 920C : 1977	I	ISO 1268 : 1974
BS 2782 : Part 9 : Method 930A : 1977	TE	ISO 2818 : 1980
BS 2782 : Part 9 : Method 931A : 1988	I	ISO 3167
BS 2782 : Part 9 : Method 940A : 1990	I	ISO 2557-1 : 1989
BS 2782 : Part 9 : Method 940B : 1989	I	ISO 2557/2 : 1976
BS 2782 : Part 9 : Method 941 : 1990	I	ISO 8328 : 1989
BS 2782 : Part 10 : Method 1001 : 1977	I	EN 59 : 1977
BS 2782 : Part 10 : Method 1002 : 1977	I R	EN 60 : 1977 ISO 1172
BS 2782 : Part 10 : Method 1003 : 1977	I R	EN 61 : 1977 ISO/R 527 ISO 3268
BS 2782 : Part 10 : Method 1004 : 1977	I R	EN 62 : 1977 ISO 291

APPENDIX G

CROSS-REFERENCE OF BRITISH, EUROPEAN AND INTERNATIONAL STANDARDS

BSI DOC.	RELATIONSHIP	ISO/EN DOC.
BS 2782 : Part 10 : Method	I	EN 63 : 1977
1005 : 1977	R	ISO 178
BS 2782 : Part 10 : Method		
1006 : 1978		
BS 2782 : Part 11 : Method		
1101A : 1981	R	ISO 3126
BS 2782 : Part 11 : Method	R	ISO 2505 : 1981
1102A : 1981		ISO 2506 : 1981
BS 2782 : Part 11 : Method		
1102B : 1981	R	ISO 3478
BS 2782 : Part 11 : Method		
1103A : 1982	R	ISO 580
BS 2782 : Part 11 : Method		
1104A : 1983	R	ISO 3474
BS 2782 : Part 11 : Method		
1106A : 1983		
BS 2782 : Part 11 : Method		
1108A : 1989	R	ISO 3127 : 1980
BS 2782 : Part 11 : Method		
1109A : 1989		
BS 2782 : Part 11 : Method		
1110 : 1989		
BS 2782 : Part 11 : Method		
1112A : 1989	R	ISO/DIS 3633
BS 2789 : 1985	R	ISO 1083
BS 2870 : 1980		
BS 2871 : Part 1 : 1971		
BS 2871 : Part 2 : 1972	R	ISO/R 196
BS 2871 : Part 3 : 1972		
BS 2872 : 1989		
BS 2873 : 1969		
BS 2874 : 1986		
BS 2875 : 1969		
BS 2917 : Part 1 : 1993	I	ISO 1219-1 : 1991
BS 3016 : 1989		
BS 3063 : 1965		
BS 3071 : 1986		
BS 3076 : 1989		
BS 3100 : 1991		
BS 3126 : 1987	R	ISO 2897/1
		ISO 2897/2
BS 3189 : 1991	I	ISO 9717 : 1990
BS 3332 : 1987	R	ISO 4381
BS 3382 : Parts 1 & 2 : 1961		
BS 3382 : Parts 3 & 4 : 1965		
BS 3382 : Parts 5 & 6 : 1967		
BS 3382 : Part 7 : 1966		
BS 3412 : 1992	R	ISO 1872-1 : 1986
		ISO 1872-2 : 1989
BS 3425 : 1966	R	ISO 362
BS 3496 : 1989		
BS 3532 : 1990		
BS 3595 : 1981		
BS 3600 : 1976	R	ISO 4200 : 1991
BS 3601 : 1987	R	ISO 2604/2
		ISO 2604/3
		ISO 2604/6
BS 3602 : Part 1 : 1987	R	ISO 2604/2
		ISO 2604/3
BS 3602 : Part 2 : 1991	R	ISO 2604-6
BS 3603 : 1991		
BS 3604 : Part 1 : 1990	R	ISO 2604/2
		ISO 2604/3
BS 3604 : Part 2 : 1991	R	ISO 2604-6
BS 3605 : Part 1 : 1991		
BS 3605 : Part 2 : 1992		
BS 3643 : Part 1 : 1981	TE	ISO 68
		ISO 261
		ISO 262
		ISO 724
		ISO 965/1
		ISO 965/3
BS 3643 : Part 2 : 1981		

BSI DOC.	RELATIONSHIP	ISO/EN DOC.
BS 3691 : 1990		
BS 3692 : 1967	TE	ISO 272
		ISO 4759/1
BS 3696 : Part 1 : 1977	R	ISO 53
		ISO 54
BS 3745 : 1970	R	ISO 1462
BS 3749 : 1991	R	ISO 472 : 1988
BS 3757 : 1978		
BS 3779 : 1985		
BS 3790 : 1981	TE	ISO 254
		ISO 1813
		ISO 4184
		ISO 5292
	R	ISO 155
		ISO 4183
BS 3832 : 1991	I	ISO 1436 : 1991
BS 3837 : Part 1 : 1986		
BS 3837 : Part 2 : 1990	TE	ISO 2896
		ISO 7616
BS 3869 : 1965		
BS 3920 : Part 1 : 1973	TE	ISO 2605
BS 3920 : Part 2 : 1986	I	ISO 2605/3 : 1985
BS 3923 : Part 1 : 1986		
BS 3923 : Part 2 : 1972		
BS 3934 : Part 1 : 1992	TE	IEC 191-1 : 1966
BS 3934 : Part 2 : 1992	I	IEC 191-2 : 1966
BS 3934 : Part 3 : 1992	TE	IEC 191-3 : 1974
BS 3934 : Part 4 : 1992	I	IEC 191-4 : 1987
BS 3934 : Part 5 : 1992	I	IEC 191-5 : 1987
BS 3934 : Part 6 : 1992	I	IEC 191-6 : 1990
BS 3934 : Part 10 : 1992		
BS 3939 : Part 1 : 1986	R	IEC 617-1
BS 3939 : Part 2 : 1985	I	IEC 617-2 : 1983
BS 3939 : Part 3 : 1985	I	IEC 617-3 : 1983
BS 3939 : Part 4 : 1985	I	IEC 617-4 : 1983
BS 3939 : Part 5 : 1985	I	IEC 617-5 : 1983
BS 3939 : Part 6 : 1985	I	IEC 617-6 : 1983
BS 3939 : Part 7 : 1985	I	IEC 617-7 : 1983
BS 3939 : Part 8 : 1985	I	IEC 617-8 : 1983
BS 3939 : Part 9 : 1985	I	IEC 617-9 : 1983
BS 3939 : Part 10 : 1985	I	IEC 617-10 : 1983
BS 3939 : Part 11 : 1985	I	IEC 617-11 : 1983
BS 3939 : Part 12 : 1991	I	IEC 617-12 : 1991
BS 3990 : 1980	TE	ISO 3336
BS 4023 : 1975		
BS 4071 : 1966		
BS 4129 : 1990		
BS 4168 : Part 1 : 1981	TE	ISO 4762
BS 4168 : Part 2 : 1981	TE	ISO 4026
BS 4168 : Part 3 : 1981	TE	ISO 4027
BS 4168 : Part 4 : 1981	TE	ISO 4028
BS 4168 : Part 5 : 1981	TE	ISO 4029
BS 4168 : Part 6 : 1982	R	ISO 7380
BS 4168 : Part 7 : 1982		
BS 4168 : Part 8 : 1982		
BS 4168 : Part 9 : 1983	TE	ISO/DIS 2936
BS 4174 : 1972	TE	ISO 1478
		ISO 1479
		ISO 1481
		ISO 1482
		ISO 1483
	R	ISO 2770
BS 4175 : 1989	R	ISO 1024
		ISO 1079
		ISO 1355
BS 4183 : 1967	TE	ISO/R 885
		ISO/R 888
		ISO 1207
		ISO/R 1580
		ISO 2009
		ISO 2010
BS 4235 : Part 1 : 1972	R	ISO/R 773
		ISO/R 774

APPENDIX G

CROSS-REFERENCE OF BRITISH, EUROPEAN AND INTERNATIONAL STANDARDS

BSI DOC.	RELATIONSHIP	ISO/EN DOC.
BS 4235 : Part 2 : 1977	I	ISO 3912 : 1977
BS 4305 : Part 1 : 1989	I	EN 198 : 1987
BS 4305 : Part 2 : 1989		
BS 4360 : 1990	R	EURONORM 113-72
		EURONORM 155-80
BS 4368 : Part 1 : 1972	R	ISO 1179
BS 4368 : Part 3 : 1974	R	ISO 1179
FR : DIN 2353		
BS 4368 : Part 4 : 1984		
BS 4375 : 1968		
BS 4480 : Part 1 : 1992	I	ISO 2795 : 1991
BS 4480 : Part 2 : 1974		
BS 4480 : Part 3 : 1993	I	ISO 4379 : 1993
BS 4480 : Part 4 : 1979	I	ISO 3547 : 1976
BS 4480 : Part 5 : 1979	I	ISO 3548 : 1978
BS 4480 : Part 6 : 1984	I	ISO 6525 : 1983
BS 4480 : Part 7 : 1984	I	ISO 6526 : 1983
BS 4480 : Part 8 : 1984	I	ISO 6864 : 1984
BS 4495 : 1969		
BS 4500 : Part 3 : 1973	R	ISO 2768-1 : 1989
BS 4500 : Part 4 : 1985	I	ISO 5166 : 1982
BS 4500A : 1970		
BS 4500B : 1970		
BS 4504 : Section 3.1 : 1989		
BS 4504 : Section 3.2 : 1989	R	ISO 7005-2
BS 4504 : Section 3.3 : 1989	R	ISO 7005/3
BS 4515 : 1984		
BS 4517 : 1969		
BS 4518 : 1982		
BS 4548 : 1987	R	ISO 5294
		ISO 5296-1
BS 4549 : Part 1 : 1970		
BS 4550 : Part 2 : 1970		
BS 4550 : Part 3 : Section 3.1 : 1978		
BS 4550 : Part 3 : Section 3.4 : 1978		
BS 4550 : Part 3 : Section 3.5 : 1978		
BS 4550 : Part 3 : Section 3.6 : 1978		
BS 4550 : Part 3 : Section 3.7 : 1978		
BS 4550 : Part 3 : Section 3.8 : 1978		
BS 4550 : Part 4 : 1978		
BS 4550 : Part 5 : 1978		
BS 4550 : Part 6 : 1978		
BS 4570 : 1985		
BS 4575 : Part 1 : 1979	I	ISO 4413 : 1978
BS 4575 : Part 2 : 1987	R	ISO 4414
BS 4575 : Part 3 : 1988		
BS 4582 : Part 1 : 1970		
BS 4582 : Part 2 : 1978		
BS 4586 : 1992	I	ISO 3862 : 1991
BS 4618 : Introduction : 1970		
BS 4618 : Section 1.1 : 1970		
BS 4618 : Subsection 1.1.1 : 1970		
BS 4618 : Subsection 1.1.2 : 1976		
BS 4618 : Subsection 1.1.3 : 1974	R	ISO 6602
BS 4618 : Section 1.2 : 1972		
BS 4618 : Section 1.3 : 1975		
BS 4618 : Subsection 1.3.1 : 1975		
BS 4618 : Subsection 1.3.3 : 1976		
BS 4618 : Section 2.1 : 1970		
BS 4618 : Section 2.2 : 1970		
BS 4618 : Section 2.3 : 1975		
BS 4618 : Section 2.4 : 1975		
BS 4618 : Section 3.1 : 1970		
BS 4618 : Section 3.2 : 1973		
BS 4618 : Section 3.3 : 1973		
BS 4618 : Section 4.1 : 1972	R	ISO 175
BS 4618 : Section 4.2 : 1972		
BS 4618 : Section 4.3 : 1974	R	ISO/R 878
		ISO/R 879
BS 4618 : Section 4.4 : 1973		
BS 4618 : Section 4.5 : 1974		
BS 4618 : Section 4.6 : 1974		
BS 4618 : Section 5.1 : 1970		
BS 4618 : Section 5.2 : 1970		
BS 4618 : Section 5.3 : 1972		
BS 4618 : Section 5.4 : 1972	R	ISO 6721
BS 4618 : Section 5.5 : 1974		
BS 4618 : Section 5.6 : 1975		
BS 4637 : 1970		
BS 4638 : 1970		
BS 4659 : 1989		
BS 4683 : Part 1 : 1971		
BS 4683 : Part 2 : 1971	TE	IEC 79-1
BS 4683 : Part 4 : 1973	R	IEC 79-7 : 1990
BS 4727 : Part 1 : Group 01 : 1983	TE	IEC 50(101)
		IEC 50(111)
		IEC 50(121)
		IEC 50(131)
BS 4727 : Part 1 : Group 02 : 1980	TE	IEC 50(151)
BS 4727 : Part 1 : Group 03 : 1971	R	IEC 50(446)
BS 4727 : Part 1 : Group 04 : 1986	TE	IEC 50(301)
		IEC 50(302)
		IEC 50(303)
BS 4727 : Part 1 : Group 05 : 1985	TE	IEC 50(521)
BS 4727 : Part 1 : Group 06 : 1973	R	IEC 50(531)
BS 4727 : Part 1 : Group 07 : 1991	I	IEC 50(221) : 1990
BS 4727 : Part 1 : Group 08 : 1992	I	IEC 50(561) : 1991
BS 4727 : Part 1 : Group 09 : 1991	I	IEC 50(161) : 1990
BS 4727 : Part 1 : Group 10 : 1991	I	IEC 50(212) : 1990
BS 4727 : Part 1 : Group 11 : 1991	I	IEC 194 : 1988
BS 4727 : Part 1 : Group 12 : 1991	I	IEC 50(471) : 1984
BS 4727 : Part 1 : Group 13 : 1991	I	IEC 50(581) : 1978
BS 4727 : Part 2 : Group 02 : 1983	TE	IEC 50(551)
BS 4727 : Part 2 : Group 03 : 1971	TE	IEC 50(411)
BS 4727 : Part 2 : Group 04 : 1991	I	IEC 50(421) : 1990
BS 4727 : Part 2 : Group 05 : 1972		
BS 4727 : Part 2 : Group 06 : 1985	TE	IEC 50(441)
BS 4727 : Part 2 : Group 07 : 1973	TE	IEC 50(691)
BS 4727 : Part 2 : Group 08 : 1986	TE	IEC 50(461)
BS 4727 : Part 2 : Group 09 : 1981	TE	IEC 50(431)
BS 4727 : Part 2 : Group 10 : 1985	TE	IEC 50(841)

APPENDIX G

CROSS-REFERENCE OF BRITISH, EUROPEAN AND INTERNATIONAL STANDARDS

BSI DOC.	RELATIONSHIP	ISO/EN DOC.
BS 4727 : Part 2 :	TE	IEC 50(601)
Group 11 : 1986		IEC 50(602)
		IEC 50(605)
		IEC 50(603)
		IEC 50(604)
BS 4727 : Part 2 :		
Group 12 : 1990	TE	IEC 50(371)
BS 4727 : Part 2 :	I	IEC 50(426) : 1990
Group 13 : 1991		
BS 4727 : Part 2 :		
Group 14 : 1991	I	IEC 50(436) : 1990
BS 4727 : Part 2 :		
Group 15 : 1991	I	IEC 50(466) : 1990
BS 4727 : Part 2 :		
Group 16 : 1991	I	IEC 50(321) : 1986
BS 4727 : Part 2 :		
Group 17 : 1992	I	IEC 50(486) : 1991
BS 4727 : Part 2 :		
Group 18 : 1992	TE	IEC 50(811) : 1991
BS 4727 : Part 3 :	TE	IEC 50(55)
Group 01 : 1971		IEC 50(60)
BS 4727 : Part 3 :		
Group 02 : 1971	TE	IEC 50(55)
BS 4727 : Part 3 :		
Group 03 : 1992	TE	IEC 50(721) : 1991
BS 4727 : Part 3 :		
Group 04 : 1976	R	IEC 50(60)
BS 4727 : Part 3 :		
Group 05 : 1971	TE	IEC 50(60)
BS 4727 : Part 3 :		
Group 06 : 1971	TE	IEC 50(60)
BS 4727 : Part 3 :		
Group 07 : 1971		
BS 4727 : Part 3 :	TE	IEC 50(60)
Group 08 : 1985		IEC 50(801)
BS 4727 : Part 3 :		
Group 09 : 1991	I	IEC 50(726) : 1982
BS 4727 : Part 3 :		
Group 10 : 1979	TE	IEC 50(806)
BS 4727 : Part 3 :		
Group 11 : 1983	TE	IEC 50(725)
BS 4727 : Part 3 :		
Group 12 : 1991	I	IEC 50(701) : 1988
BS 4727 : Part 3 :		
Group 13 : 1992	I	IEC 50(731) : 1991
BS 4727 : Part 3 :		
Group 14 : 1992	I	IEC 50(702) : 1992
BS 4727 : Part 3 :		
Group 15 : 1992	I	IEC 50(712) : 1992
BS 4727 : Part 3 :		
Group 16 : 1992	I	IEC 50(714) : 1992
BS 4727 : Part 5 :		
Group 01 : 1985	TE	IEC 50(881)
BS 4749 : 1991	I	ISO 4079 : 1991
BS 4772 : 1988	R	ISO 2531
		ISO 4179
		ISO 8179
BS 4778 : Part 1 : 1987	I	EN 28402 : 1991
		ISO 8402-1986
BS 4778 : Part 2 : 1991		
BS 4778 : Part 3 :		
Section 3.1 : 1991	R	IEC 50(191) : 1990
BS 4778 : Part 3 :		
Section 3.2 : 1991	I	IEC 50(191) : 1990
BS 4808 : Part 1 : 1972	R	IEC 189-1
BS 4808 : Part 2 : 1972	R	IEC 189-3
BS 4808 : Part 3 : 1972	R	IEC 189-5
BS 4808 : Part 4 : 1974	R	IEC 189-3
		IEC 189-4
BS 4808 : Part 5 : 1973	R	IEC 189-5
BS 4813 : 1972		
BS 4848 : Part 2 : 1991	TE	ISO 657/14 : 1982

BSI DOC.	RELATIONSHIP	ISO/EN DOC.
BS 4848 : Part 4 : 1972	TE	ISO 657-1
		ISO 657-2
	R	EURONORM 56
		EURONORM 57
BS 4848 : Part 5 : 1980	R	EURONORM 67
BS 4870 : Part 3 : 1985		
BS 4870 : Part 4 : 1988		
BS 4871 : Part 3 : 1985		
BS 4872 : Part 1 : 1982		
BS 4872 : Part 2 : 1976		
BS 4881 : 1993		
BS 4882 : 1990		
BS 4928 : 1985	R	ISO 1140 : 1990
		ISO 1141 : 1990
		ISO 1346 : 1990
		ISO 1969 : 1990
BS 4935 : 1989	R	ISO 2580/1
		ISO 2580/2
BS 4983 : 1992	I	ISO 3949 : 1991
BS 4991 : 1974	R	ISO 3212
		ISO 3213
BS 4994 : 1987		
BS 4999 : Part 0 : 1987		
BS 4999 : Part 101 : 1987	R	IEC 34-1
	H	CENELEC HD 53.1
BS 4999 : Part 102 : 1987		IEC 34-2 : 1972
	I	IEC 34-2A : 1974
BS 4999 : Part 103 : 1987	R	IEC 72-2 : 1990
BS 4999 : Part 104 : 1988	I	IEC 34-4 : 1985
BS 4999 : Part 105 : 1988	I	EN 60034 : Part 5 :
		1986
	R	IEC 34-5 : 1991
BS 4999 : Part 106 : 1987	TE	IEC 34-6
BS 4999 : Part 107 : 1987	I	IEC 34-7
BS 4999 : Part 108 : 1987	R	IEC 34-8
	H	CENELEC HD 53.8
BS 4999 : Part 109 : 1987	R	IEC 34-9
	H	CENELEC HD 53.9
BS 4999 : Part 111 : 1987	R	IEC 34-11
BS 4999 : Part 112 : 1987	R	IEC 34-12
	H	CENELEC HD 53.12
BS 4999 : Part 115 : 1992	I	IEC 34-15 : 1990
	H	CENELEC
		HD 53.15 S1
BS 4999 : Part 116 :	I	IEC 34-16-1 : 1991
Section 1 : 1992	H	CENELEC
		HD 53.16.1 S1
BS 4999 : Part 140 : 1987		
BS 4999 : Part 141 : 1987	R	IEC 72
		IEC 72A
BS 4999 : Part 142 : 1987	R	ISO 2373
		IEC 34-14
	H	CENELEC HD 347
BS 4999 : Part 143 : 1987		
BS 4999 : Part 144 : 1987	R	IEC 894
	H	CENELEC HD 345
BS 4999 : Part 145 : 1987		
BS 4999 : Part 146 : 1988	I	IEC 276 : 1968
	H	CENELEC HD 56S2
BS 4999 : Part 147 : 1988	I	IEC 136
BS 5000 : Index : 1981		
BS 5000 : Part 2 : 1992	I	IEC 34-3 : 1988
	H	CENELEC
		HD 53.3 S1 : 1991
BS 5000 : Part 3 : 1980		
BS 5000 : Part 10 : 1978	R	IEC 72
	H	CENELEC HD 231
BS 5000 : Part 11 : 1973	R	IEC 72
BS 5000 : Part 15 : 1980		
BS 5000 : Part 16 : 1985		
BS 5000 : Part 17 : 1981		
BS 5000 : Part 25 : 1981	I	IEC 34-13

APPENDIX G CROSS-REFERENCE OF BRITISH, EUROPEAN AND INTERNATIONAL STANDARDS

BSI DOC.	RELATIONSHIP	ISO/EN DOC.
BS 5000 : Part 40 : 1973		
BS 5000 : Part 50 : 1982	I	IEC 681-1
BS 5000 : Part 60 : 1982		
BS 5000 : Part 99 : 1973	R	IEC 34-1
BS 5041 : Part 1 : 1987		
BS 5041 : Part 2 : 1987		
BS 5041 : Part 3 : 1975		
BS 5041 : Part 4 : 1975		
BS 5041 : Part 5 : 1974		
BS 5070 : Part 1 : 1988		
BS 5070 : Part 2 : 1988	R	IEC 113
BS 5070 : Part 3 : 1988		
BS 5070 : Part 4 : 1990		
BS 5106 : 1988		
BS 5135 : 1984		
BS 5139 : 1991	R	ISO 1873-1
		ISO 1873-2
BS 5150 : 1990	R	ISO 5996
BS 5151 : 1974		
BS 5152 : 1974		
BS 5154 : 1991		
BS 5156 : 1985		
BS 5157 : 1989		
BS 5158 : 1989		
BS 5159 : 1974	R	ISO 7121
BS 5160 : 1989		
BS 5163 : 1986	R	ISO 7259
BS 5173 : Part 100 : 1992		
BS 5173 : Section 101.2 : 1987		
BS 5173 : Section 102.1 : 1991	R	ISO 1402 : 1984
BS 5173 : Section 102.3 : 1988		
BS 5173 : Section 102.4 : 1990		
BS 5173 : Section 102.5 : 1985	I	ISO 6803
BS 5173 : Section 102.7 : 1988	I	ISO 8032
BS 5173 : Section 102.8 : 1987	R	ISO 3994
BS 5173 : Section 102.9 : 1992	I	ISO 7233 : 1991
BS 5173 : Section 102.10 : 1990		
BS 5173 : Section 103.2 : 1990		
BS 5173 : Section 103.6 : 1990		
BS 5173 : Section 103.7 : 1991		
BS 5173 : Section 103.8 : 1991		ISO 4023 : 1988
	I	ISO 4023 : 1991
BS 5173 : Section 103.9 : 1986	I	ISO 6945
BS 5173 : Section 103.11 : 1992	I	ISO 4080 : 1991
BS 5173 : Section 103.12 : 1988	I	ISO 8308 : 1987
BS 5173 : Section 106.2 : 1990		
BS 5173 : Section 106.4 : 1989	I	ISO 8580 : 1987
BS 5200 : 1986		
BS 5214 : Part 1 : 1975	R	ISO 5893
BS 5244 : 1986		
BS 5254 : 1976		
BS 5255 : 1989	R	ISO 7671 : 1991
		ISO 8283-1 : 1991
		ISO 8770 : 1991
BS 5268 : Part 2 : 1991		
BS 5268 : Part 3 : 1985		
BS 5268 : Part 4 : Section 4.1 : 1978		
BS 5268 : Part 4 : Section 4.2 : 1989		
BS 5268 : Part 5 : 1989		
BS 5268 : Section 6.1 : 1988		
BS 5268 : Part 7 : Section 7.1 : 1989		
BS 5268 : Part 7 : Section 7.2 : 1989		
BS 5268 : Part 7 : Section 7.3 : 1989		
BS 5268 : Part 7 : Section 7.4 : 1989		
BS 5268 : Part 7 : Section 7.5 : 1990		
BS 5268 : Section 7.6 : 1990		
BS 5268 : Part 7 : Section 7.7 : 1990		
BS 5350 : Part 0 : 1987		
BS 5350 : Part A1 : 1976	R	ISO 4588
BS 5350 : Part A2 : 1990		
BS 5350 : Part B1 : 1978		
BS 5350 : Part B2 : 1976		
BS 5350 : Part B4 : 1993	I	ISO 10364 : 1993
BS 5350 : Part B5 : 1976		
BS 5350 : Part B8 : 1990		
BS 5350 : Part B9 : 1984		
BS 5350 : Part C1 : 1986		
BS 5350 : Part C4 : 1986		
BS 5350 : Part C5 : 1990		
BS 5350 : Part C6 : 1990		
BS 5350 : Part C7 : 1990		
BS 5350 : Part C9 : 1990	R	ISO 4578 : 1979
BS 5350 : Part C12 : 1979		
BS 5350 : Part C13 : 1990		
BS 5350 : Part C14 : 1979		
BS 5350 : Part C15 : 1990		
BS 5350 : Part D4 : 1976		
BS 5350 : Part E1 : 1976		
BS 5350 : Part E2 : 1979		
BS 5350 : Part F1 : 1983		
BS 5350 : Part G1 : 1987		
BS 5350 : Part G2 : 1987		
BS 5350 : Part G3 : 1987		
BS 5350 : Part H1 : 1981		
BS 5350 : Part H2 : 1982		
BS 5350 : Part H3 : 1984		
BS 5350 : Part H4 : 1984		
BS 5351 : 1986		
BS 5352 : 1981		
FR : API Standard 602		
BS 5353 : 1989		
BS 5380 : 1984	R	ISO 228/1
		ISO 1179
BS 5391 : Part 1 : 1976		
BS 5392 : Part 1 : 1976		
BS 5409 : Part 1 : 1976	R	ISO 7628/1
BS 5409 : Part 2 : 1978	R	ISO 7628/1
BS 5421 : Part 1 : 1976	I	ISO 2321 : 1975
BS 5442 : Part 1 : 1989		
BS 5442 : Part 2 : 1989		
BS 5442 : Part 3 : 1979		
BS 5493 : 1977		
BS 5501 : Part 1 : 1977	I	EN 50014 : 1977
	R	IEC 79-0
BS 5501 : Part 2 : 1977	I	EN 50015 : 1977
	R	IEC 79-6
BS 5501 : Part 3 : 1977	I	EN 50016 : 1977
	R	IEC 79-2
BS 5501 : Part 4 : 1977	I	EN 50017 : 1977
	R	IEC 79-5
BS 5501 : Part 5 : 1977	I	EN 50018 : 1977
	R	IEC 79-1
BS 5501 : Part 6 : 1977	I	EN 50019 : 1977
	R	IEC 79-7 : 1990
BS 5501 : Part 7 : 1977	I	EN 50020 : 1977
	R	IEC 79-11
BS 5501 : Part 8 : 1988	I	EN 50 028
BS 5501 : Part 9 : 1982	I	EN 50039 : 1980
	R	IEC 79-11
BS 5512 : 1991	I	ISO 281 : 1990
BS 5536 : 1988	R	ISO 6428
BS 5555 : 1993	I	ISO 1000 : 1992
BS 5600 : Part 1 : Section 1.1 : 1979		
BS 5600 : Part 1 : Section 1.2 : 1981	R	ISO 3252
BS 5600 : Subsection 2.2.3 : 1984	TE	ISO 3923/3

APPENDIX G

CROSS-REFERENCE OF BRITISH, EUROPEAN AND INTERNATIONAL STANDARDS

BSI DOC.	RELATIONSHIP	ISO/EN DOC.
BS 5600 : Part 2 : Section 2.6 : 1985	TE	ISO 4490
BS 5600 : Part 2 : Section 2.11 : 1980	I	ISO 4495 : 1978
BS 5600 : Part 3 : Section 3.2 : 1988	I	ISO 2738 : 1987
BS 5600 : Part 3 : Section 3.3 : 1987	I	ISO 7625 : 1983
BS 5600 : Part 3 : Section 3.6 : 1988	I	ISO 4022 : 1987
BS 5600 : Part 3 : Section 3.7 : 1988	I	ISO 2740 : 1986
BS 5600 : Part 3 : Section 3.8 : 1979	I	ISO 3325 : 1975
BS 5600 : Part 3 : Section 3.9 : 1979	TE	ISO 2739
BS 5600 : Part 3 : Section 3.10 : 1979	I	ISO 3928 : 1977
BS 5600 : Subsection 3.11.2 : 1984	R	ISO 4498/2
BS 5600 : Part 4 : Section 4.3 : 1979	I	ISO 3909 : 1975
BS 5600 : Part 4 : Section 4.5 : 1979	R	ISO 3738/1 : 1976
BS 5600 : Part 4 : Section 4.12 : 1980	I	ISO 4501 : 1978
BS 5600 : Part 5 : Section 5.1 : 1988	I	ISO 5755-1 : 1987
BS 5600 : Part 5 : Section 5.2 : 1988	I	ISO 5755-2 : 1987
BS 5600 : Part 5 : Section 5.3 : 1988	I	ISO 5755-3 : 1987
BS 5645 : 1987	I	ISO 76-1987
BS 5646 : Part 1 : 1978	I	ISO 2982-1972
BS 5646 : Part 2 : 1978	I	ISO 2983-1975
BS 5646 : Part 3 : 1978	R	ISO 113/1
BS 5646 : Part 4 : 1979	I	ISO 113/II-1979
	I	ISO 113/2
BS 5646 : Part 5 : 1980	I	ISO 464-1976
BS 5646 : Part 6 : 1980	I	ISO 246-1978
BS 5646 : Part 7 : 1986	I	ISO 8443-1985
BS 5735 : 1979	I	IEC 426 : 1973
BS 5750 : Part 0 :		ISO 9000-1987
Section 0.1 : 1987	I	EN 29000 : 1987
		ISO 9000 : 1987
BS 5750 : Part 0 :	I	ISO 9004-1987
Section 0.2 : 1987	I	EN 29004 : 1987
		ISO 9004 : 1987
BS 5750 : Part 1 : 1987	I	ISO 9001-1987
	I	EN 29001 : 1987
BS 5750 : Part 2 : 1987	I	EN 29002 : 1987
		ISO 9002 : 1987
BS 5750 : Part 3 : 1987		ISO 9003-1987
	I	EN 29003 : 1987
BS 5750 : Part 4 : 1990		
BS 5750 : Part 8 : 1991	I	ISO 9004-2 : 1991
BS 5750 : Part 13 : 1991	I	ISO 9000-3 : 1991
BS 5755 : 1986	TE	ISO 3320
		ISO 3322
		ISO 4393
		ISO 4395
	R	ISO 7181 : 1991
BS 5760 : Part 0 : 1986		
BS 5760 : Part 1 : 1985		
BS 5760 : Part 2 : 1981		
BS 5760 : Part 3 : 1982		
BS 5760 : Part 4 : 1986		
BS 5760 : Part 5 : 1991	R	IEC 812
BS 5760 : Part 6 : 1991	I	IEC 1014 : 1989
BS 5760 : Part 7 : 1991	I	IEC 1025 : 1990
BS 5760 : Part 9 : 1992	I	IEC 1078 : 1991
BS 5760 : Section 10.1 : 1993	I	IEC 605-1 : 1978
BS 5760 : Section 10.3 : 1993	I	IEC 1070 : 1991
BS 5760 : Part 14 : 1993	I	IEC 1160 : 1992
BS 5775 : Part 0 : 1993	I	ISO 31-0 : 1992
BS 5775 : Part 1 : 1993	I	ISO 31-1 : 1992
BS 5775 : Part 2 : 1993	I	ISO 31-2 : 1992
BS 5775 : Part 3 : 1993	I	ISO 31-3 : 1992
BS 5775 : Part 4 : 1993	I	ISO 31-4 : 1992
BS 5775 : Part 5 : 1993	I	ISO 31-5 : 1992
BS 5775 : Part 6 : 1993	I	ISO 31-6 : 1992
BS 5775 : Part 7 : 1993	I	ISO 31-7 : 1992
BS 5775 : Part 8 : 1993	I	ISO 31-8 : 1992
BS 5775 : Part 9 : 1993	I	ISO 31-9 : 1992
BS 5775 : Part 10 : 1993	I	ISO 31-10 : 1992
BS 5775 : Part 11 : 1993	I	ISO 31-11 : 1992
BS 5775 : Part 12 : 1993	I	ISO 31-12 : 1992
BS 5775 : Part 13 : 1993	I	ISO 31-13 : 1992
BS 5793 : Part 3 : Section 3.2 : 1985	I	IEC 534-3-2 : 1984
BS 5793 : Part 4 : 1987	I	IEC 534-4
BS 5793 : Part 5 : 1984	I	IEC 534-5
BS 5793 : Part 6 : 1986	I	IEC 534-6 : 1985
BS 5793 : Part 8 : Section 8.1 : 1986	I	IEC 534-8-1 : 1986
BS 5903 : 1980	TE	EURONORM 114
	R	ISO 3651/2
BS 5923 : Part 2 : 1980	R	ISO 2454
BS 5944 : Part 1 : 1992	I	ISO 4412-1 : 1991
BS 5944 : Part 2 : 1992	I	ISO 4412-2 : 1991
BS 5944 : Part 4 : 1984		
BS 5944 : Part 5 : 1985		
BS 5944 : Part 6 : 1992	I	ISO 4412-3 : 1991
BS 5950 : Part 1 : 1990		
BS 5950 : Part 2 : 1992		
BS 5950 : Part 3 : Section 3.1 : 1990		
BS 5950 : Part 4 : 1982		
BS 5950 : Part 5 : 1987		
BS 5950 : Part 7 : 1992		
BS 5950 : Part 8 : 1990		
BS 5983 : Part 1 : 1989	I	ISO 6124-1
BS 5983 : Part 2 : 1982	I	ISO 6125
BS 5983 : Part 3 : 1982	I	ISO 6124/2
BS 5983 : Part 4 : 1982	I	ISO 6124/3
BS 5983 : Part 5 : 1982	I	ISO 6126
BS 5983 : Part 6 : 1983	I	ISO 6811
BS 6005 : 1993		
BS 6086 : 1981	I	ISO 5128 : 1980
BS 6104 : Part 3 : 1981	I	ISO 898/5
BS 6105 : 1981	I	ISO 3506
BS 6107 : Part 1 : 1981	I	ISO 1132
BS 6107 : Part 2 : 1987	I	ISO 492
BS 6107 : Part 3 : 1992	I	ISO 5753 : 1991
BS 6138 : 1989	R	ISO 6354
BS 6168 : 1987		
BS 6203 : 1991		
BS 6217 : 1981	I	IEC 417
BS 6234 : 1987	R	IEC 538
		IEC 538A
		IEC 540
		IEC 811-4-2
	H	CENELEC HD 385
BS 6258 : 1988	R	ISO 2938
BS 6267 : 1982	I	ISO 15-1981
BS 6276 : 1987	TE	ISO 3019/2
		ISO 3019/3
BS 6322 : Part 1 : 1982	I	ISO 4759/1
BS 6322 : Part 2 : 1982	I	ISO 4759/2
BS 6322 : Part 3 : 1992	I	ISO 4759-3 : 1991
BS 6323 : Part 1 : 1982		
BS 6323 : Part 2 : 1982		
BS 6323 : Part 3 : 1982		
BS 6323 : Part 4 : 1982	R	ISO 3304
BS 6323 : Part 5 : 1982		
BS 6323 : Part 6 : 1982		

APPENDIX G CROSS-REFERENCE OF BRITISH, EUROPEAN AND INTERNATIONAL STANDARDS

BSI DOC.	RELATIONSHIP	ISO/EN DOC.
BS 6323 : Part 7 : 1982		
BS 6323 : Part 8 : 1982		
BS 6331 : Part 1 : 1983	TE	ISO 6020/1
	R	ISO 6099
BS 6331 : Part 2 : 1983	TE	ISO 6020/2
	R	ISO 6099
BS 6331 : Part 3 : 1983	TE	ISO 6022
	R	ISO 6099
BS 6331 : Part 4 : 1985	R	ISO 8133
		ISO 8134
BS 6340 : Part 1 : 1983		
BS 6340 : Part 2 : 1983		
BS 6340 : Part 3 : 1985		
BS 6340 : Part 4 : 1984		
BS 6340 : Part 5 : 1983		
BS 6340 : Part 6 : 1983		
BS 6340 : Part 7 : 1983		
BS 6340 : Part 8 : 1985		
BS 6346 : 1989		
BS 6374 : Part 1 : 1985		
BS 6374 : Part 2 : 1984		
BS 6374 : Part 3 : 1984		
BS 6374 : Part 4 : 1984		
BS 6374 : Part 5 : 1985		
BS 6442 : 1984	TE	ISO 3601-3
BS 6467 : Part 1 : 1985		
BS 6467 : Part 2 : 1988		
BS 6494 : Part 1 : 1984	I	ISO 4401
BS 6494 : Part 2 : 1986		
BS 6494 : Part 3 : 1989	I	ISO 6264
BS 6494 : Part 4 : 1989	I	ISO 7790
BS 6494 : Part 5 : 1989	I	ISO 6263
BS 6494 : Part 6 : 1989	I	ISO 5781
BS 6501 : Part 1 : 1991		
BS 6501 : Part 2 : 1991		
BS 6564 : Part 1 :		
Section 1.1 : 1989		
BS 6564 : Part 1 :		
Section 1.2 : 1989		
BS 6564 : Part 2 : 1991		
BS 6564 : Part 3 : 1990		
BS 6681 : 1986	R	ISO 5922
BS 6683 : 1985		
FR : MSS SP92		
BS 6747 : 1987		
BS 6840 : Part 1 : 1987	I	IEC 268-1 : 1985
	H	CENELEC
		HD 483.1 S2
BS 6840 : Part 2 : 1988	I	IEC 268-2 : 1987
	H	CENELEC
		HD 483.2 S1
BS 6840 : Part 3 : 1992	I	IEC 268-3 : 1988
	H	CENELEC
		HD 483.3 S2 : 1992
BS 6840 : Part 4 : 1987	I	IEC 268-4 : 1972
BS 6840 : Part 5 : 1990	I	IEC 268-5 : 1989
	H	CENELEC
		HD 483.5 S1
BS 6840 : Part 6 : 1987	I	IEC 268-6
BS 6840 : Part 8 : 1988	I	IEC 268-8
BS 6840 : Part 9 : 1987	I	IEC 268-9 : 1977
BS 6840 : Part 10 : 1991	I	IEC 268-10 : 1991
	H	CENELEC
		HD 483.10 S1
BS 6840 : Part 11 : 1988	I	IEC 268-11 : 1987
	H	CENELEC
		HD 483.11 S2
BS 6840 : Part 12 : 1993	I	IEC 268-12 : 1987
		IEC 268-12/A1 : 1991
	H	CENELEC
		HD 483.12 S2 : 1993
BS 6840 : Part 13 : 1987	I	IEC 268-13 : 1985
BS 6840 : Part 14 : 1987	I	IEC 268-14 : 1980

BSI DOC.	RELATIONSHIP	ISO/EN DOC.
BS 6840 : Part 15 : 1992	I	IEC 268-15 : 1987
	H	CENELEC
		HD 483.15 S4
BS 6840 : Part 16 : 1989	I	IEC 268-16
BS 6840 : Part 17 : 1991	I	IEC 268-17 : 1990
	H	CENELEC
		HD 483.17 S1 : 1992
BS 6889 : 1987		
BS 6931 : 1988	R	ISO 197
BS 6941 : 1988	R	IEC 79-15
BS 6944 : 1988		
BS 6974 : 1991		
BS 6984 : 1988	TE	ISO 7425-1
	R	ISO/DIS 7425-2
BS 6990 : 1989		
BS 6997 : 1990		
BS 7008 : Part 1 : 1988		
BS 7008 : Part 2 : 1988		
BS 7009 : 1988		
BS 7010 : 1988		
BS 7015 : 1989	I	EN 263
BS 7076 : Part 1 : 1989		
BS 7076 : Part 2 : 1989		
BS 7076 : Part 3 : 1989		
BS 7076 : Part 4 : 1989		
BS 7164 : Section 2.2 : 1990	I	ISO 4661-2 : 1987
BS 7164 : Part 3 : 1992	I	ISO 1407 : 1992
BS 7164 : Section 7.1 : 1990	I	ISO 5945 : 1989
BS 7164 : Part 14 : 1990	I	ISO 1408
BS 7164 : Part 21 : 1990	I	ISO 1656 : 1988
BS 7164 : Section 22.2 : 1992	I	ISO 7725 : 1991
BS 7164 : Section 23.1 : 1993	I	ISO 6528-1 : 1992
BS 7164 : Part 24 : 1990	I	ISO 7269 : 1987
BS 7164 : Part 25 : 1990	I	ISO 8054 : 1988
BS 7164 : Section 26.2 : 1990	I	ISO 7780 : 1987
BS 7164 : Section 28.2 : 1990	I	ISO 8053 : 1986
BS 7198 : Part 1 : 1989	I	ISO 7241-1
BS 7198 : Part 2 : 1989	I	ISO 7241/2
BS 7253 : Part 1 : 1993	I	ISO 5833 : 1992
BS 7253 : Part 2 : 1990	I	ISO 6474
BS 7253 : Part 3 : 1990		
BS 7253 : Part 4 : 1990	R	ISO 5834-1
BS 7253 : Part 5 : 1990	R	ISO 5834-2
BS 7296 : Part 1 : 1990	I	ISO 7368
BS 7303 : Part 1 : 1990	I	EN 277
BS 7344 : 1990		
BS 7350 : 1990		
BS 7389 : Part 1 : 1990	I	ISO 5599-1 : 1989
BS 8010 : Part 1 : 1989		
BS 8010 : Section 2.1 : 1987		
BS 8010 : Section 2.3 : 1988		
BS 8010 : Section 2.4 : 1988		
BS 8010 : Section 2.5 : 1989		
BS 8010 : Section 2.7 : 1989		
BS 8010 : Section 2.8 : 1992		
BS 8010 : Part 3 : 1993		
BS 8233 : 1987		
BS AU 150b : 1984	TE	ISO 5287
	R	ISO 2790
BS AU 218 : 1987	TE	ISO 254
		ISO 5288
		ISO 5295
	R	ISO 155
		ISO 5294
		ISO 5296-1
BS EN 19 : 1992	I	EN 19 : 1992
BS EN 196-6 : 1992	I	EN 196-6 : 1989
BS EN 196-7 : 1992	I	EN 196-7 : 1989
BS EN 196-21 : 1992	I	EN 196-21 : 1989
BS EN 204 : 1991	I	EN 204 : 1991
BS EN 279 : 1991	I	EN 279 : 1991
BS EN 287 : Part 1 : 1992	I	EN 287-1 : 1992
BS EN 287 : Part 2 : 1992	I	EN 287-2 : 1992

APPENDIX G

CROSS-REFERENCE OF BRITISH, EUROPEAN AND INTERNATIONAL STANDARDS

BSI DOC.	RELATIONSHIP	ISO/EN DOC.
BS EN 288 : Part 1 : 1992	I	EN 288-1 : 1992
BS EN 288 : Part 2 : 1992	I	EN 288-2 : 1992
BS EN 288 : Part 3 : 1992	I	EN 288-3 : 1992
BS EN 288 : Part 4 : 1992	I	EN 288-4 : 1992
BS EN 301 : 1992	I	EN 301 : 1992
BS EN 302-1 : 1992	I	EN 302-1 : 1992
BS EN 302-2 : 1992	I	EN 302-2 : 1992
BS EN 302-3 : 1992	I	EN 302-3 : 1992
BS EN 302-4 : 1992	I	EN 302-4 : 1992
BS EN 313-1 : 1992	I	EN 313-1 : 1992
BS EN 438 : Part 1 : 1991	I	EN 438-1 : 1991
BS EN 438 : Part 2 : 1991	I	EN 438-2 : 1991
BS EN 2243 : Part 2 : 1991	I	EN 2243 : Part 2 : 1991
BS EN 2243-3 : 1992	I	EN 2243-3 : 1991
BS EN 2243 : Part 4 : 1991	I	EN 2243 : Part 4 : 1991
BS EN 2243-5 : 1992	I	EN 2243-5 : 1992
BS EN 2285 : 1990	I	EN 2285 : 1989
BS EN 2377 : 1989	I	EN 2377
BS EN 10020 : 1991	I	EN 10020 : 1988
BS EN 10025 : 1990	I	EN 10025 : 1990
BS EN 10027-1 : 1992	I	EN 10027-1 : 1992
BS EN 10027-2 : 1992	I	EN 10027-2 : 1991
BS EN 10028-1 : 1993	I	EN 10028-1 : 1992
	R	ISO 9328-1 : 1991
BS EN 10028-2 : 1993	I	EN 10028-2 : 1992
	R	ISO 9328-2 : 1991
BS EN 10028-3 : 1993	I	EN 10028-3 : 1992
	R	ISO 9328-4 : 1991
BS EN 10029 : 1991	I	EN 10029 : 1991
BS EN 10045-1 : 1990	I	EN 10045-1 : 1990
	R	ISO 83 : 1976
		ISO 148 : 1983
BS EN 10045-2 : 1993	I	EN 10045-2 : 1993
BS EN 10083-1 : 1991	I	EN 10083-1 : 1991
BS EN 10083-2 : 1991	I	EN 10083-2 : 1991
BS EN 10113-1 : 1993	I	EN 10113-1 : 1993
	R	ISO 4950-1 : 1981
BS EN 10113-2 : 1993	I	EN 10113-2 : 1993
	R	ISO 4950-2 : 1981
BS EN 10113-3 : 1993	I	EN 10113-3 : 1993
	R	ISO 4950-3 : 1981
BS EN 10131 : 1991	I	EN 10131 : 1991
BS EN 10155 : 1993	I	EN 10155 : 1993
	R	ISO 4952 : 1981
BS EN 20140-2 : 1993	I	EN 20140-2 : 1993
BS 2750 : Part 2 : 1993		ISO 140-2 : 1991
BS EN 20140-10 : 1992	I	EN 20140-10 : 1992
		ISO 140-10 : 1991
BS EN 20225 : 1992		ISO 225 : 1983
	I	EN 20225 : 1992
BS EN 20273 : 1992		ISO 273 : 1979
	I	EN 20273 : 1992
BS EN 20286-1 : 1992	I	EN 20286-1 : 1992
		ISO 286-1 : 1988
BS EN 20286-2 : 1992	I	EN 20286-2 : 1992
		ISO 286-2 : 1988
BS EN 20898-1 : 1992	I	EN 20898-1 : 1991
		ISO 898-1 : 1988
BS EN 20898-2 : 1992	I	EN 20898-2 : 1992
		ISO 898-2 : 1980
BS EN 20898-6 : 1992	I	EN 20898-6 : 1992
		ISO 898-6 : 1988
BS EN 21746 : 1993	I	EN 21746 : 1993
		ISO 1746 : 1983
BS EN 23312 : 1993		ISO 3312 : 1987
	I	EN 23312 : 1993
BS EN 23326 : 1993		ISO 3326 : 1993
	I	EN 23326 : 1993
BS EN 23327 : 1993		ISO 3327 : 1982
	I	EN 23327 : 1993

BSI DOC.	RELATIONSHIP	ISO/EN DOC.
BS EN 23369 : 1993		ISO 3369 : 1975
	I	EN 23369 : 1993
BS EN 23878 : 1993		ISO 3878 : 1983
	I	EN 23878 : 1993
BS EN 23907 : 1993		ISO 3907 : 1985
	I	EN 23907 : 1993
BS EN 23908 : 1993		ISO 3908 : 1985
	I	EN 23908 : 1993
BS EN 23923-1 : 1993	I	EN 23923-1 : 1992
		ISO 3923-1 : 1981
BS EN 23923-2 : 1993		ISO 3923-2 : 1981
	I	EN 23923-2 : 1992
BS EN 23927 : 1993	I	EN 23927 : 1993
		ISO 3927 : 1985
BS EN 23953 : 1993		ISO 3953 : 1985
	I	EN 23953 : 1993
BS EN 23954 : 1993		ISO 3954 : 1977
	I	EN 23954 : 1993
BS EN 23995 : 1993		ISO 3995 : 1985
	I	EN 23995 : 1993
BS EN 24003 : 1993		ISO 4003 : 1977
	I	EN 24003 : 1993
BS EN 24014 : 1992		ISO 4014 : 1988
	I	EN 24014 : 1991
BS EN 24015 : 1992		ISO 4015 : 1979
	I	EN 24015 : 1991
BS EN 24016 : 1992		ISO 4016 : 1988
	I	EN 24016 : 1991
BS EN 24017 : 1992		ISO 4017 : 1988
	I	EN 24017 : 1991
BS EN 24018 : 1992		ISO 4018 : 1988
	I	EN 24018 : 1991
BS EN 24032 : 1992		ISO 4032 : 1986
	I	EN 24032 : 1991
BS EN 24033 : 1992		ISO 4033 : 1979
	I	EN 24033 : 1991
BS EN 24034 : 1992		ISO 4034 : 1986
	I	EN 24034 : 1991
BS EN 24035 : 1992		ISO 4035 : 1986
	I	EN 24035 : 1991
BS EN 24036 : 1992		ISO 4036 : 1979
	I	EN 24036 : 1991
BS EN 24063 : 1992		ISO 4063 : 1990
	I	EN 24063 : 1992
BS EN 24489 : 1993		ISO 4489 : 1978
	I	EN 24489 : 1993
BS EN 24491-2 : 1993		ISO 4491-2 : 1989
	I	EN 24491-2 : 1992
BS EN 24492 : 1993		ISO 4492 : 1985
	I	EN 24492 : 1992
BS EN 24496 : 1993		ISO 4496 : 1978
	I	EN 24496 : 1992
BS EN 24497 : 1993		ISO 4497 : 1983
	I	EN 24497 : 1993
BS EN 24498-1 : 1993		ISO 4498-1 : 1990
	I	EN 24498-1 : 1992
BS EN 24499 : 1993		ISO 4499 : 1978
	I	EN 24499 : 1993
BS EN 24503 : 1993		ISO 4503 : 1978
	I	EN 24503 : 1993
BS EN 24505 : 1993		ISO 4505 : 1978
	I	EN 24505 : 1993
BS EN 24506 : 1993		ISO 4506 : 1979
	I	EN 24506 : 1993
BS EN 24671 : 1993		ISO 4671-1984
	I	EN 24671 : 1993
BS EN 24672 : 1993		ISO 4672 : 1988
	I	EN 24672 : 1993
BS EN 24883 : 1993		ISO 4883 : 1978
	I	EN 24883 : 1992
BS EN 24884 : 1993		ISO 4884 : 1978
	I	EN 24884 : 1993

APPENDIX G

CROSS-REFERENCE OF BRITISH, EUROPEAN AND INTERNATIONAL STANDARDS

BSI DOC.	RELATIONSHIP	ISO/EN DOC.
BS EN 25817 : 1992		ISO 5817 : 1992
	I	EN 25817 : 1992
BS EN 26801 : 1993		ISO 6801-1983
	I	EN 26801 : 1993
BS EN 26802 : 1993		ISO 6802 : 1991
	I	EN 26802 : 1993
BS EN 26922 : 1993		ISO 6922 : 1987
	I	EN 26922 : 1993
BS EN 27326 : 1993	I	EN 27326 : 1993
		ISO 7326 : 1991
BS EN 27627-1 : 1993		ISO 7627-1 : 1983
	I	EN 27627-1 : 1993
BS EN 27627-2 : 1993		ISO 7627-2 : 1983
	I	EN 27627-2 : 1993
BS EN 27627-3 : 1993		ISO 7627-3 : 1983
	I	EN 27627-3 : 1993
BS EN 27627-4 : 1993	I	EN 27627-4 : 1993
		ISO 7627-4 : 1983
BS EN 27627-5 : 1993	I	EN 27627-5 : 1993
		ISO 7627-5 : 1983
BS EN 27627-6 : 1993		ISO 7627-6 : 1985
	I	EN 27627-6 : 1993
BS EN 28030 : 1993		ISO 8030-1987
	I	EN 28030 : 1993
BS EN 28031 : 1993		ISO 8031 : 1987
	I	EN 28031 : 1993
BS EN 28033 : 1993		ISO 8033 : 1991
	I	EN 28033 : 1993
BS EN 28167 : 1992		ISO 8167 : 1989
	I	EN 28167 : 1992
BS EN 28233 : 1992	I	ISO 8233 : 1988
Also numbered		
BS 2782 : Part 11 :		
Method 1131 : 1992		EN 28233 : 1990
BS EN 28510-1 : 1993	I	EN 28510-1 : 1993
		ISO 8510-1 : 1990
BS EN 28510-2 : 1993	I	ISO 8510-2 : 1990
	I	EN 28510-2 : 1993
BS EN 28659 : 1992	I	ISO 8659 : 1989
Also numbered BS 2782 :		
Part 11 : Method 1132 : 1992		EN 28659 : 1990
BS EN 50014 : 1992	I	EN 50014 : 1992
	R	IEC 79-0 : 1983
BS EN 60534-1 : 1993	I	EN 60534-1 : 1993
		IEC 534-1
BS EN 60534-2-1 : 1993	I	EN 60534-2-1 : 1993
		IEC 534-2-1 : 1978

BSI DOC.	RELATIONSHIP	ISO/EN DOC.
BS EN 60534-2-2 : 1993	I	EN 60534-2-2 : 1993
		IEC 534-2-2 : 1980
BS EN 60534-2-3 : 1993	I	EN 60534-2-3 : 1993
		IEC 534-2-3 : 1983
BS EN 60534-8-2 : 1993	I	EN 60534-8-2 : 1993
		IEC 534-8-2 : 1991
BS EN 60617-13 : 1993	I	EN 60617-13 : 1993
		IEC 617-13 : 1993
BS EN 60947-1 : 1992	I	EN 60947-1 : 1991
		IEC 947-1 : 1988
BS EN 60947-2 : 1992	I	EN 60947-2 : 1991
	TE	IEC 947-2 : 1989
BS EN 60947-3 : 1992	I	EN 60947-3 : 1992
	R	IEC 947-3 : 1990
BS EN 60947-4-1 : 1992	I	EN 60947-4-1 : 1992
		IEC 947-4-1 : 1990
BS EN 60947-5-1 : 1992	I	EN 60947-5-1 : 1991
	TE	IEC 947-5-1 : 1990
BS EN 60947-6-1 : 1992	I	EN 60947-6-1 : 1991
		IEC 947-6-1 : 1989
BS EN 60947-6-2 : 1993	I	EN 60947-6-2 : 1993
	R	IEC 947-6-2 : 1992
BS EN 60947-7-1 : 1992	I	EN 60947-7-1 : 1991
BS 8213 : Part 1 : 1991		
CP 153 : Part 2 : 1970		
CP 153 : Part 3 : 1972		
CP 3012 : 1972		
M 33 : 1970		
M 48 : 1975		
M 57 : 1985	I	ISO 7313-1984
2M 63 : 1993	I	ISO 7320 : 1992
S 201 : 1967		
S 202 : 1967		
S 203 : 1967		
S 204 : 1967		
S 205 : 1969		
SP 94 : 1964		
PD 3376 : 1959		
PD 6438 : 1969		
PD 6457 : 1970		
PD 6493 : 1991		
PD 7304 : 1991		
PP 7304 : 1991		
PP 7307 : 1989		
PP 7308 : 1986		
PP 7311 : 1984		

APPENDIX H INFORMATION ON BSI

THE WORK OF B S I

Introduction

BSI's major function is to help British industry compete effectively in world markets. Its work in standards, testing, quality assurance and export guidance is geared to enable British companies to meet the quality needs of buyers at home and abroad.

BSI is independent, operating under a Royal Charter.

Its work on standards is financed by contributions from industry, a government grant which matches these contributions and – the largest part – by sales of British Standards and associated products. The testing and quality assurance services are financed by fees paid by customers in the marketplace.

Standards are drawn up by all those who have a particular interest in the subject – manufacturers, users, research organizations, government departments and consumers. This work is coordinated by BSI staff, acting as secretaries to the 3000 committees where the work is done. All standards are made available for public comment before they are published.

Publications

Approximately 11,500 British Standards are available from stock and can be ordered by fax, phone, post or telex, directly from BSI. Also, standards can now be obtained from over 70 distributors located throughout the country.

Whilst British Standards represent BSI's core products, an increase in international trade and the Single European Market has created a greater demand for international and foreign standards. A range of technical publications and guidance documents is also now available.

Additionally, rapidly accelerating technological developments have meant that BSI is now providing information in electronic format such as CD-ROM.

Information Services

The Information Department, which is based at Milton Keynes, combines Technical Help to Exporters, Customer Services, Library and Database Sections.

Customer Services answers a wide range of questions on the documents and services available from BSI and is the first point of contact for most people. Enquiries can be made by letter, fax, telex or telephone. The information available includes price and availability of standards, current status, work in progress and detailed subject searching.

Details of all British Standards and Draft Standards are held on computer and are available online via BSI STANDARDLINE, which is a command driven bibliographic database, designed and maintained by the Database Section. Customers may ask for searches to be performed on their behalf.

The BSI Library holds a collection of some 600,000 British, international and foreign standards, EC directives, foreign legislation and technical regulations. Most of these are available on loan to UK subscribing members of BSI in exchange for library tokens.

Membership

Nearly 30,000 subscribing members form the very foundation of BSI. They range from individuals, small businesses and professional practices to some of the largest industrial groups and commercial organizations in Europe.

The BSI membership package is continually reviewed and extended. Current membership benefits include:

Account facilities.
Substantial discounts on British Standards and most foreign national standards and associated products.
Exclusive services, such as the PLUS automatic updating service.
Free copies of BSI News, a monthly update on British, European and international standards.
A free copy of the BSI Catalogue.

B S I Address:

BSI Standards, Linford Wood, Milton Keynes, MK14 6LE.

Publications: Tel (0908) 221166, Fax (0908) 322484
Information Services: Tel (0908) 226888
Membership Services: Tel (0908) 226777

(A call queueing system is in operation; when a ringing tone is obtained, please wait for answer.)

COMPLIANCE WITH A BRITISH STANDARD DOES NOT OF ITSELF CONFER IMMUNITY FROM LEGAL OBLIGATIONS

INDEX

to Handbook for Engineering Design using Standard Materials and Components

INDEX

INDEX

INDEX

INDEX